Modern
American
Prose

PERSPECTIVES IN LITERATURE

A Book of Short Stories—1
A Book of Poetry—1
A Book of Nonfiction—1
A Book of Drama—1

A Book of Short Stories—2
A Book of Poetry—2
A Book of Nonfiction—2
A Book of Drama—2

American Literature to 1900
Modern American Prose
A Book of Modern American Poetry
A Book of Drama—3

English Literature—500 to 1500
English Literature—1500 to 1700
English Literature—1700 to 1900
Modern British Prose
A Book of Modern British Poetry
A Book of Drama—4

A Book of Mythology (in preparation)

Bridges to Understanding: Essays on the Novel
    (in preparation)

PERSPECTIVES IN LITERATURE

Modern American Prose

PATRICIA J. COSTELLO
CHARLES A. CONEFREY

 HARCOURT BRACE JOVANOVICH, PUBLISHERS
Orlando   New York   Chicago   Atlanta   Dallas

Contents

Modern
American
Short
Stories

I N 1820 AN ENGLISH critic named Sydney Smith could rightly ask, "In the four quarters of the globe, who reads an American book? or goes to an American play? or looks at an American painting or sculpture?" Today such a question would be absurd because America is clearly one of the leaders in the modern arts. And although all American arts have flourished in the twentieth century, it is in literature, especially in the short story, that America has made one of its most outstanding contributions.

The contemporary American short story appears to derive from the very character of its time. It has moved from closely plotted tales of external conflicts to introspective studies of human relationships and the inner struggles of man as revealed in seemingly trivial events. Ranging from careful exploration of the motives of a single character to highly lyrical fantasy, modern stories bear the stamp of individuality and experimentation even as they retain the traditional single effect and compression so essential to the short story form.

Although any attempt to group modern writers is an oversimplification simply because it is their differences that indicate their genius, nearly all of these writers draw on the forms established by the early realists and naturalists and developed further in the stream-of-consciousness technique.

Realism

Realism is the attempt to reconstruct, in fiction, scenes and people that reflect real life. The realist may feel that life should be different from the way it is, but he does not create characters whose lives conform to his ideals. Nor does he add touches of romantic color to make common events seem more exotic or exciting. His goal is to investigate the motives, impulses, and principles that underlie human action and to form conclusions that have a direct bearing on the truths of human experience. The realist may choose any subject, but he is mainly concerned with the everyday lives of ordinary people, most often those from the middle and lower social classes.

In American letters the use of realism as a device for depicting the lives of ordinary people developed in the second half of the nineteenth century. It was influenced to some extent by Darwin's theories of evolution and the "survival of the fittest"; by the emphasis on analysis of observed and recorded data as a scientific method; and by the use of documentation in historical studies. In part it was a revolt against the emotional and subjective approaches of the earlier, romantic writers.

Among the earliest leaders in the move toward realism in fiction were local colorists such as Bret Harte, Sarah Orne Jewett, and George Washington Cable. They were exact in their description of the dress, characteristics, and customs of the particular regions of the country that they chose to write about. The movement gained in intensity under the leadership of Mark Twain and of two Americans who were influential critics as well as novelists: Henry James and William Dean Howells.

Naturalism

Other writers emphasized the social and scientific theories advanced in the nineteenth century, and were known as naturalists. Naturalism is *extreme* realism. It aims at a detached, objective, and "scientific" treatment of man. It not only details man's everyday activities, but also sees his actions and destiny as controlled by the social and economic environment into which he was born. The naturalists reject the soul and the supernatural and believe that scientific laws can account for all phenomena. The naturalists may have romantic, idealistic, or humorous elements in their work, but only as examples of illusion or hallucination. They often picture the ugly sides of American life, and usually with stark honesty.

Among the early leaders of American naturalism were Stephen Crane, Frank Norris, and Jack London. Later naturalists include Theodore Dreiser, John Dos Passos, and James T. Farrell.

Stream of Consciousness

Most recently, there has been a shift toward a realistic portrayal of the inner mind rather than of external events. This type of literary realism is called psychological realism, and one of its devices is the *stream of consciousness*, which depicts flowing inner processes of the mind.

The designation *stream of consciousness* was coined in 1890 by the American psychologist and educator William James (1842–1910), brother of the novelist-critic Henry James. He pointed out that there is a constant stream of thought that flows without order or logic through our minds. Simply stated, this means that there is a parallel between the way thoughts continuously ebb and flow in our minds and the way water ebbs and flows in a tidewater stream.

Writers who use the stream of consciousness in their novels and stories do not follow traditional rules regarding plot, chronologically ordered action, or even grammar and syntax. Rather, the story progresses through a free (and not logical) association taking place within a character's mind—one object, person, event, or thought recalls another or leads off in a new direction, back and forth. This technique gives the writer an experimental method of presenting the frequently disjointed thoughts and associations that seethe in a character's mind, but without the writer's having to use the standard pointers (*i.e.*, "He thought . . ." "I wondered . . ." etc.). Thus, the seemingly random impulses of the mind jump about, one or many at a time. In this manner the stream of consciousness can place an emphasis on those thoughts that are spontaneous, involuntary, and peripheral—the theory being that these, through revealing the inner mind, tell more about the character and his motivation than do the conscious, rational thinking and speaking he or she may engage in.

Stream of consciousness is difficult to read and is even harder to write. Its effectiveness and meaning depend on the writer's skill in making the free association understandable to the reader. American writers who have written in this manner include Sherwood Anderson, John Dos Passos, Thomas Wolfe, William Faulkner, Katherine Anne Porter, and Eudora Welty. Some critics go back to the nineteenth century and point to some of the fiction of Edgar Allan Poe, Herman Melville, and Henry James as closely resembling stream-of-consciousness writing. Poe, for example, used a similar technique in such stories as "The Tell-Tale Heart."

Today's stories range from a traditional sort of realism through an updated naturalism to the stream of consciousness. Whatever their form, they are collectively a good barometer of the social, ethical, intellectual, and moral state of the nation. They not only depict the contemporary scene but also express its attitudes.

Katherine Anne Porter

In a *Paris Review* interview—one of a series of "Writers at Work" interviews published by that literary magazine—Katherine Anne Porter spoke about her craft. The artist begins work, she said,

> . . . with the consequences of acts, not the acts themselves. Or the events. The event is important only as it affects your life and the lives of those around you. The reverberations, you might say, the overtones: that is where the artist works. In that sense it has sometimes taken me ten years to understand even a little of some important event that has happened to me. Oh, I could have given a perfectly factual account of what had happened, but I didn't know what it meant until I knew the consequences. If I didn't know the ending of a story, I wouldn't begin. I always write my last lines, my last paragraph, my last page first, and then I go back and work toward it. I know where I'm going.

Miss Porter, who was born in Indian Creek, Texas, in 1894, grew up in rural areas in that state and in Louisiana, and received her education in convents and private schools. Part of her education was her early access to good books. The old houses she knew as a child were filled with books that had been gathered over the generations by members of her family.

By the time she was twenty-one, she was supporting herself by newspaper reporting and hack writing. At the end of World War I, following a near-fatal attack of influenza, she went to Mexico to recuperate and to study Mexican art. In Mexico she became acquainted with a number of painters and revolutionaries. During this period (in fact, from the time she was fifteen), she was writing short stories and short novels. By the time a few of her stories found their way into print, in the early nineteen-twenties, she had accumulated a trunkful of manuscripts. Her first collection of short stories, *Flowering Judas and Other Stories*, was published in 1930. The next year, she was awarded a Guggenheim Fellowship, which enabled her to study in Paris, where she remained for many years. While there, she became interested in French songs

5

and translated many of them into English. These are collected in *Katherine Anne Porter's French Song-Book* (1933).

Flowering Judas, which contains "The Jilting of Granny Weatherall," was followed in 1939 by *Pale Horse, Pale Rider*, a collection of three short novels. The title story, thought to be partly autobiographical, concerns a young woman's love for a World War I soldier who dies of influenza. Many of Miss Porter's stories about the South were collected in *The Leaning Tower and Other Stories*, published in 1944.

It was not until 1962, however, that Katherine Anne Porter attained popular and commercial success for her fiction. The occasion was the appearance, after nearly twenty years of writing and revising, of her full-length novel, *Ship of Fools*. The novel was greeted with general critical praise, but Miss Porter nonetheless felt that much of the praise was for the wrong reasons and that the critics had for the most part missed the real theme of the book. What the book was about, she explained, was that "evil is always done with the collusion of good."

This theme in various forms has been a constant one in her fiction. She has also said that betrayal, especially self-betrayal, has been another lifelong theme in her fiction. "Every story I write has that at its center, and you know, I didn't realize it for years."

In "The Jilting of Granny Weatherall," Miss Porter explores a theme of betrayal, using the *stream of consciousness*. Outwardly, the story deals with the death of an old woman. Inwardly, it deals with everything that has shaped her life. This is all presented through a stream of consciousness, or a flow of perceptions and associations in the random, often confused and confusing, language of thought. In modern fiction, the stream-of-consciousness technique was first used extensively by Virginia Woolf, James Joyce, and William Faulkner. Miss Porter has used the technique only sparingly in her works, but here she found it the best way to present the inner thoughts and emotions of the dying Granny Weatherall.

The Jilting of Granny Weatherall

She flicked her wrist neatly out of Doctor Harry's pudgy careful fingers and pulled the sheet up to her chin. The brat ought to be in knee breeches. Doctoring around the country with spectacles on his nose! "Get along now, take your schoolbooks and go. There's nothing wrong with me."

Establishes setting. Character is sick in bed.

Doctor Harry spread a warm paw like a cushion on her forehead where the forked green vein danced and made her eyelids twitch. "Now, now, be a good girl, and we'll have you up in no time."

Use of simile.

"That's no way to speak to a woman nearly eighty years old just because she's down. I'd have you respect your elders, young man."

Reader learns age of character.

"Well, Missy, excuse me." Doctor Harry patted her cheek. "But I've got to warn you, haven't I? You're a marvel, but you must be careful or you're going to be good and sorry."

Characterization through dialogue and tone of voice.

"Don't tell me what I'm going to be. I'm on my feet now, morally speaking. It's Cornelia. I had to go to bed to get rid of her."

Mention of another character. Introduces possible conflict.

Her bones felt loose, and floated around in her skin, and Doctor Harry floated like a balloon around the foot of the bed. He floated and pulled down his waistcoat and swung his glasses on a cord. "Well, stay where you are, it certainly can't hurt you."

Similes used showing patient as sick and confused.

"Get along and doctor your sick," said Granny Weatherall. "Leave a well woman alone. I'll call for you when I want you. . . . Where were you forty years ago when I pulled through milk-leg and double pneumonia? You weren't even born. Don't let Cornelia lead you on," she

Reference to "milk leg," or phlebitis, an inflammation of the leg veins often occurring in women shortly after childbirth.

shouted, because Doctor Harry appeared to float up to the ceiling and out. "I pay my own bills, and I don't throw my money away on nonsense!"

She meant to wave good-by, but it was too much trouble. Her eyes closed of themselves, it was like a dark curtain drawn around the bed. The pillow rose and floated under her, pleasant as a hammock in a light wind. She listened to the leaves rustling outside the window. No, somebody was swishing newspapers; no, Cornelia and Doctor Harry were whispering together. She leaped broad awake, thinking they whispered in her ear.

Similes used again to indicate confusion and darkness.

"She was never like this, *never* like this!" "Well, what can we expect?" "Yes, eighty years old. . . ."

Well, and what if she was? She still had ears. It was like Cornelia to whisper around doors. She always kept things secret in such a public way. She was always being tactful and kind. Cornelia was dutiful; that was the trouble with her. Dutiful and good: "So good and dutiful," said Granny, "that I'd like to spank her." She saw herself spanking Cornelia and making a fine job of it.

Granny's attitude toward Cornelia.

"What'd you say, Mother?"

Granny felt her face tying up in hard knots. "Can't a body think, I'd like to know?"

"I thought you might want something."

"I do. I want a lot of things. First off, go away and don't whisper."

Establishes that Granny is Cornelia's mother.

She lay and drowsed, hoping in her sleep that the children would keep out and let her rest a minute. It had been a long day. Not that she was tired. It was always pleasant to snatch a minute now and then. There was always so much to be done, let me see: tomorrow.

Tomorrow was far away and there was nothing to trouble about. Things were finished somehow when the time came; thank God there was

Casual, yet significant revelation of Granny's phi-

always a little margin over for peace; then a person could spread out the plan of life and tuck in the edges orderly. It was good to have everything clean and folded away, with the hair brushes and tonic bottles sitting straight on the white embroidered linen; the day started without fuss and the pantry shelves laid out with rows of jelly glasses and brown jugs and white stone-china jars with blue whirligigs and words painted on them; coffee, tea, sugar, ginger, cinnamon, allspice: and the bronze clock with the lion on top nicely dusted off. The dust that lion could collect in twenty-four hours! The box in the attic with all those letters tied up, well, she'd have to go through that tomorrow. All those letters—George's letters and John's letters and her letters to them both—lying around for the children to find afterwards made her uneasy. Yes, that would be tomorrow's business. No use to let them know how silly she had been once.

While she was rummaging around she found death in her mind and it felt clammy and unfamiliar. She had spent so much time preparing for death there was no need for bringing it up again. Let it take care of itself now. When she was sixty she had felt very old, finished, and went around making farewell trips to see her children and grandchildren, with a secret in her mind: This is the very last of your mother, children! Then she made her will and came down with a long fever. That was all just a notion like a lot of other things, but it was lucky too, for she had once and for all got over the idea of dying for a long time. Now she couldn't be worried. She hoped she had better sense now. Her father had lived to be one hundred and two years old and had drunk a noggin of strong hot toddy on his last birthday. He told the reporters it was his daily habit, and he owed his long life to that. He had

losophy of life. Notice that Granny felt a person "could spread out the plan of life."

Everyday objects in her past described vividly through stream of consciousness.

George and John mentioned but not identified. Author is "planting" something to be used later in story.

Perhaps an example of Death's having "jilted" Granny.

made quite a scandal and was very pleased about it. She believed she'd just plague Cornelia a little.

"Cornelia! Cornelia!" No footsteps, but a sudden hand on her cheek. "Bless you, where have you been?"

"Here, Mother."

"Well, Cornelia, I want a noggin of hot toddy."

"Are you cold, darling?"

"I'm chilly, Cornelia. Lying in bed stops the circulation. I must have told you that a thousand times."

Well, she could just hear Cornelia telling her husband that Mother was getting a little childish and they'd have to humor her. The thing that most annoyed her was that Cornelia thought she was deaf, dumb, and blind. Little hasty glances and tiny gestures tossed around her and over her head saying, "Don't cross her, let her have her way, she's eighty years old," and she sitting there as if she lived in a thin glass cage. Sometimes Granny almost made up her mind to pack up and move back to her own house where nobody could remind her every minute that she was old. Wait, wait, Cornelia, till your own children whisper behind your back!

In her day she had kept a better house and had got more work done. She wasn't too old yet for Lydia to be driving eighty miles for advice when one of the children jumped the track, and Jimmy still dropped in and talked things over: "Now, Mammy, you've a good business head, I want to know what you think of this? . . ." Old. Cornelia couldn't change the furniture around without asking. Little things, little things! They had been so sweet when they were little. Granny wished the old days were back again with the children young and everything to be done over. It had been a hard pull, but not too much for

Note "She . . . a little." Added bit of characterization.

Passage of time indicated through dialogue.

Return to the present.

Granny resents being depend-ent on others.

Stream of con-sciousness again. Granny's mind wanders back in time.

Through her flow of thoughts we see Granny as a mother, a widow, and a young lady.

her. When she thought of all the food she had cooked, and all the clothes she had cut and sewed, and all the gardens she had made—well, the children showed it. There they were, made out of her, and they couldn't get away from that. Sometimes she wanted to see John again and point to them and say, Well, I didn't do so badly, did I? But that would have to wait. That was for tomorrow. She used to think of him as a man, but now all the children were older than their father, and he would be a child beside her if she saw him now. It seemed strange and there was something wrong in the idea. Why, he couldn't possibly recognize her. She had fenced in a hundred acres once, digging the post holes herself and clamping the wires with just a Negro boy to help. That changed a woman. John would be looking for a young woman with the peaked Spanish comb in her hair and the painted fan. Digging post holes changed a woman. Riding country roads in the winter when women had their babies was another thing; sitting up nights with sick horses and sick Negroes and sick children and hardly ever losing one. John, I hardly ever lost one of them! John would see that in a minute, that would be something he could understand, she wouldn't have to explain anything!

It made her feel like rolling up her sleeves and putting the whole place to rights again. No matter if Cornelia was determined to be everywhere at once, there were a great many things left undone on this place. She would start tomorrow and do them. It was good to be strong enough for everything, even if all you made melted and changed and slipped under your hands, so that by the time you finished you almost forgot what you were working for. What was it I set out to do? she asked herself intently, but she could not remember. A fog rose over the valley, she saw it

Some of the things Granny endured.

Some evidence of Granny's "plan of life."

Identification of John, as her husband, mentioned.

Reader given an idea of Granny's earlier life.

Again, evidence of what Granny had "weathered."

Another insight into Granny's philosophy.

marching across the creek swallowing the trees and moving up the hill like an army of ghosts. Soon it would be at the near edge of the orchard, and then it was time to go in and light the lamps. Come in, children, don't stay out in the night air.

Lighting the lamps had been beautiful. The children huddled up to her and breathed like little calves waiting at the bars in the twilight. Their eyes followed the match and watched the flame rise and settle in a blue curve, then they moved away from her. The lamp was lit, they didn't have to be scared and hang on to mother any more. Never, never, never more. God, for all my life I thank thee. Without thee, my God, I could never have done it. Hail, Mary, full of grace.[1]

I want you to pick all the fruit this year and see that nothing is wasted. There's always someone who can use it. Don't let good things rot for want of using. You waste life when you waste good food. Don't let things get lost. It's bitter to lose things. Now, don't let me get to thinking, not when I am tired and taking a little nap before supper. . . .

The pillow rose about her shoulders and pressed against her heart and the memory was being squeezed out of it: oh, push down the pillow, somebody: it would smother her if she tried to hold it. Such a fresh breeze blowing and such a green day with no threats in it. But he had not come, just the same. What does a woman do when she has put on the white veil and set out the white cake for a man and he doesn't come? She tried to remember. No, I swear he never harmed me but in that. He never harmed me but in that . . . and what if he did? There was the day, the day, but a whirl of dark smoke rose and

Personification of fog. The "army of ghosts" is a signal for recall of figures from Granny's past. Notice the references to death (army of ghosts) and life (light the lamps).

Attitude toward religion.

Granny recalls very clearly and against her will a key event in her life.

Here is a reference to the actual jilting.

1. **Hail, Mary, full of grace:** the opening line of a Roman Catholic prayer, which ends with the petition to Mary to "pray for us sinners, now and at the hour of our death."

covered it, crept up and over into the bright field where everything was planted so carefully in orderly rows. That was hell, she knew hell when she saw it. For sixty years she had prayed against remembering him and against losing her soul in the deep pit of hell, and now the two things were mingled in one and the thought of him was a smoky cloud from hell that moved and crept in her head when she had just got rid of Doctor Harry and was trying to rest a minute. Wounded vanity, Ellen, said a sharp voice in the top of her mind. Don't let your wounded vanity get the upper hand of you. Plenty of girls get jilted. You were jilted, weren't you? Then stand up to it. Her eyelids wavered and let in streamers of blue-gray light like tissue paper over her eyes. She must get up and pull the shades down or she'd never sleep. She was in bed again and the shades were not down. How could that happen? Better turn over, hide from the light, sleeping in the light gave you nightmares. "Mother, how do you feel now?" and a stinging wetness on her forehead. But I don't like having my face washed in cold water!

Hapsy? George? Lydia? Jimmy? No, Cornelia, and her features were swollen and full of little puddles. "They're coming, darling, they'll all be here soon." Go wash your face, child, you look funny.

Instead of obeying, Cornelia knelt down and put her head on the pillow. She seemed to be talking but there was no sound. "Well, are you tongue-tied? Whose birthday is it? Are you going to give a party?"

Cornelia's mouth moved urgently in strange shapes. "Don't do that, you bother me, daughter."

"Oh, no, Mother. Oh, no. . . ."

Nonsense. It was strange about children. They disputed your every word. "No what, Cornelia?"

"Here's Doctor Harry."

"That was hell" sums up intensity of her reaction.

Granny's name is given.

Question reminds reader of present and the setting— the bedroom of a dying woman. Other names, probably those of her other children. Reference to George, mentioned previously regarding letters.

"I won't see that boy again. He just left five minutes ago."

"That was this morning, Mother. It's night now. Here's the nurse."

Dialogue indicates that Granny is unaware of passage of time.

"This is Doctor Harry, Mrs. Weatherall. I never saw you look so young and happy!"

"Ah, I'll never be young again—but I'd be happy if they'd let me lie in peace and get rested."

She thought she spoke up loudly, but no one answered. A warm weight on her forehead, a warm bracelet on her wrist, and a breeze went on whispering, trying to tell her something. A shuffle of leaves in the everlasting hand of God, he blew on them and they danced and rattled. "Mother, don't mind, we're going to give you a little hypodermic." "Look here, daughter, how do ants get in this bed? I saw sugar ants yesterday." Did you send for Hapsy too?

Thoughts indicate that she is unable to communicate.

Theme expressed by an analogy.

It was Hapsy she really wanted. She had to go a long way back through a great many rooms to find Hapsy standing with a baby on her arm. She seemed to herself to be Hapsy also, and the baby on Hapsy's arm was Hapsy and himself and herself, all at once, and there was no surprise in the meeting. Then Hapsy melted from within and turned flimsy as gray gauze and the baby was a gauzy shadow, and Hapsy came up close and said, "I thought you'd never come," and looked at her very searchingly and said, "You haven't changed a bit!" They leaned forward to kiss, when Cornelia began whispering from a long way off, "Oh, is there anything you want to tell me? Is there anything I can do for you?"

Hapsy is very likely another daughter.

Notice the symbolic references to death through the use of such words as *gray, gauze,* and *gauzy shadow.*

Yes, she had changed her mind after sixty years and she would like to see George. I want you to find George. Find him and be sure to tell him I forgot him. I want him to know I had my husband just the same and my children and my house like any other woman. A good house too and a

Identifies George as the man who jilted her.

good husband that I loved and fine children out of him. Better than I hoped for even. Tell him I was given back everything he took away and more. Oh, no, oh, God, no, there was something else besides the house and the man and the children. Oh, surely they were not all? What was it? Something not given back. . . . Her breath crowded down under her ribs and grew into a monstrous frightening shape with cutting edges; it bored up into her head, and the agony was unbelievable: Yes, John, get the Doctor now, no more talk, my time has come.

When this one was born it should be the last. The last. It should have been born first, for it was the one she had truly wanted. Everything came in good time. Nothing left out, left over. She was strong, in three days she would be as well as ever. Better. A woman needed milk in her to have her full health.

"Mother, do you hear me?"

"I've been telling you—"

"Mother, Father Connolly's here."

"I went to Holy Communion only last week. Tell him I'm not so sinful as all that."

"Father just wants to speak to you."

He could speak as much as he pleased. It was like him to drop in and inquire about her soul as if it were a teething baby, and then stay on for a cup of tea and a round of cards and gossip. He always had a funny story of some sort, usually about an Irishman who made his little mistakes and confessed them, and the point lay in some absurd thing he would blurt out in the confessional showing his struggles between native piety and original sin. Granny felt easy about her soul. Cornelia, where are your manners? Give Father Connolly a chair. She had her secret comfortable understanding with a few favorite saints who cleared a straight road to God for her. All as

Another insight into lasting effect of "jilting" on her life.

Events of present conveyed through dialogue.

surely signed and sealed as the papers for the new Forty Acres. Forever . . . heirs and assigns [2] forever. Since the day the wedding cake was not cut, but thrown out and wasted. The whole bottom dropped out of the world, and there she was blind and sweating with nothing under her feet and the walls falling away. His hand had caught her under the breast, she had not fallen, there was the freshly polished floor with the green rug on it, just as before. He had cursed like a sailor's parrot and said, "I'll kill him for you." Don't lay a hand on him, for my sake leave something to God. "Now, Ellen, you must believe what I tell you. . . ."

More details on "jilting" given.

So there was nothing, nothing to worry about any more, except sometimes in the night one of the children screamed in a nightmare, and they both hustled out shaking and hunting for the matches and calling, "There, wait a minute, here we are!" John, get the doctor now, Hapsy's time has come. But there was Hapsy standing by the bed in a white cap. "Cornelia, tell Hapsy to take off her cap. I can't see her plain."

Her wandering mind constantly focuses on Hapsy.

Her eyes opened very wide and the room stood out like a picture she had seen somewhere. Dark colors with the shadows rising toward the ceiling in long angles. The tall black dresser gleamed with nothing on it but John's picture, enlarged from a little one, with John's eyes very black when they should have been blue. You never saw him, so do you know how he looked? But the man insisted the copy was perfect, it was very rich and handsome. For a picture, yes, but it's not my husband. The table by the bed had a linen cover and a candle and a crucifix.[3] The light

Another reference to darkness.

2. assigns: in law, a term used to designate the person(s) to whom a right or property is legally transferred; also called *assignee* (ə·sī′nē).
3. linen cover . . . crucifix: the objects on the table reveal that preparations had been made for the administration of Extreme Unction, a sacrament given by a priest to persons who are seriously ill or dying.

was blue from Cornelia's silk lampshades. No sort of light at all, just frippery. You had to live forty years with kerosene lamps to appreciate honest electricity. She felt very strong and she saw Doctor Harry with a rosy nimbus around him.

Granny's attraction to this light increases as death nears.

"You look like a saint, Doctor Harry, and I vow that's as near as you'll ever come to it."

"She's saying something."

"I heard you, Cornelia. What's all this carrying-on?"

"Father Connolly's saying—"

Cornelia's voice staggered and bumped like a cart in a bad road. It rounded corners and turned back again and arrived nowhere. Granny stepped up in the cart very lightly and reached for the reins, but a man sat beside her and she knew him by his hands, driving the cart. She did not look in his face, for she knew without seeing, but looked instead down the road where the trees leaned over and bowed to each other and a thousand birds were singing a Mass. She felt like singing too, but she put her hand in the bosom of her dress and pulled out a rosary, and Father Connolly murmured Latin in a very solemn voice and tickled her feet.[4] My God, will you stop that nonsense? I'm a married woman. What if he did run away and leave me to face the priest by myself? I found another a whole world better. I wouldn't have exchanged my husband for anybody except St. Michael[5] himself, and you may tell him that for me with a thank you in the bargain.

Death appears figuratively driving a cart.

Light flashed on her closed eyelids, and a deep roaring shook her. Cornelia, is that lightning? I hear thunder. There's going to be a storm.

Use of light images again.

4. tickled her feet: In administering Extreme Unction, the priest anoints the hands and feet of the sick person with holy oil, and recites a prayer (here, in Latin) for the salvation of his (or her) soul.
5. St. Michael: an angel represented as a protector of the faithful, especially when they are near death; sometimes called *St. Michael the Archangel.*

Close all the windows. Call the children in. . . . "Mother, here we are, all of us." "Is that you, Hapsy?" "Oh, no, I'm Lydia. We drove as fast as we could." Their faces drifted above her, drifted away. The rosary fell out of her hands and Lydia put it back. Jimmy tried to help, their hands fumbled together, and Granny closed two fingers around Jimmy's thumb. Beads wouldn't do, it must be something alive. She was so amazed her thoughts ran round and round. So, my dear Lord, this is my death and I wasn't even thinking about it. My children have come to see me die. But I can't, it's not time. Oh, I always hated surprises. I wanted to give Cornelia the amethyst set— Cornelia, you're to have the amethyst set, but Hapsy's to wear it when she wants, and, Doctor Harry, do shut up. Nobody sent for you. Oh, my dear Lord, do wait a minute. I meant to do something about the Forty Acres, Jimmy doesn't need it and Lydia will later on, with that worthless husband of hers. I meant to finish the altar cloth and send six bottles of wine to Sister Borgia for her dyspepsia.[6] I want to send six bottles of wine to Sister Borgia, Father Connolly, now don't let me forget.

Cornelia's voice made short turns and tilted over and crashed. "Oh, Mother, oh, Mother, oh, Mother. . . ."

"I'm not going, Cornelia. I'm taken by surprise. I can't go."

You'll see Hapsy again. What about her? "I thought you'd never come." Granny made a long journey outward, looking for Hapsy. What if I don't find her? What then? Her heart sank down and down, there was no bottom to death, she couldn't come to the end of it. The blue light from Cornelia's lampshade drew into a tiny point in the center of her brain, it flickered and

Thinks of previous storm when the children were young. Combining of the past and the present.

Granny's action reveals she must be attached to people, not things.

Final attempt to control life— and death.

Reader learns Hapsy is dead. Repetition of Hapsy's words (see page 14). Granny's inner fear unresolved.

Use again

6. **dyspepsia** (dis·pep′shə): difficulty or pain in digesting food; indigestion.

winked like an eye, quietly it fluttered and dwindled. Granny lay curled down within herself, amazed and watchful, staring at the point of light that was herself; her body was now only a deeper mass of shadow in an endless darkness and this darkness would curl around the light and swallow it up. God, give a sign!

For the second time there was no sign. Again no bridegroom and the priest in the house. She could not remember any other sorrow because this grief wiped them all away. Oh, no, there's nothing more cruel than this—I'll never forgive it. She stretched herself with a deep breath and blew out the light.

of light as symbol of life.

Final jilting— and, again, no sign.

Meaning and Method

1. As Granny Weatherall dies at the age of eighty, her mind goes back to the jilting she experienced at the age of twenty. Her stream of consciousness mixes images of the present with those of the past. The setting of the story, therefore, includes (a) the *external*, or the room in which Granny is dying, and (b) the *internal*, or her mind.

   The "external" characters, that is, those actually present in the room as she dies, include (a) Doctor Harry, (b) her daughter Cornelia, and (c) Father Connolly. What are Granny Weatherall's attitudes toward these characters, individually? Why, for example, does she resent Doctor Harry's calling her "a good girl" (see page 7)? How would you characterize her daughter Cornelia as Granny sees her?

2. What physical details in the story and what changes in Granny indicate that her death is coming nearer?

3. Many writers give their characters names that are symbolic or, at least, connotative. Katherine Anne Porter uses the name *Weatherall* to suggest such qualities as endurance, perseverance, strength through experience and survival, and self-sufficiency.

   Give examples of some of the things Granny had "weathered" or survived.

4. By using the stream-of-consciousness point of view in conjunction with a limited omniscient-author point of view, Miss Porter makes sure that the reader's focus never strays from Granny. How does

the use of these points of view limit the scope of the story? What are the disadvantages—if any—of this approach?

5. How can the reader sift out the words actually being spoken by or to Granny on her deathbed from the conversations (remembered or imagined) that are found in her stream of consciousness?

6. She planned to "spread out the plan of life and tuck in the edges orderly." (Page 19.)

Give some examples of how Granny Weatherall attempted to order and control her life. What is Miss Porter saying in the story about human attempts to control life? How is Granny's plan to control life related to her having been jilted by George, and how is it related to the last paragraph of the story, which begins, "For the second time there was no sign. Again no bridegroom and the priest in the house"? Who is the "bridegroom" at her death?

7. When Granny was sixty, she felt very old, tired, and worn out. She even went around making a farewell visit to her children and grandchildren. In what way could this time of her life be said to constitute a third "jilting," one of which she herself was probably unaware but of which the author makes *us* aware?

8. Granny calls for Hapsy. Who do you think Hapsy is or was? Is she someone living who should be there at Granny's deathbed, or is she rather someone who has died long ago and who is alive only in Granny's wandering mind? Explain.

9. Images of light and darkness are central to the story: light is life; darkness is death.

Reread the passage beginning on page 12 with "Lighting the lamps had been beautiful." Explain how light here is life for Granny as her senses fail her and how this remembering of the lamp-lighting is the story of her life—that is, how she passes the light on and then herself passes beyond the light.

Where else in the story has Miss Porter used light and darkness to represent or suggest life and death?

10. Explain whether you would accept one, neither, or both of the following as statements of the story's theme: *Man should not expect life to be predictable or logical;* and *Life has its own mysterious pattern beyond our control and comprehension.* Be prepared to support your view with references to the text.

Composition

1. Describe an experience, real or imagined, using the stream-of-consciousness technique. Decide what reaction you want to evoke in the reader and strive for effective language that will convey the effect

you want. Be sure you choose a very brief event, such as what happens between the moment you leave the bench in the dugout to take a turn at bat and the actual performance at the bat, or what occurs between the moment you see a person approaching you and the moment that person passes by.

2. Write an obituary for Granny Weatherall as it might have appeared in her local newspaper. Read the obituary notices in your local newspaper for an idea of the form of the notice.

Willa Cather
[1873–1947]

As a child growing up on a Nebraska frontier, Willa Cather witnessed firsthand the taming of the prairie by hard-working, determined settlers. For the most part they had come from across the sea—from Scandinavia, Germany, Poland, Russia, and Ireland—to seek fulfillment of the promise of America's open plains.

Willa Cather at the age of ten was in a sense an immigrant, too, for her family moved to Nebraska from a Virginia farm. They lived for a while on a ranch and then moved into the town of Red Cloud. There, Miss Cather received an early education at home, learning to read from her grandmother, learning the classics from "Uncle Billy" Drucker, who operated Red Cloud's general store. She later attended the local high school and then went on to the University of Nebraska, helping to pay her own way by doing news reporting for local papers in the college town of Lincoln.

Upon graduation in 1895, Willa Cather went East, to Pittsburgh, where she worked as a reporter and then as the drama critic for the Pittsburgh *Daily Leader*. In her spare time she took up creative writing, and she later taught high-school English, partly in order to sharpen her own language skills. During this period she produced a book of poems, *April Twilights* (1903), and a collection of short stories, the *Troll Garden* (1905).

In 1906 Willa Cather accepted an editorial job with *McClure's* Magazine, then a popular monthly published in New York. She was later the magazine's managing editor but in 1912, with the success of her first novel, *Alexander's Bridge*, she left in order to concentrate on writing fiction.

Miss Cather was at her best when she wrote about the past. "The world broke in two about 1920," she once said, "and I belonged to the former half." She felt that contemporary life put too much stress on the acquisition of material possessions. She admired people who, like the pioneers, still had a strong moral code and a firm belief in spiritual values.

Her novels that particularly reflect the conflict between old and new values include *O Pioneers!* (1913), which relates in a generation's time the passing of the tough Nebraska frontier into the rich, rolling farmland; and *My Ántonia* (1918), a narrative of an immigrant girl who survives the rigors of frontier life mainly because of her pioneer strength and solid personal values. The spiritual frontier is the setting of *Death Comes for the Archbishop* (1926), a story about the efforts of two Catholic priests to establish a mission in the Spanish Southwest.

Almost all of Willa Cather's stories and novels are economically structured and focus on character rather than on incident. Critics often use such words as *balance, control,* and *order* in describing her style. When Katherine Anne Porter was asked in 1961 to give her critical opinion of Miss Cather's stories, she wrote: "They still live with morning freshness in my memory, their clearness, warmth of feeling, calmness of intelligence, and ample human view of things; in short, the sense of an artist at work in whom one could have complete confidence. . . ."

"Neighbor Rosicky," the story presented here, was written shortly after the death of Willa Cather's father in 1928. It was published four years later in a collection entitled *Obscure Destinies.*

Neighbor Rosicky

I

When Doctor Burleigh told neighbor Rosicky he had a bad heart, Rosicky protested.

"So? No, I guess my heart was always pretty good. I got a little asthma, maybe. Just a awful short breath when I was pitchin' hay last summer, dat's all."

"Well now, Rosicky, if you know more about it than I do, what did you come to me for? It's your heart that makes you short of breath, I tell you. You're sixty-five years old, and you've always worked hard, and your heart's tired. You've got to be careful from now on, and you can't do heavy work any more. You've got five boys at home to do it for you."

The old farmer looked up at the Doctor with a gleam of amusement in his queer triangular-shaped eyes. His eyes were large and lively, but the lids were caught up in the middle in a curious way, so that they formed a triangle. He did not look like a sick man. His brown face was creased but not wrinkled, he had a ruddy color in his smooth-shaven cheeks and in his lips, under his long brown moustache. His hair was thin and ragged around his ears, but very little gray. His forehead, naturally high and crossed by deep parallel lines, now ran all the way up to his pointed crown. Rosicky's face had the habit of looking interested—suggested a contented disposition and a reflective quality that was gay rather than grave. This gave him a certain detachment, the easy manner of an onlooker and observer.

"Well, I guess you ain't got no pills fur a bad heart, Doctor Ed. I guess the only thing is fur me to git me a new one."

Doctor Burleigh swung around in his desk-chair and frowned at the old farmer. "I think if I were you I'd take a little care of the old one, Rosicky."

Rosicky shrugged. "Maybe I don't know how. I expect you mean fur me not to drink my coffee no more."

"I wouldn't, in your place. But you'll do as you choose about that. I've never yet been able to separate a Bohemian [1] from his coffee or his pipe. I've quit trying. But the sure thing is you've got to cut out farm work. You can feed the stock and do chores about the barn, but you can't do anything in the fields that makes you short of breath."

"How about shelling corn?"

"Of course not!"

Rosicky considered with puckered brows.

"I can't make my heart go no longer'n it wants to, can I, Doctor Ed?"

"I think it's good for five or six years yet, maybe more, if you'll take the strain off it. Sit around the house and help Mary. If I had a good wife like yours, I'd want to stay around the house."

His patient chuckled. "It ain't no place fur a man. I don't like no old man hanging round the kitchen too much. An' my wife, she's a awful hard worker her own self."

1. **Bohemian**: a resident of Bohemia, a region in western Czechoslovakia. In another sense, *Bohemian* denotes a person with literary or artistic tastes who lives in an unconventional manner.

"That's it; you can help her a little. My Lord, Rosicky, you are one of the few men I know who has a family he can get some comfort out of—happy dispositions, never quarrel among themselves, and they treat you right. I want to see you live a few years and enjoy them."

"Oh, they're good kids, all right," Rosicky assented.

The Doctor wrote him a prescription and asked him how his oldest son, Rudolph, who had married in the spring, was getting on. Rudolph had struck out for himself, on rented land. "And how's Polly? I was afraid Mary mightn't like an American daughter-in-law, but it seems to be working out all right."

"Yes, she's a fine girl. Dat widder woman bring her daughters up very nice. Polly got lots of spunk, an' she got some style, too. Da's nice, for young folks to have some style." Rosicky inclined his head gallantly. His voice and his twinkly smile were an affectionate compliment to his daughter-in-law.

"It looks like a storm, and you'd better be getting home before it comes. In town in the car?" Doctor Burleigh rose.

"No, I'm in de wagon. When you got five boys, you ain't got much chance to ride round in de Ford. I ain't much for cars, noway."

"Well, it's a good road out to your place; but I don't want you bumping around in a wagon much. And never again on a hayrake,[2] remember!"

Rosicky placed the Doctor's fee delicately behind the desk telephone, looking the other way, as if this were an absent-minded gesture. He put on his plush cap and his corduroy jacket with a sheepskin collar, and went out.

The Doctor picked up his stethoscope and frowned at it as if he were seriously annoyed with the instrument. He wished it had been telling tales about some other man's heart, some old man who didn't look the Doctor in the eye so knowingly, or hold out such a warm brown hand when he said good-by. Doctor Burleigh had been a poor boy in the country before he went away to medical school; he had known Rosicky almost ever since he could remember, and he had a deep affection for Mrs. Rosicky.

Only last winter he had had such a good breakfast at Rosicky's, and that when he needed it. He had been out all night on a

---

2. **hayrake:** a farm implement used to rake or collect hay, straw, etc.

long, hard confinement case at Tom Marshall's—a big rich farm where there were plenty of stock and plenty of feed and a great deal of expensive farm machinery of the newest model, and no comfort whatever. The woman had too many children and too much work, and she was no manager. When the baby was born at last, and handed over to the assisting neighbor woman, and the mother was properly attended to, Burleigh refused any breakfast in that slovenly house, and drove his buggy—the snow was too deep for a car—eight miles to Anton Rosicky's place. He didn't know another farmhouse where a man could get such a warm welcome, and such good strong coffee with rich cream. No wonder the old chap didn't want to give up his coffee!

He had driven in just when the boys had come back from the barn and were washing up for breakfast. The long table, covered with a bright oilcloth, was set out with dishes waiting for them, and the warm kitchen was full of the smell of coffee and hot biscuit and sausage. Five big handsome boys, running from twenty to twelve, all with what Burleigh called natural good manners—they hadn't a bit of the painful self-consciousness he himself had to struggle with when he was a lad. One ran to put his horse away, another helped him off with his fur coat and hung it up, and Josephine, the youngest child and the only daughter, quickly set another place under her mother's direction.

With Mary, to feed creatures was the natural expression of affection—her chickens, the calves, her big hungry boys. It was a rare pleasure to feed a young man whom she seldom saw and of whom she was as proud as if he belonged to her. Some country housekeepers would have stopped to spread a white cloth over the oilcloth, to change the thick cups and plates for their best china, and the wooden-handled knives for plated ones. But not Mary.

"You must take us as you find us, Doctor Ed. I'd be glad to put out my good things for you if you was expected, but I'm glad to get you any way at all."

He knew she was glad—she threw back her head and spoke out as if she were announcing him to the whole prairie. Rosicky hadn't said anything at all; he merely smiled his twinkling smile, put some more coal on the fire, and went into his own room to pour the Doctor a little drink in a medicine glass. When they were all seated, he watched his wife's face from his end of the table and spoke to her in Czech. Then, with the instinct of politeness which seldom failed him, he turned to the Doctor and said slyly: "I was just tellin' her not to ask you no questions about Mrs. Marshall till you eat some breakfast. My wife, she's terrible fur to ask questions."

The boys laughed, and so did Mary. She watched the Doctor devour her biscuit and sausage, too much excited to eat anything herself. She drank her coffee and sat taking in everything about her visitor. She had known him when he was a poor country boy, and was boastfully proud of his success, always saying: "What do people go to Omaha for to see a doctor, when we got the best one in the state right here?" If Mary liked people at all, she felt physical pleasure in the sight of them, personal exultation in any good fortune that came to them. Burleigh didn't know many women like that, but he knew she was like that.

When his hunger was satisfied, he did, of course, have to tell them about Mrs. Marshall, and he noticed what a friendly interest the boys took in the matter.

Rudolph, the oldest one (he was still living at home then), said: "The last time I was over there, she was lifting them big heavy milk cans, and I knew she oughtn't to be doing it."

"Yes, Rudolph told me about that when he came home, and I said it wasn't right," Mary put in warmly. "It was all right for me to do them things up to the last, for I was terrible strong, but that woman's weakly. And do you think she'll be able to nurse it, Ed?" She sometimes forgot to give him the title she was so proud of. "And to think of your being up all night and then not able to get a decent breakfast! I don't know what's the matter with such people."

"Why, Mother," said one of the boys, "if Doctor Ed had got breakfast there, we wouldn't have him here. So you ought to be glad."

"He knows I'm glad to have him, John, any time. But I'm sorry for that poor woman, how bad she'll feel the Doctor had to go away in the cold without his breakfast."

"I wish I'd been in practice when these were getting born." The Doctor looked down the row of close-clipped heads. "I missed some good breakfasts by not being."

The boys began to laugh at their mother because she flushed so red, but she stood her ground and threw up her head. "I don't care, you wouldn't have got away from this house without breakfast. No doctor ever did. I'd have had something ready fixed that Anton could warm up for you."

The boys laughed harder than ever, and exclaimed at her: "I'll bet you would!" "She would, that!"

"Father, did you get breakfast for the doctor when we were born?"

"Yes, and he used to bring me my breakfast, too, mighty nice. I was always awful hungry!" Mary admitted with a guilty laugh.

While the boys were getting the Doctor's horse, he went to the window to examine the house plants. "What do you do to your geraniums to keep them blooming all winter, Mary? I never pass this house that from the road I don't see your windows full of flowers."

She snapped off a dark red one, and a ruffled new green leaf, and put them in his buttonhole. "There, that looks better. You look too solemn for a young man, Ed. Why don't you git married? I'm worried about you. Settin' at breakfast, I looked at you real hard, and I seen you've got some gray hairs already."

"Oh, yes! They're coming. Maybe they'd come faster if I married."

"Don't talk so. You'll ruin your health eating at the hotel. I could send your wife a nice loaf of nut bread, if you only had one. I don't like to see a young man getting gray. I'll tell you something, Ed; you make some strong black tea and keep it handy in a bowl, and every morning just brush it into your hair, an' it'll keep the gray from showin' much. That's the way I do!"

Sometimes the Doctor heard the gossipers in the drug-store wondering why Rosicky didn't get on faster. He was industrious, and so were his boys, but they were rather free and easy, weren't pushers, and they didn't always show good judgment. They were comfortable, they were out of debt, but they didn't get much ahead. Maybe, Doctor Burleigh reflected, people as generous and warmhearted and affectionate as the Rosickys never got ahead much; maybe you couldn't enjoy your life and put it into the bank, too.

II

When Rosicky left Doctor Burleigh's office he went into the farm-implement store to light his pipe and put on his glasses and read over the list Mary had given him. Then he went into the general merchandise place next door and stood about until the pretty girl with the plucked eyebrows, who always waited on him, was free. Those eyebrows, two thin India-ink strokes, amused him, because he remembered how they used to be. Rosicky always prolonged his shopping by a little joking; the girl knew the old fellow admired her, and she liked to chaff with him.

"Seems to me about every other week you buy ticking, Mr. Rosicky, and always the best quality," she remarked as she measured off the heavy bolt with red stripes.

"You see, my wife is always makin' goose-fedder pillows, an' de thin stuff don't hold in dem little down fedders."

"You must have lots of pillows at your house."

"Sure. She makes quilts of dem, too. We sleeps easy. Now she's makin' a fedder quilt for my son's wife. You know Polly, that married my Rudolph. How much my bill, Miss Pearl?"

"Eight eighty-five."

"Chust make it nine, and put in some candy fur de women."

"As usual. I never did see a man buy so much candy for his wife. First thing you know, she'll be getting too fat."

"I'd like dat. I ain't much fur all dem slim women like what de style is now."

"That's one for me, I suppose, Mr. Bohunk!" [3] Pearl sniffed and elevated her India-ink strokes.

When Rosicky went out to his wagon, it was beginning to snow—the first snow of the season, and he was glad to see it. He rattled out of town and along the highway through a wonderfully rich stretch of country, the finest farms in the county. He admired this High Prairie, as it was called, and always liked to drive through it. His own place lay in a rougher territory, where there was some clay in the soil and it was not so productive. When he bought his land, he hadn't the money to buy on High Prairie; so he told his boys, when they grumbled, that if their land hadn't

3. **Bohunk:** *slang,* a derogatory term denoting any foreign-born laborer, usually unskilled and especially one from central Europe. The term is a combination of Bohemian and Hungarian.

some clay in it, they wouldn't own it at all. All the same, he enjoyed looking at these fine farms, as he enjoyed looking at a prize bull.

After he had gone eight miles, he came to the graveyard, which lay just at the edge of his own hay-land. There he stopped his horses and sat still on his wagon seat, looking about at the snowfall. Over yonder on the hill he could see his own house, crouching low, with the clump of orchard behind and the windmill before, and all down the gentle hill-slope the rows of pale gold cornstalks stood out against the white field. The snow was falling over the cornfield and the pasture and the hay land, steadily, with very little wind—a nice dry snow. The graveyard had only a light wire fence about it and was all overgrown with long red grass. The fine snow, settling into this red grass and upon the few little evergreens and the headstones, looked very pretty.

It was a nice graveyard, Rosicky reflected, sort of snug and homelike, not cramped or mournful—a big sweep all round it. A man could lie down in the long grass and see the complete arch of the sky over him, hear the wagons go by; in summer the mowing-machine rattled right up to the wire fence. And it was so near home. Over there across the cornstalks his own roof and windmill looked so good to him that he promised himself to mind the Doctor and take care of himself. He was awful fond of his place, he admitted. He wasn't anxious to leave it. And it was a comfort to think that he would never have to go farther than the edge of his own hayfield. The snow, falling over his barnyard and the graveyard, seemed to draw things together like. And they were all old neighbors in the graveyard, most of them friends; there was nothing to feel awkward or embarrassed about. Embarrassment was the most disagreeable feeling Rosicky knew. He didn't often have it—only with certain people whom he didn't understand at all.

Well, it was a nice snowstorm; a fine sight to see the snow falling so quietly and graciously over so much open country. On his cap and shoulders, on the horses' backs and manes, light, delicate, mysterious it fell; and with it a dry cool fragrance was released into the air. It meant rest for vegetation and men and beasts, for the ground itself; a season of long nights for sleep, leisurely breakfasts, peace by the fire. This and much more went through Rosicky's mind, but he merely told himself that winter was coming, clucked to his horses, and drove on.

When he reached home, John, the youngest boy, ran out to put away his team for him, and he met Mary coming up from the outside cellar with her apron full of carrots. They went into the house together. On the table, covered with oilcloth figured with clusters of blue grapes, a place was set, and he smelled hot coffee-cake of some kind. Anton never lunched in town; he thought that extravagant, and anyhow he didn't like the food. So Mary always had something ready for him when he got home.

After he was settled in his chair, stirring his coffee in a big cup, Mary took out of the oven a pan of *kolache* [4] stuffed with apricots, examined them anxiously to see whether they had got too dry, put them beside his plate, and then sat down opposite him.

Rosicky asked her in Czech if she wasn't going to have any coffee.

She replied in English, as being somehow the right language for transacting business: "Now what did Doctor Ed say, Anton? You tell me just what."

"He said I was to tell you some compliments, but I forgot 'em." Rosicky's eyes twinkled.

"About you, I mean. What did he say about your asthma?"

"He says I ain't got no asthma." Rosicky took one of the little rolls in his broad brown fingers. The thickened nail of his right thumb told the story of his past.

"Well, what is the matter? And don't try to put me off."

"He don't say nothing much, only I'm a little older, and my heart ain't so good like it used to be."

Mary started and brushed her hair back from her temples with both hands as if she were a little out of her mind. From the way she glared, she might have been in a rage with him.

"He says there's something the matter with your heart? Doctor Ed says so?"

"Now don't yell at me like I was a hog in de garden, Mary. You know I always did like to hear a woman talk soft. He didn't say anything de matter wid my heart, only it ain't so young like it used to be an' he tell me not to pitch hay or run de corn-sheller."

---

4. kolache (kō′läch): *also* kolacky, a kind of sweet bun with jam or fruit-pulp filling.

Mary wanted to jump up, but she sat still. She admired the way he never under any circumstances raised his voice or spoke roughly. He was city-bred, and she was country-bred; she often said she wanted her boys to have their papa's nice ways.

"You never have no pain there, do you? It's your breathing and your stomach that's been wrong. I wouldn't believe nobody but Doctor Ed about it. I guess I'll go see him myself. Didn't he give you no advice?"

"Chust to take it easy like, an' stay round de house dis winter. I guess you got some carpenter work for me to do. I kin make some new shelves for you, and I want dis long time to build a closet in de boys' room and make dem two little fellers keep dere clo'es hung up."

Rosicky drank his coffee from time to time, while he considered. His moustache was of the soft long variety and came down over his mouth like the teeth of a buggy rake over a bundle of hay. Each time he put down his cup, he ran his blue handkerchief over his lips. When he took a drink of water, he managed very neatly with a back of his hand.

Mary sat watching him intently, trying to find any change in his face. It is hard to see anyone who has become like your own body to you. Yes, his hair had got thin, and his high forehead had deep lines running from left to right. But his neck, always clean shaved except in the busiest seasons, was not loose or baggy. It was burned a dark reddish brown, and there were deep creases in it, but it looked firm and full of blood. His cheeks had a good color. On either side of his mouth there was a half-moon down the length of his cheek, not wrinkles, but two lines that had come there from his habitual expression. He was shorter and broader than when she married him; his back had grown broad and curved, a good deal like the shell of an old turtle, and his arms and legs were short.

He was fifteen years older than Mary, but she had hardly ever thought about it before. He was her man, and the kind of man she liked. She was rough, and he was gentle—city-bred, as she always said. They had been shipmates on a rough voyage and had stood by each other in trying times. Life had gone well with them because, at bottom, they had the same ideas about life. They agreed, without discussion, as to what was most important and what was secondary. They didn't often exchange opinions, even in Czech—it was as if they had thought the same thought together. A good deal had to be sacrificed and thrown overboard in a hard life like theirs, and they had never disagreed as to the things that could go. It had been a hard life, and a soft life, too. There wasn't anything brutal in the short, broad-backed man with the three-cornered eyes, and the forehead that went on to the top of his skull. He was a city man, a gentle man, and though he had married a rough farm girl, he had never touched her without gentleness.

They had been at one accord not to hurry through life, not to be always skimping and saving. They saw their neighbors buy more land and feed more stock than they did, without discontent. Once when the creamery agent came to the Rosickys to persuade them to sell him their cream, he told them how much money the Fasslers, their nearest neighbors, had made on their cream last year.

"Yes," said Mary, "and look at them Fassler children! Pale, pinched little things, they look like skimmed milk. I'd rather put some color into my children's faces than put money into the bank."

The agent shrugged and turned to Anton.

"I guess we'll do like she says," said Rosicky.

III

Mary very soon got into town to see Doctor Ed, and then she had a talk with her boys and set a guard over Rosicky. Even John, the youngest, had his father on his mind. If Rosicky went to throw hay down from the loft, one of the boys ran up the ladder and took the fork from him. He sometimes complained that, though he was getting to be an old man, he wasn't an old woman yet.

That winter he stayed in the house in the afternoons and carpentered, or sat in the chair between the window full of plants and the wooden bench where the two pails of drinking water stood. This spot was called "Father's corner," though it was not a corner at all. He had a shelf there, where he kept his Bohemian papers and his pipes and tobacco, and his shears and needles and thread and tailor's thimble. Having been a tailor in his youth, he couldn't bear to see a woman patching at his clothes, or at the boys'. He liked tailoring, and always patched all the overalls and jackets

and work shirts. Occasionally he made over a pair of pants one
of the older boys had outgrown, for the little fellow.

While he sewed, he let his mind run back over his life. He
had a good deal to remember, really; life in three countries. The
only part of his youth he didn't like to remember was the two
years he had spent in London, in Cheapside, working for a German tailor who was wretchedly poor. Those days, when he was
nearly always hungry, when his clothes were dropping off him for
dirt, and the sound of a strange language kept him in continual
bewilderment, had left a sore spot in his mind that wouldn't bear
touching.

He was twenty when he landed at Castle Garden in New
York, and he had a protector who got him work in a tailor shop
in Vesey Street, down near the Washington Market. He looked
upon that part of his life as very happy. He became a good workman, he was industrious, and his wages were increased from time
to time. He minded his own business and envied nobody's good
fortune. He went to night school and learned to read English. He
often did overtime work and was well paid for it, but somehow
he never saved anything. He couldn't refuse a loan to a friend, and
he was self-indulgent. He liked a good dinner, and a little went for
beer, a little for tobacco; a good deal went to the girls. He often
stood through an opera on Saturday nights; he could get standing room for a dollar. Those were the great days of opera in New
York, and it gave a fellow something to think about for the rest
of the week. Rosicky had a quick ear, and a childish love of all
the stage splendor; the scenery, the costumes, the ballet. He
usually went with a chum, and after the performance they had
beer and maybe some oysters somewhere. It was a fine life; for the
first five years or so it satisfied him completely. He was never
hungry or cold or dirty, and everything amused him: a fire, a
dog fight, a parade, a storm, a ferry ride. He thought New York the
finest, richest, friendliest city in the world.

Moreover, he had what he called a happy home life. Very near
the tailor shop was a small furniture factory, where an old Au-
strian, Loeffler, employed a few skilled men and made unusual
furniture, most of it to order, for the rich German housewives up-
town. The top floor of Loeffler's five-story factory was a loft, where
he kept his choice lumber and stored the odd pieces of furniture

left on his hands. One of the young workmen he employed was a Czech, and he and Rosicky became fast friends. They persuaded Loeffler to let them have a sleeping room in one corner of the loft. They bought good beds and bedding and had their pick of the furniture kept up there. The loft was low-pitched, but light and airy, full of windows, and good-smelling by reason of the fine lumber put up there to season. Old Loeffler used to go down to the docks and buy wood from South America and the East from the sea captains. The young men were as foolish about their house as a bridal pair. Zichec, the young cabinetmaker, devised every sort of convenience, and Rosicky kept their clothes in order. At night and on Sundays, when the quiver of machinery underneath was still, it was the quietest place in the world, and on summer nights all the sea winds blew in. Zichec often practiced on his flute in the evening. They were both fond of music and went to the opera together. Rosicky thought he wanted to live like that for ever.

But as the years passed, all alike, he began to get a little restless. When spring came round, he would begin to feel fretted, and he got to drinking. He was likely to drink too much of a Saturday night. On Sunday he was languid and heavy, getting over his spree. On Monday he plunged into work again. So he never had time to figure out what ailed him, though he knew something did. When the grass turned green in Park Place, and the lilac hedge at the back of Trinity churchyard put out its blossoms, he was tormented by a longing to run away. That was why he drank too much; to get a temporary illusion of freedom and wide horizons.

Rosicky, the old Rosicky, could remember as if it were yesterday the day when the young Rosicky found out what was the matter with him. It was on a Fourth of July afternoon, and he was sitting in Park Place in the sun. The lower part of New York was empty. Wall Street, Liberty Street, Broadway, all empty. So much stone and asphalt with nothing going on, so many empty windows. The emptiness was intense, like the stillness in a great factory when the machinery stops and the belts and bands cease running. It was too great a change, it took all the strength out of one. Those blank buildings, without the stream of life pouring through them, were like empty jails. It struck young Rosicky that this was the trouble with big cities; they built you in from the earth itself, cemented you away from any contact with the ground. You lived in an unnatural world, like the fish in an aquarium, who were probably much more comfortable than they ever were in the sea.

On that very day he began to think seriously about the articles he had read in the Bohemian papers, describing prosperous Czech farming communities in the West. He believed he would like to go out there as a farm hand; it was hardly possible that he could ever have land of his own. His people had always been workmen; his father and grandfather had worked in shops. His mother's parents had lived in the country, but they rented their farm and had a hard time to get along. Nobody in his family had ever owned any land—that belonged to a different station of life altogether. Anton's mother died when he was little, and he was sent into the country to her parents. He stayed with them until he was twelve, and formed those ties with the earth and the farm animals and growing things which are never made at all unless they are made early. After his grandfather died, he went back to live with his father and stepmother, but she was very hard on him, and his father helped him to get passage to London.

After that Fourth of July day in Park Place, the desire to return to the country never left him. To work on another man's farm would be all he asked; to see the sun rise and set and to plant things and watch them grow. He was a very simple man. He was like a tree that has not many roots, but one taproot that goes down deep. He subscribed for a Bohemian paper printed in Chicago, then for one printed in Omaha. His mind got farther and farther west. He began to save a little money to buy his liberty. When he was thirty-five, there was a great meeting in New York of Bohemian athletic societies, and Rosicky left the tailor shop and went home with the Omaha delegates to try his fortune in another part of the world.

IV

Perhaps the fact that his own youth was well over before he began to have a family was one reason why Rosicky was so fond of his boys. He had almost a grandfather's indulgence for them. He had never had to worry about any of them—except, just now, a little about Rudolph.

On Saturday night the boys always piled into the Ford, took little Josephine, and went to town to the moving-picture show. One Saturday morning they were talking at the breakfast table about starting early that evening, so that they would have an hour or so to see the Christmas things in the stores before the show began. Rosicky looked down the table.

"I hope you boys ain't disappointed, but I want you to let me have de car tonight. Maybe some of you can go in with de neighbors."

Their faces fell. They worked hard all week, and they were still like children. A new jackknife or a box of candy pleased the older ones as much as the little fellow.

"If you and Mother are going to town," Frank said, "maybe you could take a couple of us along with you, anyway."

"No, I want to take de car down to Rudolph's, and let him an' Polly go in to de show. She don't git into town enough, an' I'm afraid she's gettin' lonesome, and he can't afford no car yet."

That settled it. The boys were a good deal dashed. Their father took another piece of apple cake and went on: "Maybe next Saturday night de two little fellers can go along wid dem."

"Oh, is Rudolph going to have the car every Saturday night?"

Rosicky did not reply at once; then he began to speak seriously: "Listen, boys; Polly ain't lookin' so good. I don't like to see nobody lookin' sad. It comes hard fur a town girl to be a farmer's wife. I don't want no trouble to start in Rudolph's family. When it starts, it ain't so easy to stop. An American girl don't git used to our ways all at once. I like to tell Polly she and Rudolph can have the car every Saturday night till after New Year's, if it's all right with you boys."

"Sure it's all right, Papa," Mary cut in. "And it's good you thought about that. Town girls is used to more than country girls. I lay awake nights, scared she'll make Rudolph discontented with the farm."

The boys put as good a face on it as they could. They surely looked forward to their Saturday nights in town. That evening Rosicky drove the car the half-mile down to Rudolph's new, bare little house.

Polly was in a short-sleeved gingham dress, clearing away the supper dishes. She was a trim, slim little thing, with blue eyes and shingled yellow hair, and her eyebrows were reduced to a mere brush stroke, like Miss Pearl's.

"Good evening, Mr. Rosicky. Rudolph's at the barn, I guess." She never called him father, or Mary mother. She was sensitive about having married a foreigner. She never in the world would have done it if Rudolph hadn't been such a handsome, persuasive fellow and such a gallant lover. He had graduated in her class in the high school in town, and their friendship began in the ninth grade.

Rosicky went in, though he wasn't exactly asked. "My boys ain't goin' to town tonight, an' I brought de car over fur you two to go in to de picture show."

Polly, carrying dishes to the sink, looked over her shoulder at him. "Thank you. But I'm late with my work tonight, and pretty tired. Maybe Rudolph would like to go in with you."

"Oh, I don't go to de shows! I'm too old-fashioned. You won't feel so tired after you ride in de air a ways. It's a nice clear night, an' it ain't cold. You go an' fix yourself up, Polly, an' I'll wash de dishes an' leave everything nice fur you."

Polly blushed and tossed her bob. "I couldn't let you do that, Mr. Rosicky. I wouldn't think of it."

Rosicky said nothing. He found a big apron on a nail behind the kitchen door. He slipped it over his head and then took Polly by her two elbows and pushed her gently toward the door of her own room. "I washed up de kitchen many times fur my wife, when de babies was sick or somethin'. You go an' make yourself look nice. I like you to look prettier'n any of dem town girls when you go in. De young folks must have some fun, an' I'm goin' to look out fur you, Polly."

That kind, reassuring grip on her elbows, the old man's funny bright eyes, made Polly want to drop her head on his shoulder for a second. She restrained herself, but she lingered in his grasp at the door of her room, murmuring tearfully: "You always lived in the city when you were young, didn't you? Don't you ever get lonesome out here?"

As she turned round to him, her hand fell naturally into his, and he stood holding it and smiling into her face with his peculiar, knowing, indulgent smile without a shadow of reproach in it. "Dem big cities is all right fur de rich, but dey is terrible hard fur de poor."

"I don't know. Sometimes I think I'd like to take a chance. You lived in New York, didn't you?"

"An' London. Da's bigger still. I learned my trade dere. Here's Rudolph comin', you better hurry."

"Will you tell me about London some time?"

"Maybe. Only I ain't no talker, Polly. Run an' dress yourself up."

The bedroom door closed behind her, and Rudolph came in from the outside, looking anxious. He had seen the car and was sorry any of his family should come just then. Supper hadn't been a very pleasant occasion. Halting in the doorway, he saw his father in a kitchen apron, carrying dishes to the sink. He flushed crimson and something flashed in his eye. Rosicky held up a warning finger.

"I brought de car over fur you an' Polly to go to de picture show, an' I made her let me finish here so you won't be late. You go put on a clean shirt, quick!"

"But don't the boys want the car, Father?"

"Not tonight dey don't." Rosicky fumbled under his apron and found his pants pocket. He took out a silver dollar and said in a hurried whisper: "You go an' buy dat girl some ice cream an' candy tonight, like you was courtin'. She's awful good friends wid me."

Rudolph was very short of cash, but he took the money as if it hurt him. There had been a crop failure all over the country. He had more than once been sorry he'd married this year.

In a few minutes the young people came out, looking clean and a little stiff. Rosicky hurried them off, and then he took his own time with the dishes. He scoured the pots and pans and put away the milk and swept the kitchen. He put some coal in the stove and shut off the drafts,[5] so the place would be warm for them when they got home late at night. Then he sat down and had a pipe and listened to the clock tick.

Generally speaking, marrying an American girl was certainly a risk. A Czech should marry a Czech. It was lucky that Polly was the daughter of a poor widow woman; Rudolph was proud, and if she had a prosperous family to throw up at him, they could never make it go. Polly was one of four sisters, and they all worked;

5. drafts: devices for regulating the flow of air in a stove or furnace.

one was a bookkeeper in the bank, one taught music, and Polly and her younger sister had been clerks, like Miss Pearl. All four of them were musical, had pretty voices, and sang in the Methodist choir, which the eldest sister directed.

Polly missed the sociability of a store position. She missed the choir, and the company of her sisters. She didn't dislike housework, but she disliked so much of it. Rosicky was a little anxious about this pair. He was afraid Polly would grow so discontented that Rudy would quit the farm and take a factory job in Omaha. He had worked for a winter up there, two years ago, to get money to marry on. He had done very well, and they would always take him back at the stockyards. But to Rosicky that meant the end of everything for his son. To be a landless man was to be a wage earner, a slave, all your life; to have nothing, to be nothing.

Rosicky thought he would come over and do a little carpentering for Polly after the New Year. He guessed she needed jollying. Rudolph was a serious sort of chap, serious in love and serious about his work.

Rosicky shook out his pipe and walked home across the fields. Ahead of him the lamplight shone from his kitchen windows. Suppose he were still in a tailor shop on Vesey Street, with a bunch of pale, narrow-chested sons working on machines, all coming home tired and sullen to eat supper in a kitchen that was a parlor also; with another crowded, angry family quarreling just across the dumb-waiter shaft, and squeaking pulleys at the windows where dirty washings hung on dirty lines above a court full of old brooms and mops and ash cans. . . .

He stopped by the windmill to look up at the frosty winter stars and draw a long breath before he went inside. That kitchen with the shining windows was dear to him; but the sleeping fields and bright stars and the noble darkness were dearer still.

V

On the day before Christmas the weather set in very cold; no snow, but a bitter, biting wind that whistled and sang over the flat land and lashed one's face like fine wires. There was baking going on in the Rosicky kitchen all day, and Rosicky sat inside, making over a coat that Albert had outgrown into an overcoat for John. Mary had a big red geranium in bloom for Christmas, and a row of Jerusalem cherry trees, full of berries. It was the first year she had ever grown these; Doctor Ed brought her the seeds from Omaha when he went to some medical convention. They reminded Rosicky of plants he had seen in England; and all afternoon, as he stitched, he sat thinking about those two years in London, which his mind usually shrank from even after all this while.

He was a lad of eighteen when he dropped down into London, with no money and no connections except the address of a cousin who was supposed to be working at a confectioner's. When he went to the pastry shop, however, he found that the cousin had gone to America. Anton tramped the streets for several days, sleeping in doorways and on the Embankment,[6] until he was in utter despair. He knew no English, and the sound of the strange language all about him confused him. By chance he met a poor German tailor who had learned his trade in Vienna, and could speak a little Czech. This tailor, Lifschnitz, kept a repair shop in a Cheapside basement, underneath a cobbler. He didn't much need an apprentice, but he was sorry for the boy and took him in for no wages but his keep and what he could pick up. The pickings were supposed to be coppers given you when you took work home to a customer. But most of the customers called for their clothes themselves, and the coppers that came Anton's way were very few. He had, however, a place to sleep. The tailor's family lived upstairs in three rooms; a kitchen, a bedroom, where Lifschnitz and his wife and five children slept, and a living room. Two corners of this living room were curtained off for lodgers; in one Rosicky slept on an old horsehair sofa, with a feather quilt to wrap himself in. The other corner was rented to a wretched, dirty boy, who was studying the violin. He actually practiced there. Rosicky was dirty, too. There was no way to be anything else. Mrs. Lifschnitz got the water she cooked and washed with from a pump in a brick court, four flights down. There were bugs in the place, and multitudes of fleas, though the poor woman did the best she could. Rosicky knew she often went empty to give another potato or a spoonful of dripping to the two hungry, sad-eyed boys who lodged with her. He used to think he would never

6. **the Embankment:** the elevated bank along the Thames River, used as a public walk.

get out of there, never get a clean shirt to his back again. What would he do, he wondered, when his clothes acutally dropped to pieces and the worn cloth wouldn't hold patches any longer?

It was still early when the old farmer put aside his sewing and his recollections. The sky had been a dark gray all day, with not a gleam of sun, and the light failed at four o'clock. He went to shave and change his shirt while the turkey was roasting. Rudolph and Polly were coming over for supper.

After supper they sat round in the kitchen, and the younger boys were saying how sorry they were it hadn't snowed. Everybody was sorry. They wanted a deep snow that would lie long and keep the wheat warm, and leave the ground soaked when it melted.

"Yes, sir!" Rudolph broke out fiercely. "If we have another dry year like last year, there's going to be hard times in this country."

Rosicky filled his pipe. "You boys don't know what hard times is. You don't owe nobody, you got plenty to eat an' keep warm, an' plenty water to keep clean. When you got them, you can't have it very hard."

Rudolph frowned, opened and shut his big right hand, and dropped it clenched upon his knee. "I've got to have a good deal more than that, Father, or I'll quit this farming gamble. I can always make good wages railroading, or at the packing house, and be sure of my money."

"Maybe so," his father answered dryly.

Mary, who had just come in from the pantry and was wiping her hands on the roller towel, thought Rudy and his father were getting too serious. She brought her darning basket and sat down in the middle of the group.

"I ain't much afraid of hard times, Rudy," she said heartily. "We've had a plenty, but we've always come through. Your father wouldn't never take nothing very hard, not even hard times. I got a mind to tell you a story on him. Maybe you boys can't hardly remember the year we had that terrible hot wind, that burned everything up on the Fourth of July? All the corn an' the gardens. An' that was in the days when we didn't have alfalfa yet—I guess it wasn't invented.

"Well, that very day your father was out cultivatin' corn, and I was here in the kitchen makin' plum preserves. We had bushels of plums that year. I noticed it was terrible hot, but it's always hot in the kitchen when you're preservin', an' I was too busy with my plums to mind. Anton come in from the field about three o'clock, an' I asked him what was the matter.

" 'Nothin',' he says, 'but it's pretty hot, an' I think I won't work no more today.' He stood round for a few minutes, an' then he says: 'Ain't you near through? I want you should git up a nice supper for us tonight. It's Fourth of July.'

"I told him to git along, that I was right in the middle of preservin', but the plums would taste good on hot biscuit. 'I'm goin' to have fried chicken, too,' he says, and he went off an' killed a couple. You three oldest boys was little fellers, playin' round outside, real hot an' sweaty, an' your father took you to the horse tank down by the windmill an' took off your clothes an' put you in. Them two box-elder trees was little then, but they made shade over the tank. Then he took off all his own clothes, an' got in with you. While he was playin' in the water with you, the Methodist preacher drove into our place to say how all the neighbors was goin' to meet at the schoolhouse that night, to pray for rain. He drove right to the windmill, of course, and there was your father and you three with no clothes on. I was in the kitchen door, an' I had to laugh, for the preacher acted like he ain't never seen a naked man before. He surely was embarrassed, an' your father couldn't git to his clothes; they was all hangin' up on the windmill to let the sweat dry out of 'em. So he laid in the tank where he was, an' put one of you boys on top of him to cover him up a little, an' talked to the preacher.

"When you got through playin' in the water, he put clean clothes on you and a clean shirt on himself, an' by that time I'd begun to get supper. He says: 'It's too hot in here to eat comfortable. Let's have a picnic in the orchard. We'll eat our supper behind the mulberry hedge, under them linden trees.'

"So he carried our supper down, an' a bottle of my wild-grape wine, an' everything tasted good, I can tell you. The wind got cooler as the sun was goin' down, and it turned out pleasant, only I noticed how the leaves was curled up on the linden trees. That made me think, an' I asked your father if that hot wind all day hadn't been terrible hard on the gardens an' the corn.

" 'Corn,' he says, 'there ain't no corn.'

" 'What you talkin' about?' I said. 'Ain't we got forty acres?'

" 'We ain't got an ear,' he says, 'nor nobody else ain't got none. All the corn in this country was cooked by three o'clock today, like you'd roasted it in an oven.'

" 'You mean you won't get no crop at all?' I asked him. I couldn't believe it, after he'd worked so hard.

" 'No crop this year,' he says. 'That's why we're havin' a picnic. We might as well enjoy what we got.'

"An' that's how your father behaved, when all the neighbors was so discouraged they couldn't look you in the face. An' we enjoyed ourselves that year, poor as we was, an' our neighbors wasn't a bit better off for bein' miserable. Some of 'em grieved till they got poor digestions and couldn't relish what they did have."

The younger boys said they thought their father had the best of it. But Rudolph was thinking that, all the same, the neighbors had managed to get ahead more, in the fifteen years since that time. There must be something wrong about his father's way of doing things. He wished he knew what was going on in the back of Polly's mind. He knew she liked his father, but he knew, too, that she was afraid of something. When his mother sent over coffee cake or prune tarts or a loaf of fresh bread, Polly seemed to regard them with a certain suspicion. When she observed to him that his brothers had nice manners, her tone implied that it was remarkable they should have. With his mother she was stiff and on her guard. Mary's hearty frankness and gusts of good humor irritated her. Polly was afraid of being unusual or conspicuous in any way, of being "ordinary," as she said!

When Mary had finished her story, Rosicky laid aside his pipe.

"You boys like me to tell you about some of dem hard times I been through in London?" Warmly encouraged, he sat rubbing his forehead along the deep creases. It was bothersome to tell a long story in English (he nearly always talked to the boys in Czech), but he wanted Polly to hear this one.

"Well, you know about dat tailor shop I worked in in London? I had one Christmas dere I ain't never forgot. Times was awful bad before Christmas; de boss ain't got much work, an' have it awful hard to pay his rent. It ain't so much fun, bein' poor in a big city like London, I'll say! All de windows is full of good t'ings to eat, an' all de pushcarts in de streets is full, an' you smell 'em all de time, an' you ain't got no money—not a damn bit. I didn't mind de cold so much, though I didn't have no overcoat, chust a short jacket I'd outgrowed so it wouldn't meet on me, an' my hands was chapped raw. But I always had a good appetite, like you all know, an' de sight of dem pork pies in de windows was awful fur me!

"Day before Christmas was terrible foggy dat year, an' dat fog gits into your bones and makes you all damp like. Mrs. Lifschnitz didn't give us nothin' but a little bread an' drippin' for supper, because she was savin' to try for to give us a good dinner on Christmas Day. After supper de boss say I can go an' enjoy myself, so I went into de streets to listen to de Christmas singers. Dey sing old songs an' make very nice music, an' I run round after dem a good ways, till I got awful hungry. I t'ink maybe if I go home, I can sleep till morning an' forgit my belly.

"I went into my corner real quiet, and roll up in my feeder quilt. But I ain't got my head down, till I smell somet'ing good. Seem like it git stronger an' stronger, an' I can't git to sleep noway. I can't understand dat smell. Dere was a gas light in a hall across de court, dat always shine in at my window a little. I got up an' look round. I got a little wooden box in my corner fur a stool, 'cause I ain't got no chair. I picks up dat box, and under it dere is a roast goose on a platter! I can't believe my eyes. I carry it to de window where de light comes in, an' touch it and smell it to find out, an' den I taste it to be sure. I say, I will eat chust one little bite of dat goose, so I can go to sleep, and tomorrow I won't eat none at all. But I tell you, boys, when I stop, one half of dat goose was gone!"

The narrator bowed his head, and the boys shouted. But little Josephine slipped behind his chair and kissed him on the neck beneath his ear.

"Poor little Papa, I don't want him to be hungry!"

"Da's long ago, child. I ain't never been hungry since I had your mudder to cook fur me."

"Go on and tell us the rest, please," said Polly.

"Well, when I come to realize what I done, of course, I felt terrible. I felt better in de stomach, but very bad in de heart. I set on my bed wid dat platter on my knees, an' it all come to me; how hard dat poor woman save to buy dat goose, and how she get some neighbor to cook it dat got more fire, an' how she put it in my corner to keep it away from dem hungry children. Dey was a old carpet hung up to shut my corner off, an' de children wasn't allowed to go in dere. An' I know she put it in my corner because she trust me more'n she did de violin boy. I can't stand it to face her after I spoil de Christmas. So I put on my shoes and go out into de city. I tell myself I better throw myself in de river, but I guess I ain't dat kind of a boy.

"It was after twelve o'clock, an' terrible cold, an' I start out to walk about London all night. I walk along de river awhile, but dey was lots of drunks all along; men, and women too. I chust move along to keep away from de police. I git onto de Strand, an' den over to New Oxford Street, where dere was a big German restaurant on de ground floor, wid big windows all fixed up fine, an' I could see de people havin' parties inside. While I was lookin' in, two men and two ladies come out, laughin' and talkin' and feelin' happy about all dey been eatin' and drinkin', and dey was speakin' Czech—not like de Austrians, but like de home folks talk it.

"I guess I went crazy, an' I done what I ain't never done before nor since. I went right up to dem gay people an' begun to beg dem: 'Fellow-countrymen, for God's sake give me money enough to buy a goose!'

"Dey laugh, of course, but de ladies speak awful kind to me, an' dey take me back into de restaurant and give me hot coffee and cakes, an' make me tell all about how I happened to come to London, an' what I was doin' dere. Dey take my name and where I work down on paper, an' both of dem ladies give me ten shillings.

"De big market at Covent Garden ain't very far away, an' by dat time it was open. I go dere an' buy a big goose an' some pork pies, an' potatoes and onions, an' cakes an' oranges fur de children —all I could carry! When I git home, everybody is still asleep. I pile all I bought on de kitchen table, an' go in an' lay down on my bed, an' I ain't waken up till I hear dat woman scream when she come out into her kitchen. My goodness, but she was surprise! She laugh an' cry at de same time, an' hug me and waken all de children. She ain't stop fur no breakfast; she git de Christmas dinner ready dat morning, and we all sit down an' eat all we can hold. I ain't never seen dat violin boy have all he can hold before.

"Two three days after dat, de two men come to hunt me up, an' dey ask my boss, and he give me a good report an' tell dem I was a steady boy all right. One of dem Bohemians was very smart an' run a Bohemian newspaper in New York, an' de odder was a rich man, in de importing business, an' dey been traveling togedder. Dey told me how t'ings was easier in New York, an' offered to pay my passage when dey was goin' home soon on a boat. My boss say to me: 'You go. You ain't got no chance here, an' I like to see you git ahead, fur you always been a good boy to my woman, and fur dat fine Christmas dinner you give us all.' An' da's how I got to New York."

That night when Rudolph and Polly, arm in arm, were running home across the fields with the bitter wind at their backs, his heart leaped for joy when she said she thought they might have his family come over for supper on New Year's Eve. "Let's get up a nice supper, and not let your mother help at all; make her be company for once."

"That would be lovely of you, Polly," he said humbly. He was a very simple, modest boy, and he, too, felt vaguely that Polly and her sisters were more experienced and worldly than his people.

VI

The winter turned out badly for farmers. It was bitterly cold, and after the first light snows before Christmas there was no snow at all—and no rain. March was as bitter as February. On those days when the wind fairly punished the country, Rosicky sat by his window. In the fall he and the boys had put in a big wheat planting, and now the seed had frozen in the ground. All that land would have to be plowed up and planted over again, planted in corn. It had happened before, but he was younger then, and he never worried about what had to be. He was sure of himself and of Mary; he knew they could bear what they had to bear, that they would always pull through somehow. But he was not so sure about the young ones, and he felt troubled because Rudolph and Polly were having such a hard start.

Sitting beside his flowering window while the panes rattled and the wind blew in under the door, Rosicky gave himself to reflection as he had not done since those Sundays in the loft of the furniture factory in New York, long ago. Then he was trying to find what he wanted in life for himself; now he was trying to find what he wanted for his boys, and why it was he so hungered to feel sure they would be here, working this very land, after he was gone.

They would have to work hard on the farm, and probably they would never do much more than make a living. But if he could think of them as staying here on the land, he wouldn't have to fear any great unkindness for them. Hardships, certainly; it was a hardship to have the wheat freeze in the ground when seed was so high; and to have to sell your stock because you had no feed. But there would be other years when everything came along right, and you caught up. And what you had was your own. You didn't have to choose between bosses and strikers, and go wrong either way. You didn't have to do with dishonest and cruel people. They were the only things in his experience he had found terrifying and horrible; the look in the eyes of a dishonest and crafty man, of a scheming and rapacious woman.

In the country, if you had a mean neighbor, you could keep off his land and make him keep off yours. But in the city, all the foulness and misery and brutality of your neighbors were part of your life. The worst things he had come upon in his journey through the world were human—depraved and poisonous specimens of man. To this day he could recall certain terrible faces in the London streets. There were mean people everywhere, to be sure, even in their own country town here. But they weren't tempered, hardened, sharpened, like the treacherous people in cities who live by grinding or cheating or poisoning their fellow men. He had helped to bury two of his fellow workmen in the tailoring trade, and he was distrustful of the organized industries that see one out of the world in big cities. Here, if you were sick, you had Doctor Ed to look after you; and if you died, fat Mr. Haycock, the kindest man in the world, buried you.

It seemed to Rosicky that for good, honest boys like his, the worst they could do on the farm was better than the best they would be likely to do in the city. If he'd had a mean boy, now, one who was crooked and sharp and tried to put anything over on his brothers, then town would be the place for him. But he had no such boy. As for Rudolph, the discontented one, he would give the shirt off his back to anyone who touched his heart. What Rosicky really hoped for his boys was that they could get through the world without ever knowing much about the cruelty of human beings. "Their mother and me ain't prepared them for that," he sometimes said to himself.

These thoughts brought him back to a grateful consideration of his own case. What an escape he had had, to be sure! He, too, in his time, had had to take money for repair work from the hand of a hungry child who let it go so wistfully, because it was money due his boss. And now, in all these years, he had never had to take a cent from any one in bitter need—never had to look at the face of a woman become like a wolf's from struggle and famine. When he thought of these things, Rosicky would put on his cap and jacket and slip down to the barn and give his workhorses a little extra oats, letting them eat it out of his hand in their slobbery fashion. It was his way of expressing what he felt, and made him chuckle with pleasure.

The spring came warm, with blue skies,—but dry, dry as a bone. The boys began plowing up the wheat fields to plant them over in corn. Rosicky would stand at the fence corner and watch them, and the earth was so dry it blew up in clouds of brown dust that hid the horses and the sulky plow and the driver. It was a bad outlook.

The big alfalfa field that lay between the home place and Rudolph's came up green, but Rosicky was worried because during that open windy winter a great many Russian thistle plants had blown in there and lodged. He kept asking the boys to rake them out; he was afraid their seed would root and "take the alfalfa." Rudolph said that was nonsense. The boys were working so hard planting corn, their father felt he couldn't insist about the thistles, but he set great store by that big alfalfa field. It was a feed you could depend on—and there was some deeper reason, vague, but strong. The peculiar green of that clover woke early memories in old Rosicky, went back to something in his childhood in the old world. When he was a little boy, he had played in fields of that strong blue-green color.

One morning, when Rudolph had gone to town in the car, leaving a work team idle in his barn, Rosicky went over to his son's place, put the horses to the buggy rake, and set about quietly raking up those thistles. He behaved with guilty caution, and rather enjoyed stealing a march on Doctor Ed, who was just then taking his first vacation in seven years of practice and was attending a clinic in Chicago. Rosicky got the thistles raked up, but did not stop to burn them. That would take some time, and his breath was pretty short, so he thought he had better get the horses back to the barn.

He got them into the barn and to their stalls, but the pain had come on so sharp in his chest that he didn't try to take the harness off. He started for the house, bending lower with every step. The cramp in his chest was shutting him up like a jackknife. When he reached the windmill, he swayed and caught at the ladder. He saw Polly coming down the hill, running with the swiftness of a slim greyhound. In a flash she had her shoulder under his armpit.

"Lean on me, Father, hard! Don't be afraid. We can get to the house all right."

Somehow they did, though Rosicky became blind with pain; he could keep on his legs, but he couldn't steer his course. The next thing he was conscious of was lying on Polly's bed, and Polly bending over him wringing out bath towels in hot water and putting them on his chest. She stopped only to throw coal into the stove, and she kept the teakettle and the black pot going. She put these hot applications on him for nearly an hour, she told him afterward, and all that time he was drawn up stiff and blue, with the sweat pouring off him.

As the pain gradually loosed its grip, the stiffness went out of his jaws, the black circles round his eyes disappeared, and a little of his natural color came back. When his daughter-in-law buttoned his shirt over his chest at last, he sighed.

"Da's fine, de way I feel now, Polly. It was a awful bad spell, an' I was so sorry it all come on you like it did."

Polly was flushed and excited. "Is the pain really gone? Can I leave you long enough to telephone over to your place?"

Rosicky's eyelids fluttered. "Don't telephone, Polly. It ain't no use to scare my wife. It's nice and quiet here, an' if I ain't too much trouble to you, just let me lay still till I feel like myself. I ain't got no pain now. It's nice here."

Polly bent over him and wiped the moisture from his face.

"Oh, I'm so glad it's over!" she broke out impulsively. "It just broke my heart to see you suffer so, Father."

Rosicky motioned her to sit down on the chair where the tea-kettle had been, and looked up at her with that lively affectionate gleam in his eyes. "You was awful good to me, I won't never forgit dat. I hate it to be sick on you like dis. Down at de barn I say to myself, dat young girl ain't had much experience in sickness, I don't want to scare her, an' maybe she's got a baby comin' or somet'ing."

Polly took his hand. He was looking at her so intently and affectionately and confidingly; his eyes seemed to caress her face, to regard it with pleasure. She frowned with her funny streaks of eyebrows, and then smiled back at him.

"I guess maybe there is something of that kind going to happen. But I haven't told anyone yet, not my mother or Rudolph. You'll be the first to know."

His hand pressed hers. She noticed that it was warm again. The twinkle in his yellow-brown eyes seemed to come nearer.

"I like mighty well to see dat little child, Polly," was all he said. Then he closed his eyes and lay half-smiling. But Polly sat still, thinking hard. She had a sudden feeling that nobody in the world, not her mother, not Rudolph, or anyone, really loved her as much as old Rosicky did. It perplexed her. She sat frowning and trying to puzzle it out. It was as if Rosicky had a special gift for loving people, something that was like an ear for music or an eye for color. It was quiet, unobtrusive; it was merely there. You saw it in his eyes—perhaps that was why they were merry. You felt it in his hands, too. After he dropped off to sleep, she sat holding his warm, broad, flexible brown hand. She had never seen another in the least like it. She wondered if it wasn't a kind of gypsy hand, it was so alive and quick and light in its communications—very strange in a farmer. Nearly all the farmers she knew had huge lumps of fists, like mauls,[7] or they were knotty and bony and uncomfortable looking, with stiff fingers. But Rosicky's was like quicksilver, flexible, muscular, about the color of a pale cigar, with deep, deep creases across the palm. It wasn't nervous, it wasn't a stupid lump; it was a warm brown human hand, with some

7. **mauls:** heavy hammers.

cleverness in it, a great deal of generosity, and something else which Polly could only call "gypsylike"—something nimble and lively and sure, in the way that animals are.

Polly remembered that hour long afterward; it had been like an awakening to her. It seemed to her that she had never learned so much about life from anything as from old Rosicky's hand. It brought her to herself; it communicated some direct and untranslatable message.

When she heard Rudolph coming in the car, she ran out to meet him.

"Oh, Rudy, your father's been awful sick! He raked up those thistles he's been worrying about, and afterwards he could hardly get to the house. He suffered so I was afraid he was going to die."

Rudolph jumped to the ground. "Where is he now?"

"On the bed. He's asleep. I was terribly scared, because, you know, I'm so fond of your father." She slipped her arm through his and they went into the house. That afternoon they took Rosicky home and put him to bed, though he protested that he was quite well again.

The next morning he got up and dressed and sat down to breakfast with his family. He told Mary that his coffee tasted better than usual to him, and he warned the boys not to bear any tales to Doctor Ed when he got home. After breakfast he sat down by his window to do some patching and asked Mary to thread several needles for him before she went to feed her chickens—her eyes were better than his, and her hands steadier. He lit his pipe and took up John's overalls. Mary had been watching him anxiously all morning, and as she went out of the door with her bucket of scraps, she saw that he was smiling. He was thinking, indeed, about Polly, and how he might never have known what a tender heart she had if he hadn't got sick over there. Girls nowadays didn't wear their heart on their sleeve. But now he knew Polly would make a fine woman after the foolishness wore off. Either a woman had that sweetness at her heart or she hadn't. You couldn't always tell by the look of them; but if they had that, everything came out right in the end.

After he had taken a few stitches, the cramp began in his chest, like yesterday. He put his pipe cautiously down on the window-sill and bent over to ease the pull. No use—he had better try to get to his bed if he could. He rose and groped his way across the familiar floor, which was rising and falling like the deck of a ship. At the door he fell. When Mary came in, she found him lying there, and the moment she touched him she knew that he was gone.

Doctor Ed was away when Rosicky died, and for the first few weeks after he got home he was hard driven. Every day he said to himself that he must get out to see that family that had lost their father. One soft, warm moonlight night in early summer he started for the farm. His mind was on other things, and not until his road ran by the graveyard did he realize that Rosicky wasn't over there on the hill where the red lamplight shone, but here, in the moonlight. He stopped his car, shut off the engine, and sat there for a while.

A sudden hush had fallen on his soul. Everything here seemed strangely moving and significant, though signifying what, he did not know. Close by the wire fence stood Rosicky's mowing-machine, where one of the boys had been cutting hay that afternoon; his own work-horses had been going up and down there. The new-cut hay perfumed all the night air. The moonlight silvered the long, billowy grass that grew over the graves and hid the fence; the few little evergreens stood out black in it, like shadows in a pool. The sky was very blue and soft, the stars rather faint because the moon was full.

For the first time it struck Doctor Ed that this was really a beautiful graveyard. He thought of city cemeteries; acres of shrubbery and heavy stone, so arranged and lonely and unlike anything in the living world. Cities of the dead, indeed; cities of the forgotten, of the "put away." But this was open and free, this little square of long grass which the wind for ever stirred. Nothing but the sky overhead, and the many-colored fields running on until they met that sky. The horses worked here in summer; the neighbors passed on their way to town; and over yonder, in the cornfield, Rosicky's own cattle would be eating fodder as winter came on. Nothing could be more undeathlike than this place; nothing could be more right for a man who had helped to do the work of great cities and had always longed for the open country and had got to it at last. Rosicky's life seemed to him complete and beautiful.

Meaning and Method

1. How does Rosicky react to the news that he has a bad heart? Does he seem worried? What does the conversation with Doctor Burleigh reveal about Rosicky's personality? What character traits of Rosicky emerge from the author's description of him?

2. In Part 1, the flashback to Doctor Burleigh's last breakfast with the Rosickys is used to provide exposition, or background material. Why did the Doctor drive out of his way to have breakfast at the Rosickys'? What do we learn about the family and their relationships with one another and with others outside the family?

   What kind of woman is Mrs. Rosicky? Although there is no physical description of Mrs. Rosicky, we feel we know her. How has Willa Cather conveyed her character and her personality?

3. Rosicky stops to contemplate the country graveyard and sees it as ". . . sort of snug and homelike, not cramped and mournful" (page 30). How do the setting and the other images in this paragraph help to carry out Rosicky's acceptance of what the graveyard signifies? Consider especially the connotations of the words in these phrases: *gold cornstalks, long red grass, fine snow falling steadily, with every little wind, settling upon the few little evergreens.*

   In the next paragraph the author writes, "The snow, falling over his barnyard and graveyard, seemed to draw things together like." What words in the paragraph extend the image of snow as a link between life and death and as a symbol of rest and peace?

4. On page 32, we read of Rosicky and his wife that "He was city-bred, and she was country-bred." What to Mary are the signs of Rosicky's city-bred ways or attitudes? In spite of this difference between them, what basic ideas or attitudes do they share?

5. Rosicky's disenchantment with city life began on a Fourth of July afternoon. Reread the section beginning on page 35 with "Rosicky, the old Rosicky, remembered as if it were yesterday the day when the young Rosicky found out what was the matter with him."

   Why is the repetition in this section of the words *empty* and *emptiness* suitable for both the setting and Rosicky's feelings? What is the significance of the day?

6. What do the anecdotes told by Rosicky and his wife on Christmas add to the story? to the characterization of Rosicky? to an understanding of his philosophy? to an appreciation of the theme of the story?

7. Why do you think Willa Cather used the word *neighbor* in her

title? What is the literal meaning of the word? What are some of its connotations? How does the word reflect Rosicky's character?

8. One interpretation of the character of Rosicky is that he represents the last of a dying breed of men—the pioneers, the rugged individualists who were to be replaced by the inroads of urbanization. How do Rosicky and his son differ in their values and attitudes toward life? Is their difference the conflict in the story —that is, do they represent country or frontier life versus town or city life? Or is the conflict one philosophy of life versus another? both? neither? something else?

9. How did Rosicky help his daughter-in-law Polly? What did she learn from him? Why could she justifiably say of him that *the best thing he did for her was to exist as a person?*

10. How do you explain Rosicky's calm acceptance of death? What was he doing when he died? Is there any connection between his occupation as a farmer and as a tailor?

11. The story starts with Rosicky's being told of his bad heart, and the reader knows that the man is going to die. Yet, the story is about life and not death. Why?

12. There is another picture of the country graveyard at the end of the story. Compare it with the earlier scene in the graveyard. How does the author vary the setting? Is the mood similar? What similarities are there in the thoughts of the characters in both scenes? What understanding of life—and death—do they both have?

    Why did Rosicky's life seem to Doctor Burleigh "complete and beautiful"? How may this be said to be the theme of the story?

Composition and Discussion

"To be a landless man was to be a wage earner, a slave all your life; to have nothing, to be nothing" (page 40). "In the country if you had a mean neighbor, you could keep off his land and make him keep off yours. But in the city, all the foulness and misery and brutality of your neighbors were part of your life" (page 48). These statements represent Neighbor Rosicky's views of country and city life.

Do you think that these views are valid and realistic? Or are they distorted and exaggerated? List the relative advantages and disadvantages of both city living and country living, and be prepared to argue in favor of one way of life against the other in a panel or an open-class discussion. To prepare for the discussion, write an outline listing your major and minor arguments and points.

Sherwood Anderson

[1876–1941]

Sherwood Anderson made a dramatic entrance into the literary world at the age of thirty-six. According to his version of the story, on November 27, 1912, he stopped in the middle of writing a business letter, abandoned both his family and the paint factory he owned in Elyria, Ohio, and went to "Bohemian" * Chicago to become a writer.

Anderson had gathered ample material for his stories in his experiences in the small midwestern towns he had lived and worked in over the years. He was born in Camden, Ohio, the third of seven children. His family was poor. His father, an easy-going man who enjoyed telling stories, failed to keep a steady job, and the family had to move from one Ohio town to another. For a while they settled in Clyde, where Anderson spent most of his boyhood days. He had little time for a formal education because he often had to leave school and take odd jobs to aid his family. When Anderson was nineteen, his mother died, his father disappeared, and the family split up.

During his twenties, Anderson served for a brief time with the Army (he fought in the Spanish-American War of 1898), wrote advertising copy for a firm in Chicago, and became president of a Cleveland mail-order firm, specializing in agricultural tools. By the time he was thirty-two he was able to buy his own paint factory. After four progressively less successful years in the paint business, Anderson became dissatisfied and sold the factory, leaving Cleveland for Chicago.

For eight years he stayed in Chicago, writing advertising copy for a living, meeting other writers such as Theodore Dreiser and Carl Sandburg, writing stories and novels, and waiting to be dis‧ covered. In 1916 his first book, *Windy McPherson's Son*, was published. A semiautobiographical novel, it told the story of a boy's life in a dull Iowa town and of his eventual renunciation of a business career.

* **"Bohemian"**: *here*, the artistic or literary life of the city, particularly the unconventional life of its free-and-easy artists.

Three years later, *Winesburg, Ohio* appeared. Each one of the twenty-three "tales" in the book is a psychological portrait of a sensitive individual in a small Ohio town, to which Anderson gave the fictional name "Winesburg." In the introduction Anderson writes that he sought "the truths that make these people grotesques."

The critic and teacher Mark Schorer explains the "grotesque" as a person formed "when an individual seizes on some single truth from the whole body of truths and tries to live by that alone. A single truth, a single wish, a single memory, a single obsessive ambition that distorts the self even as it compels it—these are the motivations of Sherwood Anderson's grotesques."

Each sketch in *Winesburg* has its own title, many of them abstractions, such as "Respectability," "Loneliness," "An Awakening," and "Death." Most of the events are seen through the eyes of George Willard, a young reporter on the *Winesburg Eagle*, who observes and reports but plays no active role until the last few sketches in the book, one of which is "Sophistication," the story presented here.

If his stories seem plotless, it is only because, as he once wrote, ". . . life itself is a loose, flowing thing. There are no plot stories in life." Anderson thus neglected plot, as such, and concentrated instead on the common folk who populate his fiction. He tried to think their thoughts; he strove to capture the rhythm and tone of their language. He adopted a colloquial style that was deliberately simple and even repetitious—the language of his perplexed and often frustrated characters, people who were generally unable to understand their own natures or the advancing technology of their environment.

As Anderson grew older, he became more and more disenchanted with the Bohemian city life that had once so charmed him. He left Chicago in 1920 for visits to New York and New Orleans, and, for a while, Europe. At the age of fifty, he returned to small-town life and settled in Marion, Virginia, home base for the remainder of his life. There he took up newspaper work and edited two local weeklies. He left Marion only for occasional lecture tours and trips abroad. He died en route to South America on one such trip in 1941.

Sophistication

It was early evening of a day in the late fall and the Winesburg County Fair had brought crowds of country people into town. The day had been clear, and the night came on warm and pleasant. On the Trunion Pike, where the road after it left town stretched away between berry fields now covered with dry brown leaves, the dust from passing wagons arose in clouds. Children, curled into little balls, slept on the straw scattered on wagon beds. Their hair was full of dust and their fingers black and sticky. The dust rolled away over the fields and the departing sun set it ablaze with colors.

In the main street of Winesburg crowds filled the stores and the sidewalks. Night came on, horses whinnied, the clerks in the stores ran madly about, children became lost and cried lustily, an American town worked terribly at the task of amusing itself.

Pushing his way through the crowds in Main Street, young George Willard concealed himself in the stairway leading to Doctor Reefy's office and looked at the people. With feverish eyes he watched the faces drifting past under the store lights. Thoughts kept coming into his head and he did not want to think. He stamped impatiently on the wooden steps and looked sharply about. "Well, is she going to stay with him all day? Have I done all this waiting for nothing?" he muttered.

George Willard, the Ohio village boy, was fast growing into manhood and new thoughts had been coming into his mind. All that day, amid the jam of people at the Fair, he had gone about feeling lonely. He was about to leave Winesburg to go away to some city where he hoped to get work on a city newspaper, and he felt grown up. The mood that had taken possession of him was a thing known to men and unknown to boys. He felt old and a little tired. Memories awoke in him. To his mind his new sense of maturity set him apart, made of him a half-tragic figure. He wanted someone to understand the feeling that had taken possession of him after his mother's death.

There is a time in the life of every boy when he for the first

"Sophistication" from *Winesburg, Ohio* by Sherwood Anderson, copyright 1919 B. W. Heubsch, Inc., 1947 Eleanor Copenhaver Anderson. Reprinted by permission of The Viking Press, Inc.

time takes the backward view of life. Perhaps that is the moment when he crosses the line into manhood. The boy is walking through the street of his town. He is thinking of the future and of the figure he will cut in the world. Ambitions and regrets awake within him. Suddenly something happens; he stops under a tree and waits as for a voice calling his name. Ghosts of old things creep into his consciousness; the voices outside of himself whisper a message concerning the limitations of life. From being quite sure of himself and his future he becomes not at all sure. If he be an imaginative boy a door is torn open and for the first time he looks out upon the world, seeing, as though they marched in procession before him, the countless figures of men who before his time have come out of nothingness into the world, lived their lives and again disappeared into nothingness. The sadness of sophistication has come to the boy. With a little gasp he sees himself as merely a leaf blown by the wind through the streets of his village. He knows that in spite of all the stout talk of his fellows he must live and die in uncertainty, a thing blown by the winds, a thing destined like corn to wilt in the sun. He shivers and looks eagerly about. The eighteen years he has lived seem but a moment, a breathing space in the long march of humanity. Already he hears death calling. With all his heart he wants to come close to some other human, touch someone with his hands, be touched by the hand of another. If he prefers that the other be a woman, that is because he believes that a woman will be gentle, that she will understand. He wants, most of all, understanding.

When the moment of sophistication came to George Willard his mind turned to Helen White, the Winesburg banker's daughter. Always he had been conscious of the girl growing into womanhood as he grew into manhood. Once on a summer night when he was eighteen, he had walked with her on a country road and in her presence had given way to an impulse to boast, to make himself appear big and significant in her eyes. Now he wanted to see her for another purpose. He wanted to tell her of the new impulses that had come to him. He had tried to make her think of him as a man when he knew nothing of manhood and now he wanted to be with her and to try to make her feel the change he believed had taken place in his nature.

As for Helen White, she also had come to a period of change.

What George felt, she in her young woman's way felt also. She was no longer a girl and hungered to reach into the grace and beauty of womanhood. She had come home from Cleveland, where she was attending college, to spend a day at the Fair. She also had begun to have memories. During the day she sat in the grandstand with a young man, one of the instructors from the college, who was a guest of her mother's. The young man was of a pedantic turn of mind and she felt at once he would not do for her purpose. At the Fair she was glad to be seen in his company as he was well dressed and a stranger. She knew that the fact of his presence would create an impression. During the day she was happy, but when night came on she began to grow restless. She wanted to drive the instructor away, to get out of his presence. While they sat together in the grandstand and while the eyes of former schoolmates were upon them, she paid so much attention to her escort that he grew interested. "A scholar needs money. I should marry a woman with money," he mused.

Helen White was thinking of George Willard even as he wandered gloomily through the crowds thinking of her. She remembered the summer evening when they had walked together and wanted to walk with him again. She thought that the months she had spent in the city, the going to theaters and the seeing of great crowds wandering in lighted thoroughfares, had changed her profoundly. She wanted him to feel and be conscious of the change in her nature.

The summer evening together that had left its mark on the memory of both the young man and woman had, when looked at quite sensibly, been rather stupidly spent. They had walked out of town along a country road. Then they had stopped by a fence near a field of young corn and George had taken off his coat and let it hang on his arm. "Well, I've stayed here in Winesburg—yes— I've not yet gone away but I'm growing up," he had said. "I've been reading books and I've been thinking. I'm going to try to amount to something in life.

"Well," he explained, "that isn't the point. Perhaps I'd better quit talking."

The confused boy put his hand on the girl's arm. His voice trembled. The two started to walk back along the road toward town. In his desperation George boasted, "I'm going to be a big man, the biggest that ever lived here in Winesburg," he declared. "I want you to do something, I don't know what. Perhaps it is none of my business. I want you to try to be different from other women. You see the point. It's none of my business I tell you. I want you to be a beautiful woman. You see what I want."

The boy's voice failed and in silence the two came back into town and went along the street to Helen White's house. At the gate he tried to say something impressive. Speeches he had thought out came into his head, but they seemed utterly pointless. "I thought—I used to think—I had it in my mind you would marry Seth Richmond. Now I know you won't," was all he could find to say as she went through the gate and toward the door of her house.

On the warm fall evening as he stood in the stairway and looked at the crowd drifting through Main Street, George thought of the talk beside the field of young corn and was ashamed of the figure he had made of himself. In the street the people surged up and down like cattle confined in a pen. Buggies and wagons almost filled the narrow thoroughfare. A band played and small boys raced along the sidewalk, diving between the legs of men. Young men with shining red faces walked awkwardly about with girls on their arms. In a room above one of the stores, where a dance was to be held, the fiddlers tuned their instruments. The broken sounds floated down through an open window and out across the murmur of voices and the loud blare of the horns of the band. The medley of sounds got on young Willard's nerves. Everywhere, on all sides, the sense of crowding, moving life closed in about him. He wanted to run away by himself and think. "If she wants to stay with that fellow, she may. Why should I care? What difference does it make to me?" he growled and went along Main Street and through Hern's grocery into a side street.

George felt so utterly lonely and dejected that he wanted to weep, but pride made him walk rapidly along, swinging his arms. He came to Westley Moyer's livery barn and stopped in the shadows to listen to a group of men who talked of a race Westley's stallion, Tony Tip, had won at the Fair during the afternoon. A crowd had gathered in front of the barn and before the crowd walked Westley, prancing up and down and boasting. He held a whip in his hand and kept tapping the ground. Little puffs of dust arose in the lamplight. "Hell, quit your talking," Westley exclaimed. "I wasn't afraid, I knew I had 'em beat all the time. I wasn't afraid."

Ordinarily George Willard would have been intensely interested in the boasting of Moyer, the horseman. Now it made him angry. He turned and hurried away along the street. "Old wind bag," he sputtered. "Why does he want to be bragging? Why don't he shut up?"

George went into a vacant lot and as he hurried along, fell over a pile of rubbish. A nail protruding from an empty barrel tore his trousers. He sat down on the ground and swore. With a pin he mended the torn place and then arose and went on. "I'll go to Helen White's house, that's what I'll do. I'll walk right in. I'll say that I want to see her. I'll walk right in and sit down, that's what I'll do," he declared, climbing over a fence and beginning to run.

On the veranda of Banker White's house Helen was restless and distraught. The instructor sat between the mother and daughter. His talk wearied the girl. Although he had also been raised in an Ohio town, the instructor began to put on the airs of the city. He wanted to appear cosmopolitan. "I like the chance you have given me to study the background out of which most of our girls come," he declared. "It was good of you, Mrs. White, to have me down for the day." He turned to Helen and laughed. "Your life is still bound up with the life of this town?" he asked. "There are people here in whom you are interested?" To the girl his voice sounded pompous and heavy.

Helen arose and went into the house. At the door leading to a garden at the back she stopped and stood listening. Her mother began to talk. "There is no one here fit to associate with a girl of Helen's breeding," she said.

Helen ran down a flight of stairs at the back of the house and into the garden. In the darkness she stopped and stood trembling. It seemed to her that the world was full of meaningless people saying words. Afire with eagerness she ran through a garden gate and turning a corner by the banker's barn, went into a little side street. "George! Where are you, George?" she cried, filled with nervous excitement. She stopped running, and leaned against a tree to laugh hysterically. Along the dark little street came George Willard, still saying words. "I'm going to walk right into her house. I'll go right in and sit down," he declared as he came up to her. He stopped and stared stupidly. "Come on," he said and took hold of her hand. With hanging heads they walked away along the street under the trees. Dry leaves rustled under foot. Now that he had found her George wondered what he had better do and say.

At the upper end of the fairground in Winesburg, there is a half decayed old grandstand. It has never been painted and the boards are all warped out of shape. The fairground stands on top of a low hill rising out of the valley of Wine Creek and from the grandstand one can see at night, over a cornfield, the lights of the town reflected against the sky.

George and Helen climbed the hill to the fairground, coming by the path past Waterworks Pond. The feeling of loneliness and isolation that had come to the young man in the crowded streets of his town was both broken and intensified by the presence of Helen. What he felt was reflected in her.

In youth there are always two forces fighting in people. The warm unthinking little animal struggles against the thing that reflects and remembers, and the older, the more sophisticated thing had possession of George Willard. Sensing his mood, Helen walked beside him filled with respect. When they got to the grandstand they climbed up under the roof and sat down on one of the long benchlike seats.

There is something memorable in the experience to be had by going into a fairground that stands at the edge of a Middle Western town on a night after the annual fair has been held. The sensation is one never to be forgotten. On all sides are ghosts, not of the dead, but of living people. Here, during the day just passed, have come the people pouring in from the town and the country around. Farmers with their wives and children and all the people from the hundreds of little frame houses have gathered within these board walls. Young girls have laughed and men with beards have talked of the affairs of their lives. The place has been filled to overflowing with life. It has itched and squirmed with life and now it is night and the life has all gone away. The silence is almost terrifying. One conceals oneself standing silently beside the trunk of a tree and what there is of a reflective tendency in his nature is intensified. One shudders at the thought of the meaninglessness of life while at the same instant, and if the people of the town are his people, one loves life so intensely that tears come into the eyes.

In the darkness under the roof of the grandstand, George Willard sat beside Helen White and felt very keenly his own insignificance in the scheme of existence. Now that he had come out of town where the presence of the people stirring about, busy with a multitude of affairs, had been so irritating, the irritation was all gone. The presence of Helen renewed and refreshed him. It was as though her woman's hand was assisting him to make some minute readjustment of the machinery of his life. He began to think of the people in the town where he had always lived with something like reverence. He had reverence for Helen. He wanted to love and to be loved by her, but he did not want at the moment to be confused by her womanhood. In the darkness he took hold of her hand and when she crept close put a hand on her shoulder. A wind began to blow and he shivered. With all his strength he tried to hold and to understand the mood that had come upon him. In that high place in the darkness the two oddly sensitive human atoms held each other tightly and waited. In the mind of each was the same thought. "I have come to this lonely place and here is this other," was the substance of the thing felt.

In Winesburg the crowded day had run itself out into the long night of the late fall. Farm horses jogged away along lonely country roads pulling their portion of weary people. Clerks began to bring samples of goods in off the sidewalks and lock the doors of stores. In the Opera House a crowd had gathered to see a show and further down Main Street the fiddlers, their instruments tuned, sweated and worked to keep the feet of youth flying over a dance floor.

In the darkness in the grandstand Helen White and George Willard remained silent. Now and then the spell that held them was broken and they turned and tried in the dim light to see int each other's eyes. They kissed but that impulse did not last. At the upper end of the fairground a half dozen men worked over horses that had raced during the afternoon. The men had built a fire and were heating kettles of water. Only their legs could be seen as they passed back and forth in the light. When the wind blew, the little flames of the fire danced crazily about.

George and Helen arose and walked away into the darkness. They went along a path past a field of corn that had not yet been cut. The wind whispered among the dry corn blades. For a moment during the walk back into town the spell that held them was broken. When they had come to the crest of Waterworks Hill they stopped by a tree and George again put his hands on the girl's shoulders. She embraced him eagerly and then again they drew quickly back from that impulse. They stopped kissing and stood a little apart. Mutual respect grew big in them. They were both embarrassed and to relieve their embarrassment dropped into the animalism of youth. They laughed and began to pull and haul at each other. In some way chastened and purified by the mood they had been in they became, not man and woman, not boy and girl, but excited little animals.

It was so they went down the hill. In the darkness they played like two splendid young things in a young world. Once, running swiftly forward, Helen tripped George and he fell. He squirmed and shouted. Shaking with laughter, he rolled down the hill. Helen ran after him. For just a moment she stopped in the darkness. There is no way of knowing what woman's thoughts went through her mind but, when the bottom of the hill was reached and she came up to the boy, she took his arm and walked beside him in dignified silence. For some reason they could not have explained they had both got from their silent evening together the thing needed. Man or boy, woman or girl, they had for a moment taken hold of the thing that makes the mature life of men and women in the modern world possible.

Meaning and Method

1. In the fifth paragraph of the story, the omniscient narrator says that "the sadness of sophistication has come to the boy." What does this statement mean? Paraphrase, or restate in your own words, the examples he gives to substantiate this statement. What qualities are basic to Anderson's idea of sophistication?

   How would you describe or characterize the narrator? Is he a sophisticated person, or is he a homespun philosopher-poet? Is he aware of or insensitive to the small things in life? Does he like or dislike, glorify or downgrade country life? Explain your answers and support them with references to the text.

2. Anderson uses George Willard to hold up his own view of life. He

also writes, through his narrator, direct authorial statements and commentaries, such as that beginning on page 58 with "There is a time in the life of every boy when for the first time he takes the backward view of life. Perhaps that is the moment when he crosses the line into manhood."

Do these direct commentaries of Anderson's make the story more expository and less narrative, more a vehicle for personal expression than a work of art?

3. This story seems to be told in retrospect, as if someone were looking back at events through the experience of years. Which sentences create the impression that the narrator is an older George Willard?

4. Why, in the midst of the swarming, small-town life—epitomized by the bustling fair itself—did George Willard feel loneliness and isolation? Were his loneliness and isolation the result of his disenchantment with small-town life? Were they part of his new awareness, his new sophistication? How are his feelings tied in with his plans to leave Winesburg?

5. How does the setting help externalize the conflict of the story?

6. Why does George react as he does to the boasting of Moyer, the horseman? Is this change in attitude a temporary or a permanent feeling? In what way is this incident symbolic?

7. Helen, too, is "restless and distraught." In what ways has her day been like George's? Does she understand his mood? Give reasons to support your answer.

8. What are the characteristics of the boy-girl relationship in "Sophistication"? Is this relationship different from the usual? If so, how? If not, why not?

9. The dialogue in this story seems to have little meaning of its own, but in its totality it contributes to the general effect the author is attempting to produce. Why, for example, does Anderson relate parts of the young instructor's conversation with Helen? How does the effect of his words on Helen help to characterize her mood? How does the instructor's conversation help to characterize him? What is he like? How does he differ from George Willard?

Composition

1. To write a good description one must know how to use details. Sherwood Anderson, for example, wants us to see what the fairgrounds are like after the crowds have gone. To do this he lets the reader "see" for himself what it was like when the crowds were *present*. He mentions the activity of the farmers, wives, children, and

of the young girls in particular. When he finally writes, "The silence was almost terrifying," we can understand why.

Write a two- or three-paragraph description in which you convey your impression of a place that was previously filled with gaiety and excitement and activity but is now deserted. You may wish to describe the empty stands after a football or basketball game, a deserted classroom or lunchroom, a dancehall as the musicians prepare to leave, or any other such place. In your first sentence, state your overall impression of the vacated scene and the feeling it created in you. Then use precise details to recreate for your reader what the scene was like when it was filled with activity.

2. Perhaps you have your own ideas about what the word *sophistication* means, in terms of both its denotation and its connotation(s). List what you feel are the essential qualities or characteristics that the word brings to mind. Then give several concrete examples to illustrate these characteristics.

3. In what way is Anderson's statement that man is "merely a leaf blown by the winds through the streets of his village" similar to or different from the philosophy of life expressed by Katherine Anne Porter in "The Jilting of Granny Weatherall"?

Write an expository essay comparing and/or contrasting the philosophy of life expressed in the two stories.

Stephen Vincent Benét

[1898–1943]

"It's always seemed to me that legends and yarns
and folk tales are as much a part of the real history of a
country as proclamations and provisos and constitutional
amendments."

—Stephen Vincent Benét

Benét was born in Bethlehem, Pennsylvania, the son of a
career army officer. Both Stephen Vincent Benét and his brother,
William Rose Benét, broke a family tradition by not entering the
military life. Along with their sister, Laura Benét, they chose a
literary career. The turnabout is not surprising, however, for their
father had always kept a well-stocked library that moved with the
family from army installation to installation. He enjoyed reading
poems and stories to his children and, as they grew older, encouraged them to develop writing skills.

While Stephen Vincent Benét was still a student at Yale—
from which he received a bachelor's degree in 1919 and a master's
in 1920—he published at his own expense two early collections of
his verse, *Five Men and Pompey* (1915) and *Young Adventure*
(1918). His first novel was *The Beginning of Wisdom* (1921), a
somewhat unsuccessful attempt at a tale of "flaming youth."

By the mid 1920's, Benét was well into a special project, the
creation of an American epic about the Civil War, *John Brown's
Body*, and, with the help of a fellowship, was able to complete the
verse narrative for publication in 1928. The work begins with background about the intersectional dispute over slavery that led to the
war. It then relates episodes about John Brown's raid on the strong-
hold at Harpers Ferry, West Virginia, in 1859, his capture and
execution, and the opening of the Civil War. It also presents
individuals involved in the war—Abraham Lincoln and Jefferson
Davis, Generals Robert E. Lee, Stonewall Jackson, and U. S. Grant,
and other, fictional figures who served as common soldiers for both
sides or whose lives were otherwise disrupted by the war. Through
the narrative, Benét shows the sharp division between North and
South that, by war's end, left the Southern dream of a patriarchal,

agrarian aristocracy shattered forever and the Northern way of mechanization and industrialism in ascendancy. The epic was a popular and critical success, and won Benét the Pulitzer prize for poetry in 1929.

More poems and prose works followed, including *Ballads and Poems*, 1915–1930, collected in 1931. Shortly before the outbreak of World War II, Benét wrote *Nightmare at Noon*, an impassioned poem warning America to wake up and react against the peril of fascism. During the war, Benét wrote radio scripts and speeches, *gratis*, for the Federal Government.

Shortly before he died, Benét also completed the first section of what was to have been another American epic, this one tracing the westward-moving American frontier from the Jamestown and Plymouth settlements to California. The poem was entitled *Western Star*, and it won Benét a second Pulitzer prize, awarded posthumously in 1944.

"The Devil and Daniel Webster," presented here, takes the form of historical legend or folk tale. Of it Benét once commented, "I couldn't help trying to show [Webster] in terms of American legend; I couldn't help wondering what would happen if a man like that ever came to grips with the Devil—and not an imported devil, either, but a genuine, homegrown product, Mr. Scratch."

The Devil and Daniel Webster

It's a story they all tell in the border country, where Massachusetts joins Vermont and New Hampshire.

Yes, Dan'l Webster's dead—or, at least, they buried him. But every time there's a thunderstorm around Marshfield,[1] they say you can hear his rolling voice in the hollows of the sky. And they say that if you go to his grave and speak loud and clear,

1. **Marshfield:** the small Massachusetts town southeast of Boston where Webster maintained his farm and spent most of his private life.

"Dan'l Webster—Dan'l Webster!" the ground'll begin to shiver and the trees begin to shake. And after a while you'll hear a deep voice saying, "Neighbor, how stands the Union?" Then you better answer: the Union stands as she stood, rock-bottomed and copper-sheathed, one and indivisible, or he's liable to rear right out of the ground. At least, that's what I was told when I was a youngster.

You see, for a while, he was the biggest man in the country. He never got to be President, but he was the biggest man. There were thousands that trusted in him right next to God Almighty, and they told stories about him and all the things that belonged to him that were like the stories of patriarchs [2] and such. They said when he stood up to speak, stars and stripes came right out in the sky, and once he spoke against a river and made it sink into the ground. They said when he walked the woods with his fishing rod Killall, the trout would jump out of the streams right into his pockets, for they knew it was no use putting up a fight against him; and, when he argued a case, he could turn on the harps of the blessed and the shaking of the earth underground. That was the kind of man he was, and his big farm up at Marshfield was suitable to him. The chickens he raised were all white meat down through the drumsticks, the cows were tended like children, and the big ram he called Goliath [3] had horns with a curl like a morning-glory vine and could butt through an iron door. But Dan'l wasn't one of your gentlemen farmers; he knew all the ways of the land, and he'd be up by candlelight to see that the chores got done. A man with a mouth like a mastiff, a brow like a mountain, and eyes like burning anthracite—that was Dan'l Webster in his prime. And the biggest case he argued never got written down in the books, for he argued it against the devil, nip and tuck, and no holds barred. And that is the way I used to hear it told:

There was a man named Jabez Stone, lived at Cross Corners, New Hampshire. He wasn't a bad man to start with, but he was an unlucky man. If he planted corn, he got borers; if he planted

---

2. patriarchs (pā′trē·ärks): commonly, leaders of families, clans, or tribes who rule by paternal authority. Here, the term probably has a biblical significance and might also refer to the twelve sons of Jacob, regarded as the founders and leaders (*i.e.*, patriarchs) of the twelve tribes of Israel.
3. Goliath: the name of the biblical Philistine giant slain by young David, described in I Samuel 17:4.

potatoes, he got blight.[4] He had good enough land, but it didn't prosper him; he had a decent wife and children, but the more children he had, the less there was to feed them. If stones cropped up in his neighbor's field, boulders boiled up in his; if he had a horse with the spavins, he'd trade it for one with the staggers [5] and give something extra. There's some folks bound to be like that, apparently. But one day Jabez Stone got sick of the whole business.

He'd been plowing that morning and he'd just broke the plowshare on a rock that he could have sworn hadn't been there yesterday. And, as he stood looking at the plowshare, the off horse began to cough—that ropy kind of cough [6] that means sickness and horse doctors. There were two children down with the measles, his wife was ailing, and he had a whitlow [7] on his thumb. It was about the last straw for Jabez Stone. "I vow," he said, and he looked around him kind of desperate—"I vow it's enough to make a man want to sell his soul to the devil! And I would, too, for two cents!"

Then he felt a kind of queerness come over him at having said what he'd said; though, naturally, being a New Hampshireman, he wouldn't take it back. But, all the same, when it got to be evening and, as far as he could see, no notice had been taken, he felt relieved in his mind, for he was a religious man. But notice is always taken, sooner or later, just like the Good Book says. And, sure enough, the next day, about suppertime, a soft-spoken, dark-dressed stranger drove up in a handsome buggy and asked for Jabez Stone.

Well, Jabez told his family it was a lawyer, come to see him about a legacy. But he knew who it was. He didn't like the looks of the stranger, nor the way he smiled with his teeth. They were white teeth, and plentiful—some say they were filed to a point, but I wouldn't vouch for that. And he didn't like it when the dog took one look at the stranger and ran away howling, with his tail between his legs. But having passed his word, more or less, he stuck to it, and they went out behind the barn and made their

4. **borers . . . blight:** borers are worms that bore into and thus destroy corn plants; blight is a fungoid rust, scale, or mildew that attacks leafy plants.
5. **spavins** (spav'ins) **. . . the staggers:** spavins is a joint disease that often afflicts horses; the staggers is another disease of domestic animals, characterized by vertigo (dizziness), staggering, and stumbling.
6. **off horse . . . ropy kind of cough:** the off horse is the one on the right-hand side of a team (the other is the *near* horse); its ropy cough is a roupy cough (*roupy* is Scottish dialect for *hoarse*).
7. **whitlow:** an inflammation at the fingertip.

bargain. Jabez Stone had to prick his finger to sign, and the stranger lent him a silver pen. The wound healed clean, but it left a little white scar.

After that, all of a sudden, things began to pick up and prosper for Jabez Stone. His cows got fat and his horses sleek, his crops were the envy of the neighborhood, and lightning might strike all over the valley, but it wouldn't strike his barn. Pretty soon, he was one of the prosperous people of the county; they asked him to stand for selectman,[8] and he stood for it; there began to be talk of running him for state senate. All in all, you might say the Stone family was as happy and contented as cats in a dairy. And so they were, except for Jabez Stone.

He'd been contented enough, the first few years. It's a great thing when bad luck turns; it drives most other things out of your head. True, every now and then, especially in rainy weather, the little white scar on his finger would give him a twinge. And once a year, punctual as clockwork, the stranger with the handsome buggy would come driving by. But the sixth year, the stranger lighted, and, after that, his peace was over for Jabez Stone.

The stranger came up through the lower field, switching his boots with a cane—they were handsome black boots, but Jabez Stone never liked the look of them, particularly the toes. And, after he'd passed the time of day, he said, "Well, Mr. Stone, you're a hummer! It's a very pretty property you've got here, Mr. Stone."

"Well, some might favor it and others might not," said Jabez Stone, for he was a New Hampshireman.

"Oh, no need to decry your industry!" said the stranger, very easy, showing his teeth in a smile. "After all, we know what's been done, and it's been according to contract and specifications. So when—ahem—the mortgage falls due next year, you shouldn't have any regrets."

"Speaking of that mortgage, mister," said Jabez Stone, and he looked around for help to the earth and the sky, "I'm beginning to have one or two doubts about it."

"Doubts?" said the stranger, not quite so pleasantly.

"Why, yes," said Jabez Stone. "This being the U.S.A. and me always having been a religious man." He cleared his throat and

8. **selectman:** Many New England towns elect officials to serve as village trustees or board members.

got bolder. "Yes, sir," he said, "I'm beginning to have considerable doubts as to that mortgage holding in court."

"There's courts and courts," said the stranger, clicking his teeth. "Still, we might as well have a look at the original document." And he hauled out a big black pocketbook, full of papers. "Sherwin, Slater, Stevens, Stone," he muttered. "I, Jabez Stone, for a term of seven years— Oh, it's quite in order, I think."

But Jabez Stone wasn't listening, for he saw something else flutter out of the black pocketbook. It was something that looked like a moth, but it wasn't a moth. And as Jabez Stone stared at it, it seemed to speak to him in a small sort of piping voice, terrible small and thin, but terrible human.

"Neighbor Stone!" it squeaked. "Neighbor Stone! Help me! I beg you, help me!"

But before Jabez Stone could stir hand or foot, the stranger whipped out a big bandanna handkerchief, caught the creature in it, just like a butterfly, and started tying up the ends of the bandanna.

"Sorry for the interruption," he said. "As I was saying—"

But Jabez Stone was shaking all over like a scared horse.

"That's Miser Stevens' voice!" he said, in a croak. "And you've got him in your handkerchief!"

The stranger looked a little embarrassed.

"Yes, I really should have transferred him to the collecting box," he said with a simper, "but there were some rather unusual specimens there and I didn't want them crowded. Well, well, these little contretemps [9] will occur."

"I don't know what you mean by contertan," said Jabez Stone, "but that was Miser Stevens' voice! And he ain't dead! You can't tell me he is! He was just as spry and mean as a woodchuck, Tuesday!"

"In the midst of life—" [10] said the stranger, kind of pious. "Listen!" Then a bell began to toll in the valley, and Jabez Stone

9. **contretemps** (kôn·trə·tän′): *from the French*, an embarrassing situation or mishap.
10. **"In the midst of life—"**: part of a line from *The Book of Common Prayer*, the book of ritual of the Church of England and, slightly modified, of other Anglican churches. The full line reads, "In the midst of life we are in death."

listened, with the sweat running down his face. For he knew it was tolled for Miser Stevens and that he was dead.

"These long-standing accounts," said the stranger with a sigh; "one really hates to close them. But business is business."

He still had the bandanna in his hand, and Jabez Stone felt sick as he saw the cloth struggle and flutter.

"Are they all as small as that?" he asked hoarsely.

"Small?" said the stranger. "Oh, I see what you mean. Why, they vary." He measured Jabez Stone with his eyes, and his teeth showed. "Don't worry, Mr. Stone," he said. "You'll go with a very good grade. I wouldn't trust you outside the collecting box. Now, a man like Dan'l Webster, of course—well, we'd have to build a special box for him, and even at that, I imagine the wing-spread would astonish you. He'd certainly be a prize. I wish we could see our way clear to him. But, in your case, as I was saying—"

"Put that handkerchief away!" said Jabez Stone, and he began to beg and to pray. But the best he could get at the end was a three years' extension, with conditions.

But till you make a bargain like that, you've got no idea of how fast four years can run. By the last months of those years, Jabez Stone's known all over the state and there's talk of running him for governor—and it's dust and ashes in his mouth. For every day, when he gets up, he thinks, "There's one more night gone," and every night when he lies down, he thinks of the black pocket-book and the soul of Miser Stevens, and it makes him sick at heart. Till, finally, he can't bear it any longer, and, in the last days of the last year, he hitches up his horse and drives off to seek Dan'l Webster. For Dan'l Webster was born in New Hampshire, only a few miles from Cross Corners, and it's well known that he has a particular soft spot for old neighbors.

It was early in the morning when he got to Marshfield, but Dan'l was up already, talking Latin to the farm hands and wrestling with the ram, Goliath, and trying out a new trotter and working up speeches to make against John C. Calhoun.[11] But when he heard a New Hampshireman had come to see him, he

11. **John C. Calhoun** (1782–1850): Calhoun was the nation's Vice President from 1825 to 1832, and therefore presided over the Senate debates on the issues of tariffs, secession, and nullification. Outside the Senate he was a champion of states' rights and nullification.

dropped everything else he was doing, for that was Dan'l's way. He gave Jabez Stone a breakfast that five men couldn't eat, went into the living history of every man and woman in Cross Corners, and finally asked him how he could serve him.

Jabez Stone allowed that it was a kind of mortgage case.

"Well, I haven't pleaded a mortgage case in a long time, and I don't generally plead now, except before the Supreme Court," said Dan'l, "but if I can, I'll help you."

"Then I've got hope for the first time in ten years," said Jabez Stone, and told him the details.

Dan'l walked up and down as he listened, hands behind his back, now and then asking a question, now and then plunging his eyes at the floor, as if they'd bore through it like gimlets.[12] When Jabez Stone had finished, Dan'l puffed out his cheeks and blew. Then he turned to Jabez Stone, and a smile broke over his face like the sunrise over Monadnock.[13]

"You've certainly given yourself the devil's own row to hoe, Neighbor Stone," he said, "but I'll take your case."

"You'll take it?" said Jabez Stone, hardly daring to believe.

"Yes," said Dan'l Webster. "I've got about seventy-five other things to do and the Missouri Compromise[14] to straighten out, but I'll take your case. For if two New Hampshiremen aren't a match for the devil, we might as well give the country back to the Indians."

Then he shook Jabez Stone by the hand and said, "Did you come down here in a hurry?"

"Well, I admit I made time," said Jabez Stone.

"You'll go back faster," said Dan'l Webster, and he told 'em to hitch up Constitution and Constellation[15] to the carriage. They

12. gimlets (gim′lits): a gimlet is a small awl or auger, used for boring holes. *Gimlet eyes* is a stock figure denoting eyes that probe with piercing intensity.
13. Monadnock (mə·nad′nok): an isolated, abrupt peak rising in southern New Hampshire. As a common noun, *monadnock* denotes any mountain rising sharply from a plain.
14. Missouri Compromise: Federal legislation passed in 1821 in hopes of settling the question of slavery in states admitted to the Union after 1821. Missouri was admitted as a slave state that year, but states admitted thereafter and situated, like Missouri, above latitude (36° 30′) would be free states. Webster was instrumental in effecting the final compromise agreement.
15. Constitution and Constellation: Webster's horses were named after two famous American frigates used in the War of 1812. The *Constitution* was also called "Old Ironsides."

were matched grays with one white forefoot, and they stepped like greased lightning.

Well, I won't describe how excited and pleased the whole Stone family was to have the great Dan'l Webster for a guest, when they finally got there. Jabez Stone had lost his hat on the way, blown off when they overtook a wind, but he didn't take much account of that. But after supper he sent the family off to bed, for he had most particular business with Mr. Webster. Mrs. Stone wanted them to sit in the front parlor, but Dan'l Webster knew front parlors and said he preferred the kitchen. So it was there they sat, waiting for the stranger, with a jug on the table between them and a bright fire on the hearth—the stranger being scheduled to show up on the stroke of midnight, according to specification.

Well, most men wouldn't have asked for better company than Dan'l Webster and a jug. But with every tick of the clock Jabez Stone got sadder and sadder. His eyes roved round and though he sampled the jug, you could see he couldn't taste it. Finally, on the stroke of eleven-thirty, he reached over and grabbed Dan'l Webster by the arm.

"Mr. Webster, Mr. Webster!" he said, and his voice was shaking with fear and a desperate courage. "For God's sake, Mr. Webster, harness your horses and get away from this place while you can!"

"You've brought me a long way, neighbor, to tell me you don't like my company," said Dan'l Webster, quite peaceable, pulling at the jug.

"Miserable wretch that I am!" groaned Jabez Stone. "I've brought you a devilish way, and now I see my folly. Let him take me if he wills. I don't hanker after it, I must say, but I can stand it. But you're the Union's stay and New Hampshire's pride! He mustn't get you, Mr. Webster! He mustn't get you!"

Dan'l Webster looked at the distracted man, all gray and shaking in the firelight, and laid a hand on his shoulder.

"I'm obliged to you, Neighbor Stone," he said gently. "It's kindly thought of. But there's a jug on the table and a case in hand. And I never left a jug or a case half finished in my life."

And just at that moment there was a sharp rap on the door.

"Ah," said Dan'l Webster, very coolly, "I thought your clock was a trifle slow, Neighbor Stone." He stepped to the door and opened it. "Come in!" he said.

The stranger came in—very dark and tall he looked in the firelight. He was carrying a box under his arm—a black, japanned box with little air holes in the lid. At the sight of the box, Jabez Stone gave a low cry and shrank into a corner of the room.

"Mr. Webster, I presume," said the stranger, very polite, but with his eyes glowing like a fox's deep in the woods.

"Attorney of record for Jabez Stone," said Dan'l Webster, but his eyes were glowing too. "Might I ask your name?"

"I've gone by a good many," said the stranger carelessly. "Perhaps Scratch will do for the evening. I'm often called that in these regions."

Then he sat down at the table and poured himself a drink from the jug. The liquor was cold in the jug, but it came steaming into the glass.

"And now," said the stranger, smiling and showing his teeth, "I shall call upon you, as a law-abiding citizen, to assist me in taking possession of my property."

Well, with that the argument began—and it went hot and heavy. At first, Jabez Stone had a flicker of hope, but when he saw Dan'l Webster being forced back at point after point, he just sat scrunched in his corner, with his eyes on that japanned box. For there wasn't any doubt as to the deed or the signature—that was the worst of it. Dan'l Webster twisted and turned and thumped his fist on the table, but he couldn't get away from that. He offered to compromise the case; the stranger wouldn't hear of it. He pointed out the property had increased in value, and state senators ought to be worth more; the stranger stuck to the letter of the law. He was a great lawyer, Dan'l Webster, but we know who's the King of Lawyers, as the Good Book tells us, and it seemed as if, for the first time, Dan'l Webster had met his match.

Finally, the stranger yawned a little. "Your spirited efforts on behalf of your client do you credit, Mr. Webster," he said, "but if you have no more arguments to adduce,[16] I'm rather pressed for time—" and Jabez Stone shuddered.

---

16. **adduce:** cite; bring forward for consideration. From Latin *adducere*, to lead to, to bring to.

Dan'l Webster's brow looked dark as a thundercloud. "Pressed or not, you shall not have this man!" he thundered. "Mr. Stone is an American citizen, and no American citizen may be forced into the service of a foreign prince. We fought England for that in '12 [17] and we'll fight all hell for it again!"

"Foreign?" said the stranger. "And who calls me a foreigner?"

"Well, I never yet heard of the dev—of your claiming American citizenship," said Dan'l Webster with surprise.

"And who with better right?" said the stranger, with one of his terrible smiles. "When the first wrong was done to the first Indian, I was there. When the first slaver put out for the Congo, I stood on her deck. Am I not in your books and stories and beliefs, from the first settlements on? Am I not spoken of, still, in every church in New England? 'Tis true the North claims me for a Southerner, and the South for a Northerner, but I am neither. I am merely an honest American like yourself—and of the best descent—for, to tell the truth, Mr. Webster, though I don't like to boast of it, my name is older in this country than yours."

"Aha!" said Dan'l Webster, with the veins standing out in his forehead. "Then I stand on the Constitution! I demand a trial for my client!"

"The case is hardly one for an ordinary court," said the stranger, his eyes flickering. "And, indeed, the lateness of the hour—"

"Let it be any court you choose, so it is an American judge and an American jury!" said Dan'l Webster in his pride. "Let it be the quick [18] or the dead; I'll abide the issue!"

"You have said it," said the stranger, and pointed his finger at the door. And with that, and all of a sudden, there was a rushing of wind outside and a noise of footsteps. They came, clear and distinct, through the night. And yet, they were not like the footsteps of living men.

"In God's name, who comes by so late?" cried Jabez Stone, in an ague of fear.

"The jury Mr. Webster demands," said the stranger, sipping at his boiling glass. "You must pardon the rough appearance of one or two; they will have come a long way."

---

17. '12: the War of 1812, among the causes of which was the impressing of American sailors into the British navy.
18. the quick: the living.

And with that the fire burned blue [19] and the door blew open and twelve men entered, one by one.

If Jabez Stone had been sick with terror before, he was blind with terror now. For there was Walter Butler, the Loyalist, who spread fire and horror through the Mohawk Valley in the times of the Revolution; and there was Simon Girty, the renegade, who saw white men burned at the stake and whooped with the Indians to see them burn. His eyes were green, like a catamount's,[20] and the stains on his hunting shirt did not come from the blood of the deer. King Philip was there, wild and proud as he had been in life, with the great gash in his head that gave him his death wound, and cruel Governor Dale, who broke men on the wheel.[21] There was Morton of Merry Mount, who so vexed the Plymouth Colony, with his flushed, loose, handsome face and his hate of the godly. There was Teach, the bloody pirate, with his black beard curling on his breast. The Reverend John Smeet,[22] with his strangler's hands and his Geneva gown,[23] walked as daintily as he had to the gallows. The red print of the rope was still around his neck, but he carried a perfumed handkerchief in one hand. One and all, they came into the room with the fires of hell still upon them, and the stranger named their names and their deeds as they came, till the tale of twelve was told. Yet the stranger had told the truth—they had all played a part in America.

19. **the fire burned blue:** Blue is the color of the flame produced by burning brimstone.
20. **catamount's:** catamountain's (from *cat of the mountain*); mountain lion's or lynx's.
21. **broke men on the wheel:** The wheel, like the rack, was an instrument of torture.
22. **King Philip . . . Governor Dale . . . Morton of Merry Mount . . . Teach . . . Reverend John Smeet:** in their days and ways notable sinners in colonial history. King Philip was an Indian chief (Metacomet) who led massacres of many New England settlements, 1675–76; Governor Thomas Dale was a harsh overseer of the Virginia colony, whose years of tenure (1611–16) were called the "years of slavery" by the colonists; Thomas Morton was an English lawyer who was expelled from the Plymouth colony for selling rum and guns to the Indians and who further antagonized the pilgrims by leading a band of revelers at Merry Mount, the settlement he founded outside Plymouth; Edward Teach (or *Thatch* or *Thach*) was an English pirate known popularly as "Blackbeard," who plundered ships off the Southern coast; just who Smeet was is unclear.
23. **Geneva gown:** minister's robe. Originally the garb of scholars, the long, flowing black robes were first adapted as preacher's garb by the late-sixteenth century Calvinist clergy in Geneva and were later used by many Protestant ministers.

"Are you satisfied with the jury, Mr. Webster?" said the stranger mockingly, when they had taken their places.

The sweat stood upon Dan'l Webster's brow, but his voice was clear.

"Quite satisfied," he said. "Though I miss General Arnold from the company."

"Benedict Arnold is engaged upon other business," said the stranger, with a glower. "Ah, you asked for a justice, I believe."

He pointed his finger once more, and a tall man, soberly clad in Puritan garb, with the burning gaze of the fanatic, stalked into the room and took his judge's place.

"Justice Hathorne [24] is a jurist of experience," said the stranger. "He presided at certain witch trials once held in Salem. There were others who repented of the business later, but not he."

"Repent of such notable wonders and undertakings?" said the stern old justice. "Nay, hang them—hang them all!" And he muttered to himself in a way that struck ice into the soul of Jabez Stone.

Then the trial began, and, as you might expect, it didn't look anyways good for the defense. And Jabez Stone didn't make much of a witness in his own behalf. He took one look at Simon Girty and screeched, and they had to put him back in his corner in a kind of swoon.

It didn't halt the trial, though; the trial went on, as trials do. Dan'l Webster had faced some hard juries and hanging judges in his time, but this was the hardest he'd ever faced, and he knew it. They sat there with a kind of glitter in their eyes, and the stranger's smooth voice went on and on. Every time he'd raise an objection, it'd be "Objection sustained," but whenever Dan'l objected, it'd be "Objection denied." Well, you couldn't expect fair play from a fellow like this Mr. Scratch.

It got to Dan'l in the end, and he began to heat, like iron in the forge. When he got up to speak, he was going to flay that stranger with every trick known to the law, and the judge and jury, too. He didn't care if it was contempt of court or what would happen to him for it. He didn't care any more what happened to

24. **Justice [John] Hathorne** (hô'thôrn): presiding judge at the Salem witch trials of 1692. Hathorne was an ancestor of the American writer Nathaniel Hawthorne, and his connection with the witch trials is erroneously given as one of the reasons Hawthorne added the *w* to his surname.

Jabez Stone. He just got madder and madder, thinking of what he'd say. And yet, curiously enough, the more he thought about it, the less he was able to arrange his speech in his mind.

Till, finally, it was time for him to get up on his feet, and he did so, all ready to bust out with lightnings and denunciations. But before he started, he looked over the judge and jury for a moment, such being his custom. And he noticed the glitter in their eyes was twice as strong as before, and they all leaned forward. Like hounds just before they get the fox, they looked, and the blue mist of evil in the room thickened as he watched them. Then he saw what he'd been about to do, and he wiped his forehead, as a man might who's just escaped falling into a pit in the dark.

For it was him they'd come for, not only Jabez Stone. He read it in the glitter of their eyes and in the way the stranger hid his mouth with one hand. And if he fought them with their own weapons, he'd fall into their power; he knew that, though he couldn't have told you how. It was his own anger and horror that burned in their eyes; and he'd have to wipe that out or the case was lost. He stood there for a moment, his black eyes burning like anthracite. And then he began to speak.

He started off in a low voice, though you could hear every word. They say he could call on the harps of the blessed when he chose. And this was just as simple and easy as a man could talk. But he didn't start out by condemning or reviling. He was talking about the things that make a country a country, and a man a man.

And he began with the simple things that everybody's known and felt—the freshness of a fine morning when you're young, and the taste of food when you're hungry, and the new day that's every day when you're a child. He took them up and he turned them in his hands. They were good things for any man. But without freedom, they sickened. And when he talked of those enslaved, and the sorrows of slavery, his voice got like a big bell. He talked of the early days of America and the men who had made those days. It wasn't a spread-eagle speech, but he made you see it. He admitted all the wrong that had ever been done. But he showed how, out of the wrong and the right, the suffering and the starvations, something new had come. And everybody had played a part in it, even the traitors.

Then he turned to Jabez Stone and showed him as he was—an ordinary man who'd had hard luck and wanted to change it. And, because he'd wanted to change it, now he was going to be punished for all eternity. And yet there was good in Jabez Stone, and he showed that good. He was hard and mean, in some ways, but he was a man. There was sadness in being a man, but it was a proud thing, too. And he showed what the pride of it was till you couldn't help feeling it. Yes, even in hell, if a man was a man, you'd know it. And he wasn't pleading for any one person any more, though his voice rang like an organ. He was telling the story and the failures and the endless journey of mankind. They got tricked and trapped and bamboozled, but it was a great journey. And no demon that was ever foaled could know the inwardness of it—it took a man to do that.

The fire began to die on the hearth and the wind before morning to blow. The light was getting gray in the room when Dan'l Webster finished. And his words came back at the end to New Hampshire ground, and the one spot of land that each man loves and clings to. He painted a picture of that, and to each one of that jury he spoke of things long forgotten. For his voice could search the heart, and that was his gift and his strength. And to one, his voice was like the forest and its secrecy, and to another like the sea and the storms of the sea; and one heard the cry of his lost nation in it, and another saw a little harmless scene he hadn't remembered for years. But each saw something. And when Dan'l Webster finished, he didn't know whether or not he'd saved Jabez Stone. But he knew he'd done a miracle. For the glitter was gone from the eyes of judge and jury, and, for the moment, they were men again, and knew they were men.

"The defense rests," said Dan'l Webster, and stood there like a mountain. His ears were still ringing with his speech, and he didn't hear anything else till he heard Judge Hathorne say, "The jury will retire to consider its verdict."

Walter Butler rose in his place and his face had a dark, gay pride on it.

"The jury has considered its verdict," he said, and looked the stranger full in the eye. "We find for the defendant, Jabez Stone."

With that, the smile left the stranger's face, but Walter Butler did not flinch.

"Perhaps 'tis not strictly in accordance with the evidence," he said, "but even the damned may salute the eloquence of Mr. Webster."

With that, the long crow of a rooster split the gray morning sky, and judge and jury were gone from the room like a puff of smoke and as if they had never been there. The stranger turned to Dan'l Webster, smiling wryly. "Major Butler was always a bold man," he said. "I had not thought him quite so bold. Nevertheless, my congratulations, as between two gentlemen."

"I'll have that paper first, if you pleace," said Dan'l Webster, and he took it and tore it into four pieces. It was queerly warm to the touch. "And now," he said, "I'll have you!" and his hand came down like a bear trap on the stranger's arm. For he knew that once you bested anybody like Mr. Scratch in fair fight, his power on you was gone. And he could see that Mr. Scratch knew it too.

The stranger twisted and wriggled, but he couldn't get out of that grip. "Come, come, Mr. Webster," he said, smiling palely. "This sort of thing is ridic—ouch!—is ridiculous. If you're worried about the costs of the case, naturally, I'd be glad to pay—"

"And so you shall!" said Dan'l Webster, shaking him till his teeth rattled. "For you'll sit right down at that table and draw up a document, promising never to bother Jabez Stone nor his heirs or assigns nor any other New Hampshireman till doomsday! For any hades we want to raise in this state, we can raise ourselves, without assistance from strangers."

"Ouch!" said the stranger. "Ouch! Well, they never did run very big to the barrel, but—ouch!—I agree!"

So he sat down and drew up the document. But Dan'l Webster kept his hand on his coat collar all the time.

"And, now, may I go?" said the stranger, quite humble, when Dan'l'd seen the document was in proper and legal form.

"Go?" said Dan'l, giving him another shake. "I'm still trying to figure out what I'll do with you. For you've settled the costs of the case, but you haven't settled with me. I think I'll take you back to Marshfield," he said, kind of reflective. "I've got a ram there named Goliath that can butt through an iron door. I'd kind of like to turn you loose in his field and see what he'd do."

Well, with that the stranger began to beg and to plead. And he begged and he pled so humble that finally Dan'l, who was naturally kindhearted, agreed to let him go. The stranger seemed terrible grateful for that and said, just to show they were friends, he'd tell Dan'l's fortune before leaving. So Dan'l agreed to that, though he didn't take much stock in fortunetellers ordinarily.

But, naturally, the stranger was a little different. Well, he pried and he peered at the lines in Dan'l's hands. And he told him one thing and another that was quite remarkable. But they were all in the past.

"Yes, all that's true, and it happened," said Dan'l Webster. "But what's to come in the future?"

The stranger grinned, kind of happily, and shook his head. "The future's not as you think it," he said. "It's dark. You have a great ambition, Mr. Webster."

"I have," said Dan'l firmly, for everybody knew he wanted to be President.

"It seems almost within your grasp," said the stranger, "but you will not attain it. Lesser men will be made President and you will be passed over."

"And, if I am, I'll still be Daniel Webster," said Dan'l. "Say on."

"You have two strong sons," said the stranger, shaking his head. "You look to found a line. But each will die in war and neither reach greatness."

"Live or die, they are still my sons," said Dan'l Webster. "Say on."

"You have made great speeches," said the stranger. "You will make more."

"Ah," said Dan'l Webster.

"But the last great speech you make will turn many of your own against you," said the stranger. "They will call you Ichabod; [25]

25. **They will call you Ichabod:** the devil's "prophecy" was correct, and the abolitionists turned on Webster. In 1846, in an anonymous article in the *Anti-Slavery Standard*, James Russell Lowell wrote of Webster, "Shall not the Recording Angel write *Ichabod* after the name of this man in the great book of Doom?"; in 1850, John Greenleaf Whittier's poem "Ichabod" appeared, attacking Webster for his call for compromise on slavery, in a speech of March 7, 1850. The use of the name Ichabod in this manner is related to a passage in I Samuel 4:19–22, which describes how the wife of Phineas was delivered of a son at the same time the deaths of both her husband and her father-in-law were reported. Part of the biblical verse reads, "And she named the child Ichabod, saying, the glory is departed from Israel."

they will call you by other names. Even in New England some will say you have turned your coat and sold your country, and their voices will be loud against you till you die."

"So it is an honest speech, it does not matter what men say," said Dan'l Webster. Then he looked at the stranger and their glances locked.

"One question," he said. "I have fought for the Union all my life. Will I see that fight won against those who would tear it apart?"

"Not while you live," said the stranger, grimly, "but it will be won. And after you are dead, there are thousands who will fight for your cause, because of words that you spoke."

"Why, then, you long-barreled, slab-sided, lantern-jawed, fortune-telling note-shaver!" said Dan'l Webster, with a great roar of laughter, "be off with you to your own place before I put my mark on you! For, by the thirteen original colonies I'd go to the Pit itself to save the Union!"

And with that he drew back his foot for a kick that would have stunned a horse. It was only the tip of his shoe that caught the stranger, but he went flying out of the door with his collecting box under his arm.

"And now," said Dan'l Webster, seeing Jabez Stone beginning to rouse from his swoon, "let's see what's left in the jug, for it's dry work talking all night. I hope there's pie for breakfast, Neighbor Stone."

But they say that whenever the devil comes near Marshfield, even now, he gives it a wide berth. And he hasn't been seen in the state of New Hampshire from that day to this. I'm not talking about Massachusetts or Vermont.

Meaning and Method

1. Which words, phrases, expressions, and details of background contained in the first three paragraphs indicate that the story is going to follow the pattern of an American folk tale? Does the narrator try to present Webster as a historical figure?

2. One way to give a folk hero legendary stature is through hyperbole —to describe him and his possessions in exaggerated terms. For example, we get an idea of the size of the giant lumberjack Paul Bunyan when we hear that Babe, his blue ox, measured "forty-two

ax handles and a plug of Star tobacco" between the eyes. Pick out some examples from the early part of Benét's story that present Daniel Webster in this manner.

3. "The Devil and Daniel Webster" has many elements characteristic of a local-color story (see Glossary). Find examples of such elements and use them to explain whether or not the story may be said to be a local-color story.

4. What is the effect of having the narrator of the story address the reader directly, in such statements as "And they say that if you go to his grave . . ." and "You see, for a while, he was the biggest man in the country"?

5. In defending Jabez Stone, Daniel Webster demands that his client be tried before a jury. What is added to the tall tale by having the jury composed of actual historical figures? What is added by the references to their individual historical contexts? Why is the choice of Justice Hathorne, especially, an unfortunate one for Jabez Stone?

6. "Then he [Webster] saw what he'd been about to do, and he wiped his forehead, as a man might who's just escaped falling into a pit in the dark. For it was him they'd come for, not only Jabez Stone. . . ." (See page 81.)

What was Webster about to do? Are there any earlier indications, or foreshadowings, that the Devil had planned all along to use Jabez Stone as "bait" with which to trap Daniel Webster?

7. Why did the jury, despite the evidence against Stone, find for the defendant? Was it only because of Webster's eloquence in defending the unfortunate man?

8. Thanks to the fact that the story was written long after Daniel Webster and his age had passed into history, the Devil, Scratch, is able to prophesy a number of events in Webster's future. Why did Benét include this part of the story? What do the events the Devil foresees and the responses Webster makes about them tell about the kind of man Webster was?

Composition and Discussion

1. Notice that with Jabez Stone's prosperity come respect, fame, and power. Notice also that Scratch's list is so long it has to be arranged in alphabetical order. Then, too, the Devil uses many legal and business terms and expressions in his speech.

Is Benét commenting on man's tendency to respect wealth? Is he being ironic about the legal acquisition of property (page 77)? Is he also saying that man is a combination of good and evil, of strengths and weaknesses—and that man should not be made to pay disproportionately for his human failings?

2. In Benét's story, both Daniel Webster and Jabez Stone represent standard New England types; Scratch, too, in many ways gives the impression of being a New Englander. Compare and contrast in a brief composition the New England "Yankee" type with a typical person from another region—a Southerner, Midwesterner, Westerner, or French-Canadian. Consider special characteristics or attitudes, speech patterns, regional accents or expressions, and local customs.

James Thurber
[1894—1961]

Contemporary American writing has not generally been comic, and the recent writing that is comic has often been imbued with a sense of tragedy or of "sick" humor. One of the early practitioners of a milder form of tragi-comic writing was James Thurber. According to his own records, Thurber "was born on a night of wild portent and high wind in the year 1894, [in] Columbus, Ohio." He spent the next two decades there, growing up, surviving a childhood accident that left him partially blind, and, later, attending Ohio State University.

After graduation, Thurber worked briefly as a code clerk for the State Department in Washington, D.C., before turning to a career as a journalist and creative writer. Writing was nothing new to him; he had been productive since childhood, when he wrote his first piece, a poem dedicated to an aunt. In the early nineteen-twenties, Thurber began what turned out to be a long association with *The New Yorker* Magazine. His personal account of that association, *The Years with Ross,** was a best seller in 1957.

Over the years, Thurber produced a large number of books, many illustrated with his own drawings, for both adults and children. He had a penchant for amusing titles, such as *The Owl in the Attic and Other Perplexities* and *The Middle-Aged Man on the Flying Trapeze.*

Thurber has been treated kindly by both literary critics and the general reading public. Perhaps the reason is that critics know that humor, even serious humor, loses its appeal under close critical analysis, and that readers know that humor, especially serious humor, can delight and enrich.

The following story, "The Catbird Seat," relates one skirmish in the battle Thurber alleged was his life's battle, the Battle of the Sexes. The story is typical of Thurber's ambivalent attitudes toward the opposite sex, and it is no surprise that, when this story was made into a film, it was entitled "The Battle of the Sexes."

---

* *The Years with Ross:* Ross was the late Harold Ross, founder and editor of *The New Yorker.*

The Catbird Seat

Mr. Martin bought the pack of Camels on Monday night in the most crowded cigar store on Broadway. It was theater time and seven or eight men were buying cigarettes. The clerk didn't even glance at Mr. Martin, who put the pack in his overcoat pocket and went out. If any of the staff at F & S had seen him buy the cigarettes, they would have been astonished, for it was generally known that Mr. Martin did not smoke, and never had. No one saw him.

It was just a week to the day since Mr. Martin had decided to rub out Mrs. Ulgine Barrows. The term "rub out" pleased him because it suggested nothing more than the correction of an error —in this case an error of Mr. Fitweiler. Mr. Martin had spent each night of the past week working out his plan and examining it. As he walked home now he went over it again. For the hundredth time he resented the element of imprecision, the margin of guess-work that entered into the business. The project as he had worked it out was casual and bold, the risks were considerable. Something might go wrong anywhere along the line. And therein lay the cunning of his scheme. No one would ever see in it the cautious, painstaking hand of Erwin Martin, head of the filing department at F & S, of whom Mr. Fitweiler had once said, "Man is fallible but Martin isn't." No one would see his hand, that is, unless it were caught in the act.

Sitting in his apartment, drinking a glass of milk, Mr. Martin reviewed his case against Mrs. Ulgine Barrows, as he had every night for seven nights. He began at the beginning. Her quacking voice and braying laugh had first profaned the halls of F & S on March 7, 1941 (Mr. Martin had a head for dates). Old Roberts, the personnel chief, had introduced her as the newly appointed special adviser to the president of the firm, Mr. Fitweiler. The woman had appalled Mr. Martin instantly, but he hadn't shown it. He had given her his dry hand, a look of studious concentration, and a faint smile. "Well," she had said, looking at the papers on his desk, "are you lifting the oxcart out of the ditch?" As Mr.

Martin recalled that moment, over his milk, he squirmed slightly. He must keep his mind on her crimes as a special adviser, not on her peccadillos [1] as a personality. This he found difficult to do, in spite of entering an objection and sustaining it. The faults of the woman as a woman kept chattering on in his mind like an unruly witness. She had, for almost two years now, baited him. In the halls, in the elevator, even in his own office, into which she romped now and then like a circus horse, she was constantly shouting these silly questions at him. "Are you lifting the oxcart out of the ditch? Are you tearing up the pea patch? Are you hollering down the rain barrel? Are you scraping around the bottom of the pickle barrel? Are you sitting in the catbird seat?"

It was Joey Hart, one of Mr. Martin's two assistants, who had explained what the gibberish meant. "She must be a Dodger fan," he had said. "Red Barber announces the Dodger games over the radio and he uses those expressions—picked 'em up down South." Joey had gone on to explain one or two. "Tearing up the pea patch" meant going on a rampage; "sitting in the catbird seat" meant sitting pretty, like a batter with three balls and no strikes on him. Mr. Martin dismissed all this with an effort. It had been annoying, it had driven him near to distraction, but he was too solid a man to be moved to murder by anything so childish. It was fortunate, he reflected as he passed on to the important charges against Mrs. Barrows, that he had stood up under it so well. He had maintained always an outward appearance of polite tolerance. "Why, I even believe you like the woman," Miss Paird, his other assistant, had once said to him. He had simply smiled.

A gavel rapped in Mr. Martin's mind and the case proper was resumed. Mrs. Ulgine Barrows stood charged with willful, blatant, and persistent attempts to destroy the efficiency and system of F & S. It was competent, material, and relevant to review her advent and rise to power. Mr. Martin had got the story from Miss Paird, who seemed always able to find things out. According to her, Mrs. Barrows had met Mr. Fitweiler at a party, where she had rescued him from the embraces of a powerfully built drunken man who had mistaken the president of F & S for a famous retired Middle Western football coach. She had led him to a sofa and

1. **peccadillos:** faults; trifling sins. The word is from Spanish *pecadillo*, a diminutive of *pecado*, "sin," from the Latin verb *peccare*, to sin.

somehow worked upon him a monstrous magic. The aging gentle-man had jumped to the conclusion there and then that this was a woman of singular attainments, equipped to bring out the best in him and in the firm. A week later he had introduced her into F & S as his special adviser. On that day confusion got its foot in the door. After Miss Tyson, Mr. Brundage, and Mr. Bartlett had been fired and Mr. Munson had taken his hat and stalked out, mailing in his resignation later, old Roberts had been emboldened to speak to Mr. Fitweiler. He mentioned that Mr. Munson's department had been "a little disrupted" and hadn't they perhaps better resume the old system there? Mr. Fitweiler had said certainly not. He had the greatest faith in Mrs. Barrows' ideas. "They require a little seasoning, a little seasoning, is all," he had added. Mr. Roberts had given it up. Mr. Martin reviewed in detail all the changes wrought by Mrs. Barrows. She had begun chipping at the cornices of the firm's edifice and now she was swinging at the foundation stones with a pickaxe.

Mr. Martin came now, in his summing up, to the afternoon of Monday, November 2, 1942—just one week ago. On that day, at 3:00 P.M., Mrs. Barrows had bounced into his office. "Boo!" she had yelled. "Are you scraping around the bottom of the pickle barrel?" Mr. Martin had looked at her from under his green eye-shade, saying nothing. She had begun to wander about the office, taking it in with her great, popping eyes. "Do you really need *all* these filing cabinets?" she had demanded suddenly. Mr. Martin's heart had jumped. "Each of these files," he had said, keeping his voice even, "plays an indispensable part in the system of F & S." She had brayed at him, "Well, don't tear up the pea patch!" and gone to the door. From there she had bawled, "But you sure have got a lot of fine scrap in here!" Mr. Martin could no longer doubt that the finger was on his beloved department. Her pickaxe was on the upswing, poised for the first blow. It had not come yet; he had received no blue memo from the enchanted Mr. Fitweiler bearing nonsensical instructions deriving from the obscene woman. But there was no doubt in Mr. Martin's mind that one would be forthcoming. He must act quickly. Already a precious week had gone by. Mr. Martin stood up in his living room, still holding his milk glass. "Gentlemen of the jury," he said to himself, "I demand the death penalty for this horrible person."

The next day Mr. Martin followed his routine, as usual. He

polished his glasses more often and once sharpened an already sharp pencil, but not even Miss Paird noticed. Only once did he catch sight of his victim; she swept past him in the hall with a patronizing "Hi!" At five-thirty he walked home, as usual, and had a glass of milk, as usual. He had never drunk anything stronger in his life—unless you could count ginger ale. The late Sam Schlosser, the S of F & S, had praised Mr. Martin at a staff meeting several years before for his temperate habits. "Our most efficient worker neither drinks nor smokes," he had said. "The results speak for themselves." Mr. Fitweiler had sat by, nodding approval.

Mr. Martin was still thinking about that red-letter day as he walked over to the Schrafft's on Fifth Avenue near Forty-Sixth Street. He got there, as he always did, at eight o'clock. He finished his dinner and the financial page of the Sun at a quarter to nine, as he always did. It was his custom after dinner to take a walk. This time he walked down Fifth Avenue at a casual pace. His gloved hands felt moist and warm, his forehead cold. He transferred the Camels from his overcoat to a jacket pocket. He wondered, as he did so, if they did not represent an unnecessary note of strain. Mrs. Barrows smoked only Luckies. It was his idea to puff a few puffs on a Camel (after the rubbing-out), stub it out in the ashtray holding her lipstick-stained Luckies, and thus drag a small red herring across the trail. Perhaps it was not a good idea. It would take time. He might even choke, too loudly.

Mr. Martin had never seen the house on West Twelfth Street where Mrs. Barrows lived, but he had a clear enough picture of it. Fortunately, she had bragged to everybody about her ducky first-floor apartment in the perfectly darling three-story red-brick. There would be no doorman or other attendants; just the tenants of the second and third floors. As he walked along, Mr. Martin realized that he would get there before nine-thirty. He had considered walking north on Fifth Avenue from Schrafft's to a point from which it would take him until ten o'clock to reach the house. At that hour people were less likely to be coming in or going out. But the procedure would have made an awkward loop in the straight thread of his casualness, and he had abandoned it. It was impossible to figure when people would be entering or leaving the house, anyway. There was a great risk at any hour. If he ran into anybody, he would simply have to place the rubbing-out of Ulgine

Barrows in the inactive file forever. The same thing would hold true if there were someone in her apartment. In that case he would just say that he had been passing by, recognized her charming house, and thought to drop in.

It was eighteen minutes after nine when Mr. Martin turned into Twelfth Street. A man passed him, and a man and a woman, talking. There was no one within fifty paces when he came to the house, halfway down the block. He was up the steps and in the small vestibule in no time, pressing the bell under the card that said "Mrs. Ulgine Barrows." When the clicking in the lock started, he jumped forward against the door. He got inside fast, closing the door behind him. A bulb in a lantern hung from the hall ceiling on a chain seemed to give a monstrously bright light. There was nobody on the stair, which went up ahead of him along the left wall. A door opened down the hall in the wall on the right. He went toward it swiftly, on tiptoe.

"Well, for God's sake, look who's here!" bawled Mrs. Barrows, and her braying laugh rang out like the report of a shotgun. He rushed past her like a football tackle, bumping her. "Hey, quit shoving!" she said, closing the door behind them. They were in her living room, which seemed to Mr. Martin to be lighted by a hundred lamps. "What's after you?" she said. "You're as jumpy as a goat." He found he was unable to speak. His heart was wheezing in his throat. "I—yes," he finally brought out. She was jabbering and laughing as she started to help him off with his coat. "No, no," he said. "I'll put it here." He took it off and put it on a chair near the door. "Your hat and gloves, too," she said. "You're in a lady's house." He put his hat on top of the coat. Mrs. Barrows seemed larger than he had thought. He kept his gloves on. "I was passing by," he said. "I recognized—is there anyone here?" She laughed louder than ever. "No," she said. "We're all alone. You're as white as a sheet, you funny man. Whatever *has* come over you? I'll mix you a toddy." She started toward a door across the room. "Scotch-and-soda be all right? But say, you don't drink, do you?" She turned and gave him her amused look. Mr. Martin pulled himself together. "Scotch-and-soda will be all right," he heard himself say. He could hear her laughing in the kitchen.

Mr. Martin looked quickly around the living room for the weapon. He had counted on finding one there. There were andirons and a poker and something in a corner that looked like an Indian club. None of them would do. It couldn't be that way. He began to pace around. He came to a desk. On it lay a metal paper knife with an ornate handle. Would it be sharp enough? He reached for it and knocked over a small brass jar. Stamps spilled out of it and it fell to the floor with a clatter. "Hey," Mrs. Barrows yelled from the kitchen, "are you tearing up the pea patch?" Mr. Martin gave a strange laugh. Picking up the knife, he tried its point against his left wrist. It was blunt. It wouldn't do.

When Mrs. Barrows reappeared, carrying two highballs, Mr. Martin, standing there with his gloves on, became acutely conscious of the fantasy he had wrought. Cigarettes in his pocket, a drink prepared for him—it was all too grossly improbable. It was more than that; it was impossible. Somewhere in the back of his mind a vague idea stirred, sprouted. "For heaven's sake, take off those gloves," said Mrs. Barrows. "I always wear them in the house," said Mr. Martin. The idea began to bloom, strange and wonderful. She put the glasses on a coffee table in front of a sofa and sat on the sofa. "Come over here, you odd little man," she said. Mr. Martin went over and sat beside her. It was difficult getting a cigarette out of the pack of Camels, but he managed it. She held a match for him, laughing. "Well," she said, handing him his drink, "this is perfectly marvelous. You with a drink and a cigarette."

Mr. Martin puffed, not too awkwardly, and took a gulp of the highball. "I drink and smoke all the time," he said. He clinked his glass against hers. "Here's nuts to that old windbag, Fitweiler," he said, and gulped again. The stuff tasted awful, but he made no grimace. "Really, Mr. Martin," she said, her voice and posture changing, "you are insulting our employer." Mrs. Barrows was now all special adviser to the president. "I am preparing a bomb," said Mr. Martin, "which will blow the old goat higher than hell." He had only had a little of the drink, which was not strong. It couldn't be that. "Do you take dope or something?" Mrs. Barrows asked coldly. "Heroin," said Mr. Martin. "I'll be coked to the gills when I bump that old buzzard off." "Mr. Mar-tin!" she shouted, getting to her feet. "That will be all of that. You must go at once." Mr. Martin took another swallow of his drink. He tapped his cigarette out in the ashtray and put the pack of Camels on the coffee table. Then he got up. She stood glaring at him. He walked over and put on his hat and coat. "Not a word about this," he said, and laid an index finger against his lips. All Mrs. Barrows could bring out was "Really!" Mr. Martin put his hand on the doorknob. "I'm sitting in the catbird seat," he said. He stuck his tongue out at her and left. Nobody saw him go.

Mr. Martin got to his apartment, walking, well before eleven. No one saw him go in. He had two glasses of milk after brushing his teeth, and he felt elated. It wasn't tipsiness, because he hadn't been tipsy. Anyway, the walk had worn off all effects of the whis-key. He got in bed and read a magazine for a while. He was asleep before midnight.

Mr. Martin got to the office at eight-thirty the next morning, as usual. At a quarter to nine, Ulgine Barrows, who had never before arrived at work before ten, swept into his office. "I'm re-porting to Mr. Fitweiler now!" she shouted. "If he turns you over to the police, it's no more than you deserve!" Mr. Martin gave her a look of shocked surprise. "I beg your pardon?" he said. Mrs. Barrows snorted and bounced out of the room, leaving Miss Paird and Joey Hart staring after her. "What's the matter with that old devil now?" asked Miss Paird. "I have no idea," said Mr. Martin, resuming his work. The other two looked at him and then at each other. Miss Paird got up and went out. She walked slowly past the closed door of Mr. Fitweiler's office. Mrs. Barrows was yelling inside, but she was not braying. Miss Paird could not hear what the woman was saying. She went back to her desk.

Forty-five minutes later, Mrs. Barrows left the president's office and went into her own, shutting the door. It wasn't until half an hour later that Mr. Fitweiler sent for Mr. Martin. The head of the filing department, neat, quiet, attentive, stood in front of the old man's desk. Mr. Fitweiler was pale and nervous. He took his glasses off and twiddled them. He made a small, bruffing sound in his throat. "Martin," he said, "you have been with us more than twenty years." "Twenty-two, sir," said Mr. Martin. "In that time," pursued the president, "your work and your—uh—manner have been exemplary." "I trust so, sir," said Mr. Martin. "I have understood, Martin," said Mr. Fitweiler, "that you have never taken a drink or smoked." "That is correct, sir," said Mr. Martin. "Ah, yes." Mr. Fitweiler polished his glasses. "You may describe what you did after leaving the office yesterday, Martin," he said. Mr. Martin allowed less than a second for his bewildered pause. "Certainly, sir," he said. "I walked home. Then I went to Schrafft's for dinner. Afterward I walked home again. I went to bed early, sir, and read a magazine for a while. I was asleep before eleven." "Ah, yes," said Mr. Fitweiler again. He was silent for a moment, searching for the proper words to say to the head of the filing department. "Mrs. Barrows," he said finally, "Mrs. Barrows has worked hard, Martin, very hard. It grieves me to report that she has suffered a severe breakdown. It has taken the form of a persecution complex accompanied by distressing hallucinations." "I am very sorry, sir," said Mr. Martin. "Mrs. Barrows is under the delusion," continued Mr. Fitweiler, "that you visited her last evening and behaved yourself in an—uh—unseemly manner." He raised his hand to silence Mr. Martin's little pained outcry. "It is the nature of these psychological diseases," Mr. Fitweiler said, "to fix upon the least likely and most innocent party as the—uh—source of persecution. These matters are not for the lay mind to grasp, Martin. I've just had my psychiatrist, Doctor Fitch, on the phone. He would not, of course, commit himself, but he made enough generalizations to substantiate my suspicions. I suggested to Mrs. Barrows, when she had completed her—uh—story to me this morning, that she visit Doctor Fitch, for I suspected a condition at once. She flew, I regret to say, into a rage, and demanded —uh—requested that I call you on the carpet. You may not know, Martin, but Mrs. Barrows had planned a reorganization of your department—subject to my approval, of course, subject to my approval. This brought you, rather than anyone else, to her mind—but again that is a phenomenon for Doctor Fitch and not for us. So, Martin, I am afraid Mrs. Barrows' usefulness here is at an end." "I am dreadfully sorry, sir," said Mr. Martin.

It was at this point that the door to the office blew open with the suddenness of a gas-main explosion and Mrs. Barrows catapulted through it. "Is the little rat denying it?" she screamed. "He can't get away with that!" Mr. Martin got up and moved discreetly to a point beside Mr. Fitweiler's chair. "You drank and smoked at my apartment," she bawled at Mr. Martin, "and you know it! You called Mr. Fitweiler an old windbag and said you were going to blow him up when you got coked to gills on your heroin!" She stopped yelling to catch her breath and a new glint came into her popping eyes. "If you weren't such a drab, ordinary little man," she said, "I'd think you'd planned it all. Sticking your tongue out, saying you were sitting in the catbird seat, because you thought no one would believe me when I told it! My God, it's really too perfect!" She brayed loudly and hysterically, and the fury was on her again. She glared at Mr. Fitweiler. "Can't you see how he has tricked us, you old fool? Can't you see his little game?" But Mr. Fitweiler had been surreptitiously pressing all the buttons under the top of his desk and employees of F & S began pouring into the room. "Stockton," said Mr. Fitweiler, "you and Fishbein will take Mrs. Barrows to her home. Mrs. Powell, you will go with them." Stockton, who had played a little football in high school, blocked Mrs. Barrows as she made for Mr. Martin. It took him and Fishbein together to force her out of the door into the hall, crowded with stenographers and office boys. She was still screaming imprecations at Mr. Martin, tangled and contradictory imprecations. The hubbub finally died down the corridor.

"I regret that this has happened," said Mr. Fitweiler. "I shall ask you to dismiss it from your mind, Martin." "Yes, sir," said Mr. Martin, anticipating his chief's "That will be all" by moving to the door. "I will dismiss it." He went out and shut the door, and his step was light and quick in the hall. When he entered his department he had slowed down to his customary gait, and he walked quietly across the room to the W20 file, wearing a look of studious concentration.

Meaning and Method

1. How does the first paragraph pique the reader's interest and create an element of suspense? What do you learn about Mr. Martin here? What do you want to know or find out about him?

2. The conflict in this story is clear-cut: Erwin Martin must somehow "rub out Mrs. Ulgine Barrows," or he will be rubbed out by her.

Why does Mr. Martin abandon his initial plan? Why is his alternate solution just as effective as "rubbing her out"?

3. Beginning with the second paragraph, Thurber presents action as if he were depicting a courtroom scene. In a sense, we are witnessing how Mr. Martin prepares his case against Mrs. Barrows. Review this section and point out particular words and phrases that extend the courtroom metaphor. What "verdict" does Thurber wish us, his readers, to reach?

4. In his characterization of Mrs. Ulgine Barrows, Thurber avoids detailed descriptions and, rather, lets the woman's own words and actions characterize her. Explain what the following verbs tell about her: *bounced, yelled, wander, demand, brayed,* and *bawled,* (see page 91 for context, if you wish). What impression of the woman do you get from her name, Ulgine Barrows? What are the connotations in the name?

5. Does the name Erwin Martin convey any connotations? Explain. Thurber characterizes Mr. Martin by letting the reader view the action (and reaction) through Martin's eyes and by letting the reader share Martin's thoughts. What do we learn about Mr. Martin through these methods of characterization? What sort of man is he? Even though Thurber has not described him physically, can you "see" what he looks like? Describe him.

6. The title of the story, "The Catbird Seat" is from one of Mrs. Barrows's favorite expressions, of which she has quite a few (see page 90). Why is the title a good one? How is it related to the outcome of the story?

   Would any of the other expressions Mrs. Barrows used have made a good or even better title?

7. The English poet, critic, and playwright T. S. Eliot once said of Thurber's humor that it was a "humor which is also a way of saying something serious." Explain whether the humor in "The Catbird Seat" is simply humor for humor's sake or whether, instead, it substantiates Eliot's observation.

Ernest Hemingway

[1898–1961]

In recent years, Ernest Hemingway and his works have been the object of reappraisal. Like many other American institutions, Hemingway and his philosophy have been questioned by a new generation of readers and critics. For his admirers, Hemingway remains the great realist among writers of American fiction in the twentieth century. To his detractors, perhaps the main problem was that Hemingway, as he grew older, too readily accepted critical and public laurels. He spent less time in writing and increasingly more time in acting out the role of the worldly and wise "Papa" that both he and his public had created. With the notable exception of *The Old Man and the Sea* (1952), he produced little of real merit during his last years. However, the 1969 biography of Hemingway by Carlos Baker shed new light on the man and his writing. This book increased the respect his admirers have for him and may have caused many of his detractors to reevaluate him.

Hemingway was born in Oak Park, Illinois, the son of a doctor who could afford to indulge in his love of the out-of-doors and who passed this love on to his son Ernest. At the family summer place up in Michigan, young Hemingway learned the skills of fishing and small-game hunting—pursuits which, in modified forms, were used as a basic metaphor in some of Hemingway's fiction. He also learned the code of sportsmanlike conduct, which served as a basis for his adult values.

At Oak Park, Hemingway attended the local high school without distinguishing himself as a scholar but managing to make his contributions to high school sports and, frequently, to the school paper and literary magazine. He was graduated in 1917 and immediately wanted to go off to the war his country had just entered.

Partly because of a high-school football injury and partly because of his father's efforts to stop him, Hemingway was unable to enlist. He went instead to Kansas City to be a cub reporter on the Kansas City *Star*. There he learned the basics of journalistic writing, the principles that became the controlling guidelines for his creative writing style.

In 1918 Hemingway left the paper, hoping again to serve in World War I. He was unable to enlist as an infantryman but did manage to join the Red Cross as an ambulance driver, and was sent to the front lines in Italy. Within a short time, he was wounded in the legs by a shellburst and had to spend three weeks recuperating in a hospital in Milan, after which he was sent home. His recovery from the war, emotionally as well as physically, was slow, just as it was to be slow for Nick Adams, the fictional "Hemingway" hero in many of his short stories.

In 1921 the Toronto *Star* offered Hemingway a job as foreign correspondent and sent him to Paris. Between writing articles and dispatches for the *Star*, he began writing fiction and developed his deceptively simple prose style, with its sometimes monotonously rhythmic arrangement of words, simple diction, and visualization.

He drew on his personal experiences for many of his stories, and he presented themes of isolation, disillusionment, initiation into the harshness of life, and near-defeat in terms of things he had seen or done. There are close parallels between the writer's life and the stories that appeared in *In Our Time* (1924) and in his first major novels, *The Sun Also Rises* (1926) and *A Farewell to Arms* (1929). These two works established his reputation as a major writer.

Hemingway continued to write and travel and to pursue his interest in sports. His fascination for the ritual life-death struggle in the Spanish bullfight, already evident in his first novel, was the subject for *Death in the Afternoon* (1932), a study of the bull-fight. With the success of his books, he could afford big-game hunting in Africa, which provided material for his nonfiction book *The Green Hills of Africa* (1935), and for two of his best short stories, "The Snows of Kilimanjaro" and "The Short Happy Life of Francis Macomber." Spain was again the setting, and its Civil War (1936–1939) the subject, of his play *The Fifth Column* (1938), and a novel, *For Whom the Bell Tolls* (1940).

After World War II, Hemingway made Cuba his home base, though he continued to make trips to Europe. In 1952, *The Old Man and the Sea* was published, and won him a Pulitzer prize. It also contributed to his being awarded the Nobel prize for literature in 1954.

Like Nick Adams in the story that follows, Hemingway believed a man had a good chance of regenerating a worn-down spirit by going out into the open country. This feeling is reflected in the way Hemingway spent his last years. In the late 1950's, when his health had deteriorated and he suffered increasingly from periods of deep depression, he spent more and more time at his hunting lodge in Ketchum, Idaho. But for all his effort, he could not rally; nature seemed to have let him down. In the late spring of 1961, he took a last look at the wilderness around Ketchum and, apparently, took his own life by shotgun blast.

"Big Two-Hearted River" is the last of fifteen stories in *In Our Time*. Nick Adams, the collection's central character, spends his boyhood in the Middle West and, like Hemingway, goes away to war and is wounded. In "Big Two Hearted River," Nick returns from Europe and retreats to the Michigan woods to recover both physically and emotionally from his having been wounded in the war.

Big Two-Hearted River

Part I

The train went on up the track out of sight, around one of the hills of burnt timber. Nick sat down on the bundle of canvas and bedding the baggage man had pitched out of the door of the baggage car. There was no town, nothing but the rails and the burned over country. The thirteen saloons that had lined the one street of Seney had not left a trace. The foundations of the Mansion House hotel stuck up above the ground. The stone was chipped and split by the fire. It was all that was left of the town of Seney. Even the surface had been burned off the ground.

Nick looked at the burned-over stretch of hillside, where he had expected to find the scattered houses of the town and then walked down the railroad track to the bridge over the river. The river was there. It swirled against the log spiles [1] of the bridge. Nick

---

1. **spiles:** supporting structures made of timber, steel, or concrete.

looked down into the clear, brown water, colored from the pebbly bottom, and watched the trout keeping themselves steady in the current with wavering fins. As he watched them they changed their positions by quick angles, only to hold steady in the fast water again. Nick watched them a long time.

He watched them holding themselves with their noses into the current, many trout in deep, fast-moving water, slightly distorted as he watched far down through the glassy convex surface of the pool, its surface pushing and swelling smooth against the resistance of the logdriven piles of the bridge. At the bottom of the pool were the big trout. Nick did not see them at first. Then he saw them at the bottom of the pool, big trout looking to hold themselves on the gravel bottom in a varying mist of gravel and sand, raised in spurts by the current.

Nick looked down into the pool from the bridge. It was a hot day. A kingfisher flew up the stream. It was a long time since Nick had looked into a stream and seen trout. They were very satisfactory. As the shadow of the kingfisher [2] moved up the stream, a big trout shot upstream in a long angle, only his shadow marking the angle, then lost his shadow as he came through the surface of the water, caught the sun, and then, as he went back into the stream under the surface, his shadow seemed to float down the stream with the current, unresisting, to his post under the bridge where he tightened facing up into the current.

Nick's heart tightened as the trout moved. He felt all the old feeling.

He turned and looked down the stream. It stretched away, pebbly-bottomed with shallows and big boulders and a deep pool as it curved away around the foot of a bluff.

Nick walked back up the ties to where his pack lay in the cinders beside the railway track. He was happy. He adjusted the pack harness around the bundle, pulling straps tight, slung the pack on his back, got his arms through the shoulder straps and took some of the pull off his shoulders by leaning his forehead against the wide band of the tumpline.[3] Still, it was too heavy. It

2. **kingfisher:** a crested, long-billed, bird of bright blue color that plunges straight into the water after minnows and other prey.
3. **tumpline:** a strap that passes across the forehead or chest to help support a back-pack.

was much too heavy. He had his leather rod-case in his hand and leaning forward to keep the weight of the pack high on his shoulders he walked along the road that paralleled the railway track, leaving the burned town behind in the heat, and then turned off around a hill with a high, fire-scarred hill on either side onto a road that went back into the country. He walked along the road feeling the ache from the pull of the heavy pack. The road climbed steadily. It was hard work walking uphill. His muscles ached and the day was hot, but Nick felt happy. He felt he had left everything behind, the need for thinking, the need to write, other needs. It was all back of him.

From the time he had gotten down off the train and the baggage man had thrown his pack out of the open car door things had been different. Seney was burned, the country was burned over and changed, but it did not matter. It could not all be burned. He knew that. He hiked along the road, sweating in the sun, climbing to cross the range of hills that separated the railway from the pine plains.

The road ran on, dipping occasionally, but always climbing. Nick went on up. Finally the road after going parallel to the burnt hillside reached the top. Nick leaned back against a stump and slipped out of the pack harness. Ahead of him, as far as he could see, was the pine plain. The burned country stopped off at the left with the range of hills. On ahead islands of dark pine trees rose out of the plain. Far off to the left was the line of the river. Nick followed it with his eye and caught glints of the water in the sun.

There was nothing but the pine plain ahead of him, until the far blue hills that marked the Lake Superior height of land. He could hardly see them, faint and far away in the heat-light over the plain. If he looked too steadily they were gone. But if he only half looked they were there, the far off hills of the height of land.

Nick sat down against the charred stump and smoked a cigarette. His pack balanced on the top of the stump, harness holding ready, a hollow molded in it from his back. Nick sat smoking, looking out over the country. He did not need to get his map out. He knew where he was from the position of the river.

As he smoked, his legs stretched out in front of him, he noticed a grasshopper walk along the ground and up onto his woolen sock. The grasshopper was black. As he had walked along the road, climbing, he had started many grasshoppers from the dust. They were all black. They were not the big grasshoppers with yellow and black or red and black wings whirring out from their black wing sheathing as they fly up. These were just ordinary hoppers, but all a sooty black in color. Nick had wondered about them as he walked, without really thinking about them. Now, as he watched the black hopper that was nibbling at the wool of his sock with its fourway lip, he realized that they had all turned black from living in the burned-over land. He realized that the fire must have come the year before, but the grasshoppers were all black now. He wondered how long they would stay that way.

Carefully he reached his hand down and took hold of the hopper by the wings. He turned him up, all his legs walking in the air, and looked at his jointed belly. Yes, it was black too, iridescent where the back and head were dusty.

"Go on, hopper," Nick said, speaking out loud for the first time, "Fly away somewhere."

He tossed the grasshopper up into the air and watched him sail away to a charcoal stump across the road.

Nick stood up. He leaned his back against the weight of his pack where it rested upright on the stump and got his arms through the shoulder straps. He stood with the pack on his back on the brow of the hill looking out across the country, toward the distant river and then struck down the hillside away from the road. Underfoot the ground was good walking. Two hundred yards down the hillside the fire line stopped. Then it was sweet fern, growing ankle high, to walk through, and clumps of jack pines; a long undulating country with frequent rises and descents, sandy underfoot and the country alive again.

Nick kept his direction by the sun. He knew where he wanted to strike the river and he kept on through the pine plain, mounting small rises to see other rises ahead of him and sometimes from the top of a rise a great solid island of pines off to his right or his left. He broke off some sprigs of the heathery sweet fern, and put them under his pack straps. The chafing crushed it and he smelled it as he walked.

He was tired and very hot, walking across the uneven, shadeless pine plain. At any time he knew he could strike the river by turning off to his left. It could not be more than a mile away. But he kept on toward the north to hit the river as far upstream as he could go in one day's walking.

For some time as he walked Nick had been in sight of one of the big islands of pine standing out above the rolling high ground he was crossing. He dipped down and then as he came slowly up to the crest of the ridge he turned and made toward the pine trees.

There was no underbrush in the island of pine trees. The trunks of the trees went straight up or slanted toward each other. The trunks were straight and brown without branches. The branches were high above. Some interlocked to make a solid shadow on the brown forest floor. Around the grove of trees was a bare space. It was brown and soft underfoot as Nick walked on it. This was the overlapping of the pine needle floor, extending out beyond the width of the high branches. The trees had grown tall and the branches moved high, leaving in the sun this bare space they had once covered with shadow. Sharp at the edge of this extension of the forest floor commenced the sweet fern.

Nick slipped off his pack and lay down in the shade. He lay on his back and looked up into the pine trees. His neck and back and the small of his back rested as he stretched. The earth felt good against his back. He looked up at the sky, through the branches, and then shut his eyes. He opened them and looked up again. There was a wind high up in the branches. He shut his eyes again and went to sleep.

Nick woke stiff and cramped. The sun was nearly down. His pack was heavy and the straps painful as he lifted it on. He leaned over with the pack on and picked up the leather rod-case and started out from the pine trees across the sweet fern swale,[4] toward the river. He knew it could not be more than a mile.

He came down a hillside covered with stumps into a meadow. At the edge of the meadow flowed the river. Nick was glad to get to the river. He walked upstream through the meadow. His trousers were soaked with the dew as he walked. After the hot day, the dew had come quickly and heavily. The river made no sound. It was too fast and smooth. At the edge of the meadow,

4. **swale:** low, marshy ground.

before he mounted to a piece of high ground to make camp, Nick looked down the river at the trout rising. They were rising to insects come from the swamp on the other side of the stream when the sun went down. The trout jumped out of water to take them. While Nick walked through the little stretch of meadow alongside the stream, trout had jumped high out of water. Now as he looked down the river, the insects must be settling on the surface, for the trout were feeding steadily all down the stream. As far down the long stretch as he could see, the trout were rising, making circles all down the surface of the water, as though it were starting to rain.

The ground rose, wooded and sandy, to overlook the meadow, the stretch of river and the swamp. Nick dropped his pack and rod-case and looked for a level piece of ground. He was very hungry and he wanted to make his camp before he cooked. Between two jack pines, the ground was quite level. He took the ax out of the pack and chopped out two projecting roots. That leveled a piece of ground large enough to sleep on. He smoothed out the sandy soil with his hand and pulled all the sweet fern bushes by their roots. His hands smelled good from the sweet fern. He smoothed the uprooted earth. He did not want anything making lumps under the blankets. When he had the ground smooth, he spread his three blankets. One he folded double, next to the ground. The other two he spread on top.

With the ax he slit off a bright slab of pine from one of the stumps and split it into pegs for the tent. He wanted them long and solid to hold in the ground. With the tent unpacked and spread on the ground, the pack, leaning against a jack pine, looked much smaller. Nick tied the rope that served the tent for a ridge-pole to the trunk of one of the pine trees and pulled the tent up off the ground with the other end of the rope and tied it to the other pine. The tent hung on the rope like a canvas blanket on a clothes line. Nick poked a pole he had cut up under the back peak of the canvas and then made it a tent by pegging out the sides. He pegged the sides out taut and drove the pegs deep, hitting them down into the ground with the flat of the ax until the rope loops were buried and the canvas was drum tight.

Across the open mouth of the tent Nick fixed cheesecloth to keep out mosquitoes. He crawled inside under the mosquito bar with various things from the pack to put at the head of the bed under the slant of the canvas. Inside the tent the light came through the brown canvas. It smelled pleasantly of canvas. Already there was something mysterious and homelike. Nick was happy as he crawled inside the tent. He had not been unhappy all day. This was different though. Now things were done. There had been this to do. Now it was done. It had been a hard trip. He was very tired. That was done. He had made his camp. He was settled. Nothing could touch him. It was a good place to camp. He was there, in the good place. He was in his home where he had made it. Now he was hungry.

He came out, crawling under the cheesecloth. It was quite dark outside. It was lighter in the tent.

Nick went over to the pack and found, with his fingers, a long nail in a paper sack of nails, in the bottom of the pack. He drove it into the pine tree, holding it close and hitting it gently with the flat of the ax. He hung the pack up on the nail. All his supplies were in the pack. They were off the ground and sheltered now.

Nick was hungry. He did not believe he had ever been hungrier. He opened and emptied a can of pork and beans and a can of spaghetti into the frying pan.

"I've got a right to eat this kind of stuff, if I'm willing to carry it," Nick said. His voice sounded strange in the darkening woods. He did not speak again.

He started a fire with some chunks of pine he got with the ax from a stump. Over the fire he stuck a wire grill, pushing the four legs down into the ground with his boot. Nick put the frying pan on the grill over the flames. He was hungrier. The beans and spaghetti warmed. Nick stirred them and mixed them together. They began to bubble, making little bubbles that rose with difficulty to the surface. There was a good smell. Nick got out a bottle of tomato ketchup and cut four slices of bread. The little bubbles were coming faster now. Nick sat down beside the fire and lifted the frying pan off. He poured about half the contents out into the tin plate. It spread slowly on the plate. Nick knew it was too hot. He poured on some tomato ketchup. He knew the beans and spaghetti were still too hot. He looked at the fire, then at the tent, he was not going to spoil it all by burning his tongue. For years he had never enjoyed fried bananas because he had never been able to wait for them to cool. His tongue was very sensitive. He was very hungry. Across the river in the swamp, in the almost dark, he saw a mist rising. He looked at the tent once more. All right. He took a full spoonful from the plate.

He ate the whole plateful before he remembered the bread. Nick finished the second plateful with the bread, mopping the plate shiny. He had not eaten since a cup of coffee and a ham sandwich in the station restaurant at St. Ignace.[5] It had been a very fine experience. He had been that hungry before, but had not been able to satisfy it. He could have made camp hours before if he had wanted to. There were plenty of good places to camp on the river. But this was good.

Nick tucked two big chips of pine under the grill. The fire flared up. He had forgotten to get water for the coffee. Out of the pack he got a folding canvas bucket and walked down the hill, across the edge of the meadow, to the stream. The other bank was in the white mist. The grass was wet and cold as he knelt on the bank and dipped the canvas bucket into the stream. It bellied and pulled hard in the current. The water was ice cold. Nick rinsed the bucket and carried it full up to the camp. Up away from the stream it was not so cold.

Nick drove another big nail and hung up the bucket full of water. He dipped the coffee pot half full, put some more chips under the grill onto the fire and put the pot on. He could not remember which way he made coffee. He could remember an argument about it with Hopkins, but not which side he had taken. He decided to bring it to a boil. He remembered now that was Hopkins's way. He had once argued about everything with Hopkins. While he waited for the coffee to boil, he opened a small can of apricots. He liked to open cans. He emptied the can of apricots out into a tin cup. While he watched the coffee on the fire, he drank the juice syrup of the apricots, carefully at first to keep from spilling, then meditatively, sucking the apricots down. They were better than fresh apricots.

The coffee boiled as he watched. The lid came up and coffee and grounds ran down the side of the pot. Nick took it off the grill. It was a triumph for Hopkins. He put sugar in the empty apricot

5. **St. Ignace** (ig′nas): a resort and fishing center in the upper Michigan peninsula.

cup and poured some of the coffee out to cool. It was too hot to pour and he used his hat to hold the handle of the coffee pot. He would not let it steep in the pot at all. Not the first cup. It should be straight Hopkins all the way. Hop deserved that. He was a very serious coffee maker. He was the most serious man Nick had ever known. Not heavy, serious. That was a long time ago. Hopkins spoke without moving his lips. He had played polo. He made millions of dollars in Texas. He had borrowed carfare to go to Chicago, when the wire came that his first big well had come in. He could have wired for money. That would have been too slow. They called Hop's girl the Blonde Venus. Hop did not mind because she was not his real girl. Hopkins said very confidently that none of them would make fun of his real girl. He was right. Hopkins went away when the telegram came. That was on the Black River.[6] It took eight days for the telegram to reach him. Hopkins gave away his .22 caliber Colt automatic pistol to Nick. He gave his camera to Bill. It was to remember him always by. They were all going fishing again next summer. The Hop Head was rich. He would get a yacht and they would all cruise along the north shore of Lake Superior. He was excited but serious. They said good-by and all felt bad. It broke up the trip. They never saw Hopkins again. That was a long time ago on the Black River.

Nick drank the coffee, the coffee according to Hopkins. The coffee was bitter. Nick laughed. It made a good ending to the story. His mind was starting to work. He knew he could choke it because he was tired enough. He spilled the coffee out of the pot and shook the grounds loose into the fire. He lit a cigarette and went inside the tent. He took off his shoes and trousers, sitting on the blankets, rolled the shoes up inside the trousers for a pillow and got in between the blankets.

Out through the front of the tent he watched the glow of the fire, when the night wind blew on it. It was a quiet night. The swamp was perfectly quiet. Nick stretched under the blanket comfortably. A mosquito hummed close to his ear. Nick sat up and lit a match. The mosquito was on the canvas, over his head. Nick moved the match quickly up to it. The mosquito made a satisfactory hiss in the flame. The match went out. Nick lay down

6. **Black River:** a stream in the northern lower peninsula of Michigan.

again under the blankets. He turned on his side and shut his eyes. He was sleepy. He felt sleep coming. He curled up under the blanket and went to sleep.

Part II

In the morning the sun was up and the tent was starting to get hot. Nick crawled out under the mosquito netting stretched across the mouth of the tent, to look at the morning. The grass was wet on his hands as he came out. He held his trousers and his shoes in his hands. The sun was just up over the hill. There was the meadow, the river, and the swamp. There were birch trees in the green of the swamp on the other side of the river.

The river was clear and smoothly fast in the early morning. Down about two hundred yards were three logs all the way across the stream. They made the water smooth and deep above them. As Nick watched, a mink crossed the river on the logs and went into the swamp. Nick was excited. He was excited by the early morning and the river. He was really too hurried to eat breakfast, but he knew he must. He built a little fire and put on the coffee pot. While the water was heating in the pot he took an empty bottle and went down over the edge of the high ground to the meadow. The meadow was wet with dew and Nick wanted to catch grasshoppers for bait before the sun dried the grass. He found plenty of good grasshoppers. They were at the base of the grass stems. Sometimes they clung to a grass stem. They were cold and wet with the dew, and could not jump until the sun warmed them. Nick picked them up, taking only the medium sized brown ones, and put them into the bottle. He turned over a log, and just under the shelter of the edge were several hundred hoppers. It was a grasshopper lodging house. Nick put about fifty of the medium browns into the bottle. While he was picking up the hoppers the others warmed in the sun and commenced to hop away. They flew when they hopped. At first they made one flight and stayed stiff when they landed, as though they were dead.

Nick knew that by the time he was through with breakfast they would be as lively as ever. Without dew in the grass it would take him all day to catch a bottle full of good grasshoppers and he would have to crush many of them, slamming at them with his hat. He washed his hands at the stream. He was excited to be near it. Then he walked up to the tent. The hoppers were already jumping stiffly in the grass. In the bottle, warmed by the sun, they were jumping in a mass. Nick put in a pine stick as a cork. It plugged the mouth of the bottle enough, so the hoppers could not get out, and left plenty of air passage.

He had rolled the log back and knew he could get grass-hoppers there every morning.

Nick laid the bottle full of jumping grasshoppers against a pine trunk. Rapidly he mixed some buckwheat flour with water and stirred it smooth, one cup of flour, one cup of water. He put a handful of coffee in the pot and dipped a lump of grease out of a can and slid it sputtering across the hot skillet. On the smoking skillet he poured smoothly the buckwheat batter. It spread like lava, the grease spitting sharply. Around the edges the buckwheat cake began to firm, then brown, then crisp. The surface was bubbling slowly to porousness. Nick pushed under the browned under surface with a fresh pine chip. He shook the skillet sideways and the cake was loose on the surface. I won't try and flop it, he thought. He slid the chip of clean wood all the way under the cake, and flopped it over onto its face. It sputtered in the pan.

When it was cooked Nick regreased the skillet. He used all the batter. It made another big flapjack and one smaller one.

Nick ate a big flapjack and a smaller one, covered with apple butter. He put apple butter on the third cake, folded it over twice, wrapped it in oiled paper and put it in his shirt pocket. He put the apple butter jar back in the pack and cut bread for two sandwiches.

In the pack he found a big onion. He sliced it in two and peeled the silky outer skin. Then he cut one half into slices and made onion sandwiches. He wrapped them in oiled paper and buttoned them in the other pocket of his khaki shirt. He turned the skillet upside down on the grill, drank the coffee, sweetened and yellow brown with the condensed milk in it, and tidied up the camp. It was a nice little camp.

Nick took his fly rod out of the leather rod-case, jointed it, and shoved the rod-case back into the tent. He put on the reel and threaded the line through the guides. He had to hold it from hand to hand, as he threaded it, or it would slip back through its own weight. It was a heavy, double tapered fly line. Nick had paid eight dollars for it a long time ago. It was made heavy to lift back in the air and come forward flat and heavy and straight to make it possible to cast a fly which has no weight. Nick opened the aluminum leader box.[7] The leaders were coiled between the damp flannel pads. Nick had wet the pads at the water cooler on the train up to St. Ignace. In the damp pads the gut leaders had softened and Nick unrolled one and tied it by a loop at the end to the heavy fly line. He fastened a hook on the end of the leader. It was a small hook; very thin and springy.

Nick took it from his hook book, sitting with the rod across his lap. He tested the knot and the spring of the rod by pulling the line taut. It was a good feeling. He was careful not to let the hook bite into his finger.

He started down to the stream, holding his rod, the bottle of grasshoppers hung from his neck by a thong tied in half hitches around the neck of the bottle. His landing net hung by a hook from his belt. Over his shoulder was a long flour sack tied at each corner into an ear. The cord went over his shoulder. The sack flapped against his legs.

Nick felt awkward and professionally happy with all his equipment hanging from him. The grasshopper bottle swung against his chest. In his shirt the breast pockets bulged against him with the lunch and his fly book.

He stepped into the stream. It was a shock. His trousers clung tight to his legs. His shoes felt the gravel. The water was a rising cold shock.

Rushing, the current sucked against his legs. Where he stepped in, the water was over his knees. He waded with the current. The gravel slid under his shoes. He looked down at the swirl of water below each leg and tipped up the bottle to get a grasshopper.

The first grasshopper gave a jump in the neck of the bottle and went out into the water. He was sucked under in the whirl by Nick's right leg and came to the surface a little way down stream. He floated rapidly, kicking. In a quick circle, breaking the smooth surface of the water, he disappeared. A trout had taken him.

7. **leader box:** box for carrying leaders, lengths of catgut or monofilament used for attaching flies, fishhooks, lures, etc., to the end of a fly line.

Another hopper poked his head out of the bottle. His antennæ wavered. He was getting his front legs out of the bottle to jump. Nick took him by the head and held him while he threaded the slim hook under his chin, down through his thorax and into the last segments of his abdomen. The grasshopper took hold of the hook with his front feet, spitting tobacco juice on it. Nick dropped him into the water.

Holding the rod in his right hand he let out line against the pull of the grasshopper in the current. He stripped off line from the reel with his left hand and let it run free. He could see the hopper in the little waves of the current. It went out of sight.

There was a tug on the line. Nick pulled against the taut line. It was his first strike. Holding the now living rod across the current, he brought in the line with his left hand. The rod bent in jerks, the trout pumping against the current. Nick knew it was a small one. He lifted the rod straight up in the air. It bowed with the pull.

He saw the trout in the water jerking with his head and body against the shifting tangent of the line in the stream.

Nick took the line in his left hand and pulled the trout, thumping tiredly against the current, to the surface. His back was mottled the clear, water-over-gravel color, his side flashing in the sun. The rod under his right arm, Nick stooped, dipping his right hand into the current. He held the trout, never still, with his moist right hand, while he unhooked the barb from his mouth, then dropped him back into the stream.

He hung unsteadily in the current, then settled to the bottom beside a stone. Nick reached down his hand to touch him, his arm to the elbow under water. The trout was steady in the moving stream, resting on the gravel, beside a stone. As Nick's fingers touched him, touched his smooth, cool, underwater feeling he was gone, gone in a shadow across the bottom of the stream.

He's all right, Nick thought. He was only tired.

He had wet his hand before he touched the trout, so he would not disturb the delicate mucus that covered him. If a trout was touched with a dry hand, a white fungus attacked the unprotected spot. Years before when he had fished crowded streams, with fly fishermen ahead of him and behind him, Nick had again and again come on dead trout, furry with white fungus, drifted against a rock, or floating belly up in some pool. Nick did not like to fish with other men on the river. Unless they were of your party, they spoiled it.

He wallowed down the stream, above his knees in the current, through the fifty yards of shallow water above the pile of logs that crossed the stream. He did not rebait his hook and held it in his hand as he waded. He was certain he could catch small trout in the shallows, but he did not want them. There would be no big trout in the shallows this time of day.

Now the water deepened up his thighs sharply and coldly. Ahead was the smooth dammed-back flood of water above the logs. The water was smooth and dark; on the left, the lower edge of the meadow; on the right the swamp.

Nick leaned back against the current and took a hopper from the bottle. He threaded the hopper on the hook and spat on him for good luck. Then he pulled several yards of line from the reel and tossed the hopper out ahead onto the fast, dark water. It floated down towards the logs, then the weight of the line pulled the bait under the surface. Nick held the rod in his right hand, letting the line run out through his fingers.

There was a long tug. Nick struck and the rod came alive and dangerous, bent double, the line tightening, coming out of water, tightening, all in a heavy, dangerous, steady pull. Nick felt the moment when the leader would break if the strain increased and let the line go.

The reel ratcheted [8] into a mechanical shriek as the line went out in a rush. Too fast. Nick could not check it, the line rushing out, the reel note rising as the line ran out.

With the core of the reel showing, his heart feeling stopped with the excitement, leaning back against the current that mounted icily his thighs, Nick thumbed the reel hard with his left hand. It was awkward getting his thumb inside the fly reel frame.

As he put on pressure the line tightened into sudden hardness and beyond the logs a huge trout went high out of water. As he jumped, Nick lowered the tip of the rod. But he felt, as he dropped the tip to ease the strain, the moment when the strain was too great; the hardness too tight. Of course, the leader had

---

8. ratcheted: clicked sharply. A ratchet is a toothed wheel that moves freely in one direction only; fishing reels use ratchet-type brakes to put a drag on the line, to make the fish work hard to drag the line out.

broken. There was no mistaking the feeling when all spring left the line and it became dry and hard. Then it went slack.

His mouth dry, his heart down, Nick reeled in. He had never seen so big a trout. There was a heaviness, a power not to be held, and then the bulk of him, as he jumped. He looked as broad as a salmon.

Nick's hand was shaky. He reeled in slowly. The thrill had been too much. He felt, vaguely, a little sick, as though it would be better to sit down.

The leader had broken where the hook was tied to it. Nick took it in his hand. He thought of the trout somewhere on the bottom, holding himself steady over the gravel, far down below the light, under the logs, with the hook in his jaw. Nick knew the trout's teeth would cut through the snell [9] of the hook. The hook would imbed itself in his jaw. He'd bet the trout was angry. Anything that size would be angry. That was a trout. He had been solidly hooked. Solid as a rock. He felt like a rock, too, before he started off. By God, he was a big one. By God, he was the biggest one I ever heard of.

Nick climbed out onto the meadow and stood, water running down his trousers and out of his shoes, his shoes squelchy. He went over and sat on the logs. He did not want to rush his sensations any.

He wriggled his toes in the water, in his shoes, and got out a cigarette from his breast pocket. He lit it and tossed the match into the fast water below the logs. A tiny trout rose at the match, as it swung around in the fast current. Nick laughed. He would finish the cigarette.

He sat on the logs, smoking, drying in the sun, the sun warm on his back, the river shallow ahead entering the woods, curving into the woods, shallows, light glittering, big water-smooth rocks, cedars along the bank and white birches, the logs warm in the sun, smooth to sit on, without bark, gray to the touch; slowly the feeling of disappointment left him. It went away slowly, the feeling of disappointment that came sharply after the thrill that made his shoulders ache. It was all right now. His rod lying out on the logs, Nick tied a new hook on the leader, pulling the gut tight until it grimped [10] into itself in a hard knot.

9. **snell:** the strand of catgut leader attached to the hook.
10. **grimped:** a combination of *grip* and *crimp*.

He baited up, then picked up the rod and walked to the far end of the logs to get into the water, where it was not too deep. Under and beyond the logs was a deep pool. Nick walked around the shallow shelf near the swamp shore until he came out on the shallow bed of the stream.

On the left, where the meadow ended and the woods began, a great elm tree was uprooted. Gone over in a storm, it lay back into the woods, its roots clotted with dirt, grass growing in them, rising a solid bank beside the stream. The river cut to the edge of the uprooted tree. From where Nick stood he could see deep channels, like ruts, cut in the shallow bed of the stream by the flow of the current. Pebbly where he stood and pebbly and full of boulders beyond; where it curved near the tree roots, the bed of the stream was marly [11] and between the ruts of deep water green weed fronds swung in the current.

Nick swung the rod back over his shoulder and forward, and the line, curving forward, laid the grasshopper down on one of the deep channels in the weeds. A trout struck and Nick hooked him.

Holding the rod far out toward the uprooted tree and sloshing backward in the current, Nick worked the trout, plunging, the rod bending alive, out of the danger of the weeds into the open river. Holding the rod, pumping alive against the current, Nick brought the trout in. He rushed, but always came, the spring of the rod yielding to the rushes, sometimes jerking under water, but always bringing him in. Nick eased downstream with the rushes. The rod above his head he led the trout over the net, then lifted.

The trout hung heavy in the net, mottled trout back and silver sides in the meshes. Nick unhooked him; heavy sides, good to hold, big undershot jaw, and slipped him, heaving and big sliding, into the long sack that hung from his shoulders in the water.

Nick spread the mouth of the sack against the current and it filled, heavy with water. He held it up, the bottom in the stream, and the water poured out through the sides. Inside at the bottom was the big trout, alive in the water.

Nick moved downstream. The sack out ahead of him, sunk, heavy in the water, pulling from his shoulders.

11. **marly:** composed of clay or sand, or a firm mixture of both.

It was getting hot, the sun hot on the back of his neck.

Nick had one good trout. He did not care about getting many trout. Now the stream was shallow and wide. There were trees along both banks. The trees of the left bank made short shadows on the current in the forenoon sun. Nick knew there were trout in each shadow. In the afternoon, after the sun had crossed toward the hills, the trout would be in the cool shadows on the other side of the stream.

The very biggest ones would lie up close to the bank. You could always pick them up there on the Black. When the sun was down they all moved out into the current. Just when the sun made the water blinding in the glare before it went down, you were liable to strike a big trout anywhere in the current. It was almost impossible to fish then, the surface of the water was blinding as a mirror in the sun. Of course, you could fish upstream, but in a stream like the Black, or this, you had to wallow against the current and in a deep place, the water piled up on you. It was no fun to fish upstream with this much current.

Nick moved along through the shallow stretch watching the banks for deep holes. A beech tree grew close beside the river, so that the branches hung down into the water. The stream went back in under the leaves. There were always trout in a place like that.

Nick did not care about fishing that hole. He was sure he would get hooked in the branches.

It looked deep though. He dropped the grasshopper so the current took it under water, back in under the overhanging branch. The line pulled hard and Nick struck. The trout threshed heavily, half out of water in the leaves and branches. The line was caught. Nick pulled hard and the trout was off. He reeled in and holding the hook in his hand, walked down the stream.

Ahead, close to the left bank, was a big log. Nick saw it was hollow; pointing up river the current entered it smoothly, only a little ripple spread each side of the log. The water was deepening. The top of the hollow log was gray and dry. It was partly in the shadow.

Nick took the cork out of the grasshopper bottle and a hopper clung to it. He picked him off, hooked him and tossed him out. He held the rod far out so that the hopper on the water moved into the current flowing into the hollow log. Nick lowered the rod and the hopper floated in. There was a heavy strike. Nick swung the rod against the pull. It felt as though he were hooked into the log itself, except for the live feeling.

He tried to force the fish out into the current. It came, heavily.

The line went slack and Nick thought the trout was gone. Then he saw him, very near, in the current, shaking his head, trying to get the hook out. His mouth was clamped shut. He was fighting the hook in the clear flowing current.

Looping in the line with his left hand, Nick swung the rod to make the line taut and tried to lead the trout toward the net, but he was gone, out of sight, the line pumping. Nick fought him against the current, letting him thump in the water against the spring of the rod. He shifted the rod to his left hand, worked the trout upstream, holding his weight, fighting on the rod, and then let him down into the net. He lifted him clear of the water, a heavy half circle in the net, the net dripping, unhooked him and slid him into the sack.

He spread the mouth of the sack and looked down in at the two big trout alive in the water.

Through the deepening water, Nick waded over to the hollow log. He took the sack off, over his head, the trout flopping as it came out of water, and hung it so the trout were deep in the water. Then he pulled himself up on the log and sat, the water from his trousers and boots running down into the stream. He laid his rod down, moved along to the shady end of the log and took the sandwiches out of his pocket. He dipped the sandwiches in the cold water. The current carried away the crumbs. He ate the sandwiches and dipped his hat full of water to drink, the water running out through his hat just ahead of his drinking.

It was cool in the shade, sitting on the log. He took a cigarette out and struck a match to light it. The match sunk into the gray wood, making a tiny furrow. Nick leaned over the side of the log, found a hard place and lit the match. He sat smoking and watching the river.

Ahead the river narrowed and went into a swamp. The river became smooth and deep and the swamp looked solid with cedar trees, their trunks close together, their branches solid. It would not be possible to walk through a swamp like that. The branches grew so low. You would have to keep almost level with the ground to move at all. You could not crash through the branches. That must be why the animals that lived in swamps were built the way they were, Nick thought.

He wished he had brought something to read. He felt like reading. He did not feel like going on into the swamp. He looked down the river. A big cedar slanted all the way across the stream. Beyond that the river went into the swamp.

Nick did not want to go in there now. He felt a reaction against deep wading with the water deepening up under his armpits, to hook big trout in places impossible to land them. In the swamp the banks were bare, the big cedars came together overhead, the sun did not come through, except in patches; in the fast deep water, in the half light, the fishing would be tragic. In the swamp fishing was a tragic adventure. Nick did not want it. He did not want to go down the stream any further today.

He took out his knife, opened it and stuck it in the log. Then he pulled up the sack, reached into it and brought out one of the trout. Holding him near the tail, hard to hold, alive, in his hand, he whacked him against the log. The trout quivered, rigid. Nick laid him on the log in the shade and broke the neck of the other fish the same way. He laid them side by side on the log. They were fine trout.

Nick cleaned them, slitting them from the vent to the tip of the jaw. All the insides and the gills and tongue came out in one piece. They were both males; long gray-white strips of milt,[12] smooth and clean. All the insides clean and compact, coming out all together. Nick tossed the offal ashore for the minks to find.

He washed the trout in the stream. When he held them back up in the water they looked like live fish. Their color was not gone yet. He washed his hands and dried them on the log. Then he laid the trout on the sack spread out on the log, rolled them up in it, tied the bundle and put it in the landing net. His knife was still standing, blade stuck in the log. He cleaned it on the wood and put it in his pocket.

Nick stood up on the log, holding his rod, the landing net

12. **milt:** the reproductive organs of the male fish when filled with seminal fluid.

hanging heavy, then stepped into the water and splashed ashore. He climbed the bank and cut up into the woods, toward the high ground. He was going back to camp. He looked back. The river just showed through the trees. There were plenty of days coming when he could fish the swamp.

Meaning and Method

1. Nick Adams returned to the familiar surroundings of the upper peninsula in Michigan, leaving behind a war-ravaged Europe and retaining many of the ill effects—physical and emotional—the war had inflicted upon him. In what ways does the burned-up town of Seney parallel and even symbolize (a) Europe after the war and (b) Nick's own state of mind as the story unfolds? What does Nick see in the landscape, despite the scars of the fire, that pleases him and makes him hopeful? What thoughts give Nick a feeling of contentment?

2. After reaching a suitable campsite, Nick laboriously sets about putting up his tent and getting the camp in order. What does the manner in which he sets up camp tell about his state of mind? In what ways is his manner ritualistic?

   War is a time of rapid, violent change and almost total chaos and insecurity. How does Nick's method of setting up camp indicate that he is putting off thinking about serious matters, that he desires a more stable set of living conditions?

3. Beginning on page 108, mention of Nick's friend Hopkins begins to dart in and out of the narrative. What do the references to his friend tell about how Nick relates to others? Does he seem to regard them the same way he regards his relationship with nature? Does he take people as they are? Explain. Why does Nick not let himself think too much about Hopkins and the others?

4. Notice the care Nick takes in handling the grasshoppers he uses for bait and, especially, in handling the first small trout he catches and then releases (page 113). Why does he first wet his hands before handling the trout? Why is he relieved when the fish darts away, unharmed? Why does all this tell about Nick and his attitudes toward life and toward wildlife in particular? Does he follow a code of behavior here?

5. Nick undergoes a subtle change in the story. Compare, for example, his reactions on the two occasions in Part II (see pages 115 and 117) when he fails to land a trout he has hooked. After the first loss, he is shaken and disappointed, somehow threatened, and has to sit down on a log and have a cigarette in order to get

hold of himself. What is his reaction after losing the second trout? What does he do after losing it? How do the different reactions reflect the change in his emotional state?

6. In the story the river Nick fishes has "two hearts" in the sense that he looks at fishing two sections of the river in different ways. On the first section, once he gets back "the old feeling," there are health, life, goodness, regeneration. How does this part of the river differ in physical detail from the section Nick does not wish to fish just yet? Why is fishing in the second section "a tragic adventure" (page 119)? What does the second part of the river symbolize in terms of Nick Adams?

Language: Journalistic Style

As a cub reporter for the Kansas City *Star*, Hemingway was instructed to observe the rules contained in the newspaper's manual of style. Part of the manual that stuck with him was its opening paragraph: "Use short sentences. Use short first paragraphs. Use vigorous English. Be positive, not negative." Hemingway also learned to write with an objective tone, with many physical and factual details, and with verbs of action. In his later career he once said that he particularly admired Mark Twain's dictum, "As to the adjective—when in doubt, strike it out."

Apply the principles of journalistic writing to the following expressions. Simplify them, deleting all unnecessary modifiers and all redundancies, and making indirect statement into direct statement:

1. in the city of Boston, Massachusetts
2. a talk on the subject of charity
3. the present incumbent
4. for a short space of time
5. made an investigation of
6. ended his talk with the following statement
7. uniform in both size and shape
8. old traditions of the past
9. a container made out of steel
10. during the month of June

Composition

1. For a book review, read one of Hemingway's full-length works (novels: *The Sun Also Rises, A Farewell to Arms, For Whom the Bell Tolls,* and *The Old Man and the Sea;* other books: *Death in the Afternoon* and *A Moveable Feast*).

In your review, concentrate on an evaluation of the major themes which, singly or in combination, run through most of Hemingway's writing: (1) the nature of the hero and of individual heroism; (2) the subtle wounding—psychologically as well as physically—of the protagonist, and his consequent "separate peace" with whatever forces buffet him; and (3) the isolation of Hemingway's protagonists (their number includes himself). Remember, too, that the quality of writing in Hemingway's works varies widely—from book to book and even within a single work.

2. A parody is the conscious, usually exaggerated imitation of a recognizable literary style or individual work. It aims at humor through distortion. Select a short narrative passage from another story in this collection—paragraphs, for example, from "Neighbor Rosicky" or "Sophistication"—and rewrite it by parodying Hemingway's style.

William Faulkner

[1897–1962]

By 1945, popular and critical interest in William Faulkner's writing had reached its low point. All of Faulkner's fiction was out of print, and scholars, if they mentioned him at all, dismissed him as a minor figure. In 1946, however, the publication of *The Portable Faulkner*, edited by Malcolm Cowley, revived general interest in his work and caused literary critics to reevaluate his importance. Although Faulkner was once considered a regional writer because almost all of his stories and novels are set in the South, he was discovered to be actually a critic of contemporary society in general. This critical reevaluation led to his being awarded the Nobel prize for literature in 1949.

Faulkner was a native Mississippian, and illustrated his ideas about contemporary society by tracing the development of southern society during the pre-Civil War age and by showing its decline since the war. Almost all of his books, such as *Sartoris* (1929) and *Absalom, Absalom!* (1936), are set in Yoknapatawpha * County. This land, modeled after his own Lafayette County in Mississippi, is a microcosm of the South. Faulkner outlined the history of the territory from the time when the wealthy, slave-owning families wrested it from the Indians to the twentieth century. The central event in this history of Faulkner's Yoknapatawpha was the Civil War. After the war, the once-powerful white families, now decadent remnants of a bygone era, are pushed aside by the northern carpetbaggers and by such unwashed and unethical southern whites as the Snopes family.† The older families live in the past, obsessed by idealized dreams of former greatness and paralyzed by a fear of the "modern" world, especially the industrialized North. Tied to a code of honor, they are unable to resist the forces of a modern world that does not recognize the code to which they cling.

William Faulkner knew intimately the land in northwest Mississippi around the towns of New Albany, where he was born, and

---

* **Yoknapatawpha** (yok′nə·pä·tow′fä).
† **Snopes family:** their arrival and eventual takeover in Yoknapatawpha are traced in *The Snopes Trilogy*, made up of the novels *The Hamlet* (1940), *The Town* (1957), and *The Mansion* (1960).

Oxford, where he spent most of his life. The fictional town of Jefferson, the setting for many of his works, resembles both these towns.

Faulkner's education was unstructured; after the fifth grade, his schooling was sporadic. Instead he read widely, although, as he said, it was "undirected and uncorrelated." During World War I, Faulkner left home to enlist in the Canadian Royal Flying Corps but didn't see any combat. At the end of the war, he returned to Mississippi and entered the state university. A poor student, he soon left school to become at various times a carpenter, a housepainter, and the university's postmaster. And, from time to time, he supported himself as a screenwriter in Hollywood. But primarily he devoted his time to writing fiction.

Popular and critical approval of Faulkner's work came slowly, partially because he broke many of the traditional conventions for novels. Characterization is often developed through interior monologues that are filled with distortions. As a result, objective reality is intermingled with subjective reactions. In addition to creating difficulties for the reader by the stream-of-consciousness technique, Faulkner's narratives also present problems because they seldom move forward in regular chronological time sequence. Rather, as in *The Sound and the Fury*, they shift back and forth in response to the thematic demands of the story. And the confusion sometimes caused by the shifting is compounded by Faulkner's frequently long, syntactically complex sentences. For example, one sentence in the story *The Bear* (1942) is more than sixteen hundred words long.

Despite the forces aligned against man today, Faulkner refused to accept man's final defeat. In his Nobel prize acceptance speech, he expressed his belief that man would not only endure but would prevail: "He [man] is immortal, not because he alone among creatures has an inexhaustible voice, but because he has a soul, a spirit capable of compassion and sacrifice and endurance."

A Rose for Emily

I

When Miss Emily Grierson died, our whole town went to her funeral: the men through a sort of respectful affection for a fallen monument, the women mostly out of curiosity to see the inside of her house, which no one save an old manservant — a combined gardener and cook — had seen in at least ten years.

It was a big, squarish frame house that had once been white, decorated with cupolas [1] and spires and scrolled balconies in the heavily lightsome style of the seventies, set on what had once been our most select street. But garages and cotton gins had encroached and obliterated even the august names of that neighborhood; only Miss Emily's house was left, lifting its stubborn and coquettish decay above the cotton wagons and the gasoline pumps — an eyesore among eyesores. And now Miss Emily had gone to join the representatives of those august names where they lay in the cedar-bemused cemetery among the ranked and anonymous graves of Union and Confederate soldiers who fell at the battle of Jefferson.

Alive, Miss Emily had been a tradition, a duty, and a care; a sort of hereditary obligation upon the town, dating from that day in 1894 when Colonel Sartoris, the mayor — he who fathered the edict that no Negro woman should appear on the streets without an apron — remitted her taxes, the dispensation dating from the death of her father on into perpetuity. Not that she would have accepted charity. Colonel Sartoris invented an involved tale to the effect that Miss Emily's father had loaned money to the town, which the town, as a matter of business, preferred this way of repaying. Only a man of Colonel Sartoris' generation and thought could have invented it, and only a woman could have believed it.

When the next generation, with its more modern ideas, became mayors and aldermen, this arrangement created some little dissatisfaction. On the first of the year they mailed her a tax notice. February came, and there was no reply. They wrote her a formal

1. cupolas (kyo͞o′pə·ləz): small coop-like structures rising above the roof of a house.

letter, asking her to call at the sheriff's office at her convenience. A week later the mayor wrote her himself, offering to call or to send his car for her, and received in reply a note on paper of an archaic shape, in a thin, flowing calligraphy [2] in faded ink, to the effect that she no longer went out at all. The tax notice was also enclosed, without comment.

They called a special meeting of the Board of Aldermen. A deputation waited upon her, knocked at the door through which no visitor had passed since she ceased giving china-painting lessons eight or ten years earlier. They were admitted by the old Negro into a dim hall from which a stairway mounted into still more shadow. It smelled of dust and disuse — a close, dank smell. The Negro led them into the parlor. It was furnished in heavy, leather-covered furniture. When the Negro opened the blinds of one window, they could see that the leather was cracked; and when they sat down, a faint dust rose sluggishly about their thighs, spinning with slow motes [3] in the single sunray. On a tarnished gilt easel before the fireplace stood a crayon portrait of Miss Emily's father.

They rose when she entered — a small, fat woman in black, with a thin gold chain descending to her waist and vanishing into her belt, leaning on an ebony cane with a tarnished gold head. Her skeleton was small and spare; perhaps that was why what would have been merely plumpness in another was obesity in her. She looked bloated, like a body long submerged in motionless water, and of that pallid hue. Her eyes, lost in the fatty ridges of her face, looked like two small pieces of coal pressed into a lump of dough as they moved from one face to another while the visitors stated their errand.

She did not ask them to sit. She just stood in the door and listened quietly until the spokesman came to a stumbling halt. Then they could hear the invisible watch ticking at the end of the gold chain.

Her voice was dry and cold. "I have no taxes in Jefferson. Colonel Sartoris explained it to me. Perhaps one of you can gain access to the city records and satisfy yourselves."

"But we have. We are the city authorities, Miss Emily. Didn't you get a notice from the sheriff, signed by him?"

2. **calligraphy** (kə·lig′rə·fē) : handwriting.
3. **motes:** minute specks of dust.

"I received a paper, yes," Miss Emily said. "Perhaps he considers himself the sheriff. . . . I have no taxes in Jefferson."

"But there is nothing on the books to show that, you see. We must go by the — "

"See Colonel Sartoris. I have no taxes in Jefferson."

"But, Miss Emily — "

"See Colonel Sartoris." (Colonel Sartoris had been dead almost ten years.) "I have no taxes in Jefferson. Tobe!" The Negro appeared. "Show these gentlemen out."

II

So she vanquished them, horse and foot, just as she had vanquished their fathers thirty years before about the smell. That was two years after her father's death and a short time after her sweetheart — the one we believed would marry her — had deserted her. After her father's death she went out very little; after her sweetheart went away, people hardly saw her at all. A few of the ladies had the temerity to call, but were not received, and the only sign of life about the place was the Negro man — a young man then — going in and out with a market basket.

"Just as if a man — any man — could keep a kitchen properly," the ladies said; so they were not surprised when the smell developed. It was another link between the gross, teeming world and the high and mighty Griersons.

A neighbor, a woman, complained to the mayor, Judge Stevens, eighty years old.

"But what will you have me do about it, madam?" he said.

"Why, send her word to stop it," the woman said. "Isn't there a law?"

"I'm sure that won't be necessary," Judge Stevens said. "It's probably just a snake or a rat that nigger of hers killed in the yard. I'll speak to him about it."

The next day he received two more complaints, one from a man who came in diffident deprecation.[4] "We really must do something about it, Judge. I'd be the last one in the world to bother Miss Emily, but we've got to do something." That night the Board of Aldermen met — three graybeards and one younger man, a member of the rising generation.

4. **diffident deprecation:** timid protest.

"It's simple enough," he said. "Send her word to have her place cleaned up. Give her a certain time to do it in, and if she don't . . ."

"Dammit, sir," Judge Stevens said, "will you accuse a lady to her face of smelling bad?"

So the next night, after midnight, four men crossed Miss Emily's lawn and slunk about the house like burglars, sniffing along the base of the brickwork and at the cellar openings while one of them performed a regular sowing motion with his hand out of a sack slung from his shoulder. They broke open the cellar door and sprinkled lime there, and in all the outbuildings. As they recrossed the lawn, a window that had been dark was lighted and Miss Emily sat in it, the light behind her, and her upright torso motionless as that of an idol. They crept quietly across the lawn and into the shadow of the locusts that lined the street. After a week or two the smell went away.

That was when people had begun to feel really sorry for her. People in our town, remembering how old lady Wyatt, her great-aunt, had gone completely crazy at last, believed that the Griersons held themselves a little too high for what they really were. None of the young men were quite good enough for Miss Emily and such. We had long thought of them as a tableau,[5] Miss Emily a slender figure in white in the background, her father a spraddled [6] silhouette in the foreground, his back to her and clutching a horsewhip, the two of them framed by the back-flung front door. So when she got to be thirty and was still single, we were not pleased exactly, but vindicated; even with insanity in the family she wouldn't have turned down all of her chances if they had really materialized.

When her father died, it got about that the house was all that was left to her; and in a way, people were glad. At last they could pity Miss Emily. Being left alone, and a pauper, she had become humanized. Now she too would know the old thrill and the old despair of a penny more or less.

The day after his death all the ladies prepared to call at the house and offer condolence and aid, as is our custom. Miss Emily met them at the door, dressed as usual and with no trace of grief on her face. She told them that her father was not dead. She did

5. **tableau** (tab'lō): picture.
6. **spraddled**: sprawling.

that for three days, with the ministers calling on her, and the doctors, trying to persuade her to let them dispose of the body. Just as they were about to resort to law and force, she broke down, and they buried her father quickly.

We did not say she was crazy then. We believed she had to do that. We remembered all the young men her father had driven away, and we knew that with nothing left, she would have to cling to that which had robbed her, as people will.

III

She was sick for a long time. When we saw her again, her hair was cut short, making her look like a girl, with a vague resemblance to those angels in colored church windows — sort of tragic and serene.

The town had just let the contracts for paving the sidewalks, and in the summer after her father's death they began the work. The construction company came with niggers and mules and machinery, and a foreman named Homer Barron, a Yankee — a big, dark, ready man, with a big voice and eyes lighter than his face. The little boys would follow in groups to hear him cuss the niggers, and the niggers singing in time to the rise and fall of picks. Pretty soon he knew everybody in town. Whenever you heard a lot of laughing anywhere about the square, Homer Barron would be in the center of the group. Presently we began to see him and Miss Emily on Sunday afternoons driving in the yellow-wheeled buggy and the matched team of bays from the livery stable.

At first we were glad that Miss Emily would have an interest, because the ladies all said, "Of course a Grierson would not think seriously of a Northerner, a day laborer." But there were still others, older people, who said that even grief could not cause a real lady to forget *noblesse oblige* [7] — without calling it *noblesse oblige*. They just said, "Poor Emily. Her kinsfolk should come to her." She had some kin in Alabama; but years ago her father had fallen out with them over the estate of old lady Wyatt, the crazy woman, and there was no communication between the two families. They had not even been represented at the funeral.

7. *noblesse oblige* (nō·bles′ ō·blēzh′): *French,* nobility obligates; signifying the responsibility the well-off have to the poor.

And as soon as the old people said, "Poor Emily," the whispering began. "Do you suppose it's really so?" they said to one another. "Of course it is. What else could . . ." This behind their hands; rustling of craned silk and satin behind jalousies [8] closed upon the sun of Sunday afternoon as the thin, swift clop-clop-clop of the matched team passed: "Poor Emily."

She carried her head high enough — even when we believed that she was fallen. It was as if she demanded more than ever the recognition of her dignity as the last Grierson; as if it had wanted that touch of earthiness to reaffirm her imperviousness. Like when she bought the rat poison, the arsenic. That was over a year after they had begun to say "Poor Emily," and while the two female cousins were visiting her.

"I want some poison," she said to the druggist. She was over thirty then, still a slight woman, though thinner than usual, with cold, haughty black eyes in a face the flesh of which was strained across the temples and about the eyesockets as you imagine a lighthouse-keeper's face ought to look. "I want some poison," she said.

"Yes, Miss Emily. What kind? For rats and such? I'd recom — "

"I want the best you have. I don't care what kind."

The druggist named several. "They'll kill anything up to an elephant. But what you want is — "

"Arsenic," Miss Emily said. "Is that a good one?"

"Is . . . arsenic? Yes, ma'am. But what you want — "

"I want arsenic."

The druggist looked down at her. She looked back at him, erect, her face like a strained flag. "Why, of course," the druggist said. "If that's what you want. But the law requires you to tell what you are going to use it for."

Miss Emily just stared at him, her head tilted back in order to look him eye for eye, until he looked away and went and got the arsenic and wrapped it up. The Negro delivery boy brought her the package; the druggist didn't come back. When she opened the package at home there was written on the box, under the skull and bones: "For rats."

8. **jalousies:** window blinds or shutters.

IV

So the next day we all said, "She will kill herself"; and we said it would be the best thing. When she had first begun to be seen with Homer Barron, we had said, "She will marry him." Then we said, "She will persuade him yet," because Homer himself had remarked — he liked men, and it was known that he drank with the younger men in the Elks' Club — that he was not a marrying man. Later we said, "Poor Emily" behind the jalousies as they passed on Sunday afternoon in the glittering buggy, Miss Emily with her head high and Homer Barron with his hat cocked and a cigar in his teeth, reins and whip in a yellow glove.

Then some of the ladies began to say that it was a disgrace to the town and a bad example to the young people. The men did not want to interfere, but at last the ladies forced the Baptist minister — Miss Emily's people were Episcopal — to call upon her. He would never divulge what happened during that interview, but he refused to go back again. The next Sunday they again drove about the streets, and the following day the minister's wife wrote to Miss Emily's relations in Alabama.

So she had blood-kin under her roof again and we sat back to watch developments. At first nothing happened. Then we were sure that they were to be married. We learned that Miss Emily had been to the jeweler's and ordered a man's toilet set in silver, with the letters H.B. on each piece. Two days later we learned that she had bought a complete outfit of men's clothing, including a night-shirt, and we said, "They are married." We were really glad. We were glad because the two female cousins were even more Grierson than Miss Emily had ever been.

So we were not surprised when Homer Barron — the streets had been finished some time since — was gone. We were a little disappointed that there was not a public blowing-off, but we believed that he had gone on to prepare for Miss Emily's coming, or to give her a chance to get rid of the cousins. (By that time it was a cabal,[9] and we were all Miss Emily's allies to help circumvent the cousins.) Sure enough, after another week they departed. And, as we had expected all along, within three days Homer Barron was

9. **cabal** (kə·bal′) : conspiracy.

back in town. A neighbor saw the Negro man admit him at the kitchen door at dusk one evening.

And that was the last we saw of Homer Barron. And of Miss Emily for some time. The Negro man went in and out with the market basket, but the front door remained closed. Now and then we would see her at a window for a moment, as the men did that night when they sprinkled the lime, but for almost six months she did not appear on the streets. Then we knew that this was to be expected too; as if that quality of her father which had thwarted her woman's life so many times had been too virulent [10] and too furious to die.

When we next saw Miss Emily, she had grown fat and her hair was turning gray. During the next few years it grew grayer and grayer until it attained an even pepper-and-salt iron gray, when it ceased turning. Up to the day of her death at seventy-four it was still that vigorous iron gray, like the hair of an active man.

From that time on her front door remained closed, save during a period of six or seven years, when she was about forty, during which she gave lessons in china-painting. She fitted up a studio in one of the downstairs rooms, where the daughters and granddaughters of Colonel Sartoris' contemporaries were sent to her with the same regularity and in the same spirit that they were sent to church on Sundays with a twenty-five-cent piece for the collection plate. Meanwhile her taxes had been remitted.

Then the newer generation became the backbone and the spirit of the town, and the painting pupils grew up and fell away and did not send their children to her with boxes of color and tedious brushes and pictures cut from the ladies' magazines. The front door closed for good. When the town got free postal delivery, Miss Emily alone refused to let them fasten the metal numbers above her door and attach a mailbox to it. She would not listen to them.

Daily, monthly, yearly we watched the Negro grow grayer and more stooped, going in and out with the market basket. Each December we sent her a tax notice, which would be returned by the post office a week later, unclaimed. Now and then we would see her in one of the downstairs windows — she had evidently shut up the top floor of the house — like the carven torso of an idol in a

10. virulent: harsh; venomous.

niche, looking or not looking at us, we could never tell which. Thus she passed from generation to generation — dear, inescapable, impervious, tranquil, and perverse.

And so she died. Fell ill in the house filled with dust and shadows, with only a doddering Negro man to wait on her. We did not even know she was sick; we had long since given up trying to get any information from the Negro. He talked to no one, probably not even to her, for his voice had grown harsh and rusty, as if from disuse.

She died in one of the downstairs rooms, in a heavy walnut bed with a curtain, her gray head propped on a pillow yellow and moldy with age and lack of sunlight.

V

The Negro met the first of the ladies at the front door and let them in, with their hushed, sibilant voices and their quick, curious glances, and then he disappeared. He walked right through the house and out the back and was not seen again.

The two female cousins came at once. They held the funeral on the second day, with the town coming to look at Miss Emily beneath a mass of bought flowers, with the crayon face of her father musing profoundly above the bier and the ladies sibilant and macabre; and the very old men — some in their brushed Confederate uniforms — on the porch and the lawn, talking of Miss Emily as if she had been a contemporary of theirs, believing that they had danced with her and courted her perhaps, confusing time with its mathematical progression, as the old do, to whom all the past is not a diminishing road but, instead, a huge meadow which no winter ever quite touches, divided from them now by the narrow bottleneck of the most recent decade of years.

Already we knew that there was one room in that region above stairs which no one had seen in forty years, and which would have to be forced. They waited until Miss Emily was decently in the ground before they opened it.

The violence of breaking down the door seemed to fill this room with pervading dust. A thin, acrid pall as of the tomb seemed to lie everywhere upon this room decked and furnished as for a bridal: upon the valance curtains of faded rose color, upon the rose-shaded lights, upon the dressing table, upon the delicate array of crystal and the man's toilet things backed with tarnished silver, silver so tarnished that the monogram was obscured. Among them lay a collar and tie, as if they had just been removed, which, lifted, left upon the surface a pale crescent in the dust. Upon a chair hung the suit, carefully folded; beneath it the two mute shoes and the discarded socks.

The man himself lay in the bed.

For a long while we just stood there, looking down at the profound and fleshless grin. The body had apparently once lain in the attitude of an embrace, but now the long sleep that outlasts love, that conquers even the grimace of love, had cuckolded him.[11] What was left of him, rotted beneath what was left of the nightshirt, had become inextricable from the bed in which he lay; and upon him and upon the pillow beside him lay that even coating of the patient and biding dust.

Then we noticed that in the second pillow was the indentation of a head. One of us lifted something from it, and leaning forward, that faint and invisible dust dry and acrid in the nostrils, we saw a long strand of iron-gray hair.

11. **cuckolded him:** cheated him. A cuckold is the unsuspecting husband of an unfaithful wife.

Meaning and Method

1. The point of view in "A Rose for Emily" is that of one of Emily Grierson's neighbors. Does the narrator present his own thoughts? the opinions of the entire town? both? Why would the narrator have to be only a few years younger than Emily?

2. How would you describe Emily Grierson? Which methods of characterization does Faulkner use? (See Glossary.) Give examples from the text.

3. What is the attitude of the narrator toward Miss Emily? How do the men of the town regard her? What do the women think of her? What is the effect of always referring to her as *Miss* Emily? How does the community feeling change from generation to generation?

4. The story, although it is clearly a narrative, does not run from beginning to end in chronological order. For example, the story starts in the present but moves to the past and then works up to the present again. Trace the chronological sequence of the events narrated. How does the narrative sequence create suspense? Does

the shifting from the near past to the distant past to the present approximate the way the mind remembers things?

5. *Miss Emily was unwilling to live in the present.* How is this statement supported by Miss Emily's actions when her father died? by her response to the deputation which called on her about her taxes? by her attitude toward the new postal numbers for the houses?

6. Why did the townspeople think it unlikely that Miss Emily would fall in love with Homer Barron? What was his job? Where was he from? What codes did she break when she took Homer for a lover? Why is the choice of his name, *Barron*, ironic? What is the significance of the fact that Miss Emily was buried "in a cedar-bemused cemetery among the ranked and anonymous graves of the Union and Confederate soldiers"? Why is it ironic?

7. Foreshadowing is hinting, by means of an action, image, or comment, at what is to come in the story. Point out specific examples of foreshadowing in the story.

8. How might Miss Emily seem like another person if Tobe had told the story? Why do you think he stayed all those years? Why do you think he disappeared after he let the townspeople into the house?

9. Why did Miss Emily kill Homer?

10. Miss Emily was confused between the past and the present, between reality and illusion. How does her keeping Homer's body in the room illustrate this?

11. To what does the "rose" in the title refer? Does it refer to the entire story, which is like a flower tossed on her grave as a last remembrance? Or does it refer to a flower pressed between the pages of a book, kept as a remembrance of the past? Or does it refer to Miss Emily herself, who must be protected from the world?

Composition and Discussion

1. One critic calls Miss Emily "a tragic—and heroic—figure." In the first place, she has been frustrated by her father and, secondly, "when she attempts to achieve freedom, she is betrayed by a man who represents the new morality. . . ."

Do you agree with this critic?

2. When asked about the conflict in "A Rose for Emily," Faulkner said it was between God and Satan and, furthermore, "The conflict was in Miss Emily, that she knew that you do not murder people. . . . And she knew she was doing wrong, and that's why her own life was

wrecked. Instead of murdering one lover, and then to go on and take another and when she used him up to murder him, she was expiating her crime."

Discuss how Miss Emily expiates her crime. Does this explain why she keeps a picture of her father in the living room? Does this idea of expiation keep the story from becoming just another macabre ghost story?

3. The word *nigger* appears a few times in this story, and another derogatory word, *Bohunk*, appears in Willa Cather's story, "Neighbor Rosicky."

Is the use of such offensive words in relation to racial, national, or religious groups ever permissible in writing? Does it matter that some members of the same group may use, within the group, words that would be offensive if used by outsiders? Who is to determine if a word is objectionable or offensive to an ethnic or a religious group?

Consider these and related questions in a panel discussion on the use in fiction of certain derogatory words and expressions. Keep in mind these points: (a) the possible distinction between the narrator of a story and the author of a story; (b) the historical and social context of a story; (c) the characterization of the person using the derogatory words in the story; and (d) the character's educational and cultural background.

John Steinbeck

[1902–1968]

"There would seem to be only one commandment
for all living things. Survive!"
—John Steinbeck, *The Sea of Cortez.*

As a result of his college study of marine biology, Steinbeck
came to believe that all living creatures, particularly man, are the
product of their environment and their heredity. Steinbeck's novels
and stories illustrate this point of view. His characters, generally
simple and unlettered but with a native innocence and dignity, are
battered by forces they neither know nor can control. Trapped by
their environment, they are unable to rise out of the situation into
which fate and society have placed them.

Steinbeck's early writing grew out of his life around the Salinas
Valley, where he was born, and the mountainous Monterey Peninsula in California, where he grew up. On the farms where he
worked while in high school, he met the laborers who populate his
stories. After graduation from high school, he attended Stanford
University on and off for five years but never received a degree. His
real education came from the odd jobs, such as fruit-picking and
construction work, that he held before he established his literary
reputation.

The economic depression which began with the stock market
crash of 1929 made Steinbeck aware of the terrible inequities in
American society. In his Pulitzer prize-winning novel, *The Grapes
of Wrath* (1939), he traces the odyssey of the Joad family, Oklahoma farmers who were forced from their land during the Depression, across the country to California. The family, spurred on
in their trek by handbills promising work, arrived in California only
to find the state overrun with other migrants—farmers who, like
themselves, had been driven off their land. With not enough work
to go around, those who did find something to do were paid pitifully little. All were systematically exploited by the landowners, but
many survived and looked to the future.

Critics feel Steinbeck's later novels, such as *East of Eden*
(1952), did not equal his earlier writings. Nevertheless, he was

awarded the Nobel prize for literature in 1962. In making the award, the committee cited Steinbeck for his feeling for nature and his concern for the oppressed. Steinbeck felt that the man close to nature is more content than the man whose life is dominated by a craving for money. But even for those close to nature, dangers such as drought or the greed of others make life precarious.

Flight

About fifteen miles below Monterey,[1] on the wild coast, the Torres family had their farm, a few sloping acres above a cliff that dropped to the brown reefs and to the hissing white waters of the ocean. Behind the farm the stone mountains stood up against the sky. The farm buildings huddled like the clinging aphids[2] on the mountain skirts, crouched low to the ground as though the wind might blow them into the sea. The little shack, the rattling, rotting barn were gray-bitten with sea salt, beaten by the damp wind until they had taken on the color of the granite hills. Two horses, a red cow and a red calf, half a dozen pigs and a flock of lean, multicolored chickens stocked the place. A little corn was raised on the sterile slope, and it grew short and thick under the wind, and all the cobs formed on the landward sides of the stalks.

Mama Torres, a lean, dry woman with ancient eyes, had ruled the farm for ten years, ever since her husband tripped over a stone in the field one day and fell full length on a rattlesnake. When one is bitten on the chest there is not much that can be done.

Mama Torres had three children, two undersized black ones of twelve and fourteen, Emilio[3] and Rosy, whom Mama kept fishing on the rocks below the farm when the sea was kind and when the truant officer was in some distant part of Monterey County. And there was Pepé,[4] the tall smiling son of nineteen, a gentle, affectionate boy, but very lazy. Pepé had a tall head, pointed at the top,

1. **Monterey:** a city in California, a few miles south of San Francisco.
2. **aphids** (ă'fidz): small insects that suck the juices of plants.
3. **Emilio** (ā·mēl'yō): *Spanish,* Emile.
4. **Pepé** (pā·pā'): *Spanish,* Joe.

and from its peak coarse black hair grew down like a thatch all around. Over his smiling little eyes Mama cut a straight bang so he could see. Pepé had sharp Indian cheekbones and an eagle nose, but his mouth was as sweet and shapely as a girl's mouth, and his chin was fragile and chiseled. He was loose and gangling, all legs and feet and wrists, and he was very lazy. Mama thought him fine and brave, but she never told him so. She said, "Some lazy cow must have got into thy father's family, else how could I have a son like thee." And she said, "When I carried thee, a sneaking lazy coyote came out of the brush and looked at me one day. That must have made thee so."

Pepé smiled sheepishly and stabbed at the ground with his knife to keep the blade sharp and free from rust. It was his inheritance, that knife, his father's knife. The long heavy blade folded back into the black handle. There was a button on the handle. When Pepé pressed the button, the blade leaped out ready for use. The knife was with Pepé always, for it had been his father's knife.

One sunny morning when the sea below the cliff was glinting and blue and the white surf creamed on the reef, when even the stone mountains looked kindly, Mama Torres called out the door of the shack, "Pepé, I have a labor for thee."

There was no answer. Mama listened. From behind the barn she heard a burst of laughter. She lifted her full long skirt and walked in the direction of the noise.

Pepé was sitting on the ground with his back against a box. His white teeth glistened. On either side of him stood the two black ones, tense and expectant. Fifteen feet away a redwood post was set in the ground. Pepé's right hand lay limply in his lap, and in the palm the big black knife rested. The blade was closed back into the handle. Pepé looked smiling at the sky.

Suddenly Emilio cried, "Ya!"

Pepé's wrist flicked like the head of a snake. The blade seemed to fly open in midair, and with a thump the point dug into the redwood post, and the black handle quivered. The three burst into excited laughter. Rosy ran to the post and pulled out the knife and brought it back to Pepé. He closed the blade and settled the knife carefully in his listless palm again. He grinned self-consciously at the sky.

"Ya!"

The heavy knife lanced out and sunk into the post again. Mama moved forward like a ship and scattered the play.

"All day you do foolish things with the knife, like a toy baby," she stormed. "Get up on thy huge feet that eat up shoes. Get up!" She took him by one loose shoulder and hoisted at him. Pepé grinned sheepishly and came halfheartedly to his feet. "Look!" Mama cried. "Big lazy, you must catch the horse and put on him thy father's saddle. You must ride to Monterey. The medicine bottle is empty. There is no salt. Go thou now, Peanut! Catch the horse."

A revolution took place in the relaxed figure of Pepé. "To Monterey, me? Alone? *Sí*, Mama."

She scowled at him. "Do not think, big sheep, that you will buy candy. No, I will give you only enough for the medicine and the salt."

Pepé smiled. "Mama, you will put the hatband on the hat?"

She relented then. "Yes, Pepé. You may wear the hatband."

His voice grew insinuating. "And the green handkerchief, Mama?"

"Yes, if you go quickly and return with no trouble, the silk green handkerchief will go. If you make sure to take off the handkerchief when you eat so no spot may fall on it."

"*Sí*, Mama. I will be careful. I am a man."

"Thou? A man? Thou art a peanut."

He went into the rickety barn and brought out a rope, and he walked agilely enough up the hill to catch the horse.

When he was ready and mounted before the door, mounted on his father's saddle that was so old that the oaken frame showed through torn leather in many places, then Mama brought out the round black hat with the tooled leather band, and she reached up and knotted the green silk handkerchief about his neck. Pepé's blue denim coat was much darker than his jeans, for it had been washed much less often.

Mama handed up the big medicine bottle and the silver coins. "That for the medicine," she said, "and that for the salt. That for a candle to burn for the papa. That for *dulces* [5] for the little ones.

5. *dulces*: *Spanish*, candies; sweets.

Our friend Mrs. Rodriguez [6] will give you dinner and maybe a bed for the night. When you go to the church, say only ten Pater Nosters [7] and only twenty-five Ave Marias.[8] Oh! I know, big coyote. You would sit there flapping your mouth over Aves all day while you looked at the candles and the holy pictures. That is not good devotion to stare at the pretty things."

The black hat, covering the high pointed head and black thatched hair of Pepé, gave him dignity and age. He sat the rangy horse well. Mama thought how handsome he was, dark and lean and tall. "I would not send thee now alone, thou little one, except for the medicine," she said softly. "It is not good to have no medicine, for who knows when the toothache will come, or the sadness of the stomach. These things are."

"*Adiós*, Mama," Pepé cried. "I will come back soon. You may send me often alone. I am a man."

"Thou art a foolish chicken."

He straightened his shoulders, flipped the reins against the horse's shoulder, and rode away. He turned once and saw that they still watched him, Emilio and Rosy and Mama. Pepé grinned with pride and gladness and lifted the tough buckskin horse to a trot.

When he had dropped out of sight over a little dip in the road, Mama turned to the black ones, but she spoke to herself. "He is nearly a man now," she said. "It will be a nice thing to have a man in the house again." Her eyes sharpened on the children. "Go to the rocks now. The tide is going out. There will be abalones [9] to be found." She put the iron hooks into their hands and saw them down the steep trail to the reefs. She brought the smooth stone *metate* [10] to the doorway and sat grinding her corn to flour and looking occasionally at the road over which Pepé had gone. The noonday came and then the afternoon, when the little ones beat the abalones on a rock to made them tender and Mama patted the tortillas [11] to make them thin. They ate their dinner as

6. **Rodriguez** (rò·drē′gäs).
7. **Pater Nosters** (pa′tər nos′tərz) : Latin for the Lord's Prayer. (Literally, "Our Father.")
8. **Ave Marias:** Latin for the prayer to the Virgin Mary, beginning "Hail, Mary."
9. **abalones** (äb′ə·lō′nēz) : an edible shellfish.
10. **metate:** *Spanish*, a stone used to grind cereal seeds.
11. **tortillas:** *Spanish*, flat cakes made out of baked cornmeal.

the red sun was plunging down toward the ocean. They sat on the doorsteps and watched a big white moon come over the mountain-tops.

Mama said, "He is now at the house of our friend Mrs. Rodriguez. She will give him nice things to eat and maybe a present."

Emilio said, "Some day I, too, will ride to Monterey for medicine. Did Pepé come to be a man today?"

Mama said wisely, "A boy gets to be a man when a man is needed. Remember this thing. I have known boys forty years old because there was no need for a man."

Soon afterward they retired, Mama in her big oak bed on one side of the room, Emilio and Rosy in their boxes full of straw and sheepskins on the other side of the room.

The moon went over the sky and the surf roared on the rocks. The roosters crowed the first call. The surf subsided to a whispering surge against the reef. The moon dropped toward the sea. The roosters crowed again.

The moon was near down to the water when Pepé rode on a winded horse to his home flat. His dog bounced out and circled the horse, yelping with pleasure. Pepé slid off the saddle to the ground. The weathered little shack was silver in the moonlight and the square shadow of it was black to the north and east. Against the east the piling mountains were misty with light; their tops melted into the sky.

Pepé walked wearily up the three steps and into the house. It was dark inside. There was a rustle in the corner.

Mama cried out from her bed. "Who comes? Pepé, is it thou?"

"Sí, Mama."

"Did you get the medicine?"

"Sí, Mama."

"Well, go to sleep, then. I thought you would be sleeping at the house of Mrs. Rodriguez." Pepé stood silently in the dark room. "Why do you stand there, Pepé? Did you drink wine?"

"Sí, Mama."

"Well, go to bed then and sleep out the wine."

His voice was tired and patient, but very firm. "Light the candle, Mama. I must go away into the mountains."

"What is this, Pepé? You are crazy." Mama struck a sulfur

match and held the little blue burr until the flame spread up the stick. She set light to the candle on the floor beside her bed. "Now, Pepé, what is this you say?" She looked anxiously into his face.

He was changed. The fragile quality seemed to have gone from his chin. His mouth was less full than it had been, the lines of the lips were straighter, but in his eyes the greatest change had taken place. There was no laughter in them any more, nor any bashfulness. They were sharp and bright and purposeful.

He told her in a tired monotone, told her everything just as it had happened. A few people came into the kitchen of Mrs. Rodriguez. There was wine to drink. Pepé drank wine. The little quarrel—the man started toward Pepé and then the knife—it went almost by itself. It flew, it darted before Pepé knew it. As he talked, Mama's face grew stern, and it seemed to grow more lean. Pepé finished. "I am a man now, Mama. The man said names to me I could not allow."

Mama nodded. "Yes, thou art a man, my poor little Pepé. Thou art a man. I have seen it coming on thee. I have watched you throwing the knife into the post, and I have been afraid." For a moment her face had softened, but now it grew stern again. "Come! We must get you ready. Go. Awaken Emilio and Rosy. Go quickly."

Pepé stepped over to the corner where his brother and sister slept among the sheepskins. He leaned down and shook them gently. "Come, Rosy! Come, Emilio! The Mama says you must arise."

The little black ones sat up and rubbed their eyes in the candlelight. Mama was out of bed now, her long black skirt over her nightgown. "Emilio," she cried. "Go up and catch the other horse for Pepé. Quickly, now! Quickly." Emilio put his legs in his overalls and stumbled sleepily out the door.

"You heard no one behind you on the road?" Mama demanded.

"No, Mama. I listened carefully. No one was on the road."

Mama darted like a bird about the room. From a nail on the wall she took a canvas water bag and threw it on the floor. She stripped a blanket from her bed and rolled it into a tight tube and tied the ends with string. From a box beside the stove she lifted a flour sack half full of black stringy jerky.[12] "Your father's black coat, Pepé. Here, put it on."

Pepé stood in the middle of the floor watching her activity. She reached behind the door and brought out the rifle, a long 38–56, worn shiny the whole length of the barrel. Pepé took it from her and held it in the crook of his elbow. Mama brought a little leather bag and counted the cartridges into his hand. "Only ten left," she warned. "You must not waste them."

Emilio put his head in the door. " *'Qui 'st 'l caballo*,[13] Mama."

"Put on the saddle from the other horse. Tie on the blanket. Here, tie the jerky to the saddle horn."

Still Pepé stood silently watching his mother's frantic activity. His chin looked hard, and his sweet mouth was drawn and thin. His little eyes followed Mama about the room almost suspiciously.

Rosy asked softly, "Where goes Pepé?"

Mama's eyes were fierce. "Pepé goes on a journey. Pepé is a man now. He has a man's thing to do."

Pepé straightened his shoulders. His mouth changed until he looked very much like Mama.

At last the preparation was finished. The loaded horse stood outside the door. The water bag dripped a line of moisture down the bay shoulder.

The moonlight was being thinned by the dawn, and the big white moon was near down to the sea. The family stood by the shack. Mama confronted Pepé. "Look, my son! Do not stop until it is dark again. Do not sleep even though you are tired. Take care of the horse in order that he may not stop of weariness. Remember to be careful with the bullets—there are only ten. Do not fill thy stomach with jerky or it will make thee sick. Eat a little jerky and fill thy stomach with grass. When thou comest to the high mountains, if thou seest any of the dark watching men, go not near to them nor try to speak to them. And forget not thy prayers." She put her lean hands on Pepé's shoulders, stood on her toes and kissed him formally on both cheeks, and Pepé kissed her on both cheeks. Then he went to Emilio and Rosy and kissed both of their cheeks.

12. **jerky:** meat cured by being cut into strips and dried.
13. *'Qui 'st 'l caballo:* colloquial Spanish for *Aquí está el caballo*, Here is the horse.

Pepé turned back to Mama. He seemed to look for a little softness, a little weakness in her. His eyes were searching, but Mama's face remained fierce. "Go now," she said. "Do not wait to be caught like a chicken."

Pepé pulled himself into the saddle. "I am a man," he said.

It was the first dawn when he rode up the hill toward the little canyon which let a trail into the mountains. Moonlight and daylight fought with each other, and the two warring qualities made it difficult to see. Before Pepé had gone a hundred yards, the outlines of his figure were misty; and long before he entered the canyon, he had become a gray, indefinite shadow.

Mama stood stiffly in front of her doorstep, and on either side of her stood Emilio and Rosy. They cast furtive glances at Mama now and then.

When the gray shape of Pepé melted into the hillside and disappeared, Mama relaxed. She began the high, whining keen [14] of the death wail. "Our beautiful—our brave," she cried. "Our protector, our son is gone." Emilio and Rosy moaned beside her. "Our beautiful—our brave, he is gone." It was the formal wail. It rose to a high piercing whine and subsided to a moan. Mama raised it three times and then she turned and went into the house and shut the door.

Emilio and Rosy stood wondering in the dawn. They heard Mama whimpering in the house. They went out to sit on the cliff above the ocean. They touched shoulders. "When did Pepé come to be a man?" Emilio asked.

"Last night," said Rosy. "Last night in Monterey." The ocean clouds turned red with the sun that was behind the mountains.

"We will have no breakfast," said Emilio. "Mama will not want to cook." Rosy did not answer him. "Where is Pepé gone?" he asked.

Rosy looked around at him. She drew her knowledge from the quiet air. "He has gone on a journey. He will never come back."

"Is he dead? Do you think he is dead?"

Rosy looked back at the ocean again. A little steamer, drawing a line of smoke, sat on the edge of the horizon. "He is not dead," Rosy explained. "Not yet."

14. keen: lamentation for the dead.

Pepé rested the big rifle across the saddle in front of him. He let the horse walk up the hill and he didn't look back. The stony slope took on a coat of short brush so that Pepé found the entrance to a trail and entered it.

When he came to the canyon opening, he swung once in his saddle and looked back, but the houses were swallowed in the misty light. Pepé jerked forward again. The high shoulder of the canyon closed in on him. His horse stretched out its neck and sighed and settled to the trail.

It was a well-worn path, dark soft leaf-mold earth strewn with broken pieces of sandstone. The trail rounded the shoulder of the canyon and dropped steeply into the bed of the stream. In the shallows the water ran smoothly, glinting in the first morning sun. Small round stones on the bottom were as brown as rust with sun moss. In the sand along the edges of the stream the tall, rich, wild mint grew, while in the water itself the cress,[15] old and tough, had gone to heavy seed.

The path went into the stream and emerged on the other side. The horse sloshed into the water and stopped. Pepé dropped his bridle and let the beast drink of the running water.

Soon the canyon sides became steep and the first giant sentinel redwoods guarded the trail, great round red trunks bearing foliage as green and lacy as ferns. Once Pepé was among the trees, the sun was lost. A perfumed and purple light lay in the pale green of the underbrush. Gooseberry bushes and blackberries and tall ferns lined the stream, and overhead the branches of the redwoods met and cut off the sky.

Pepé drank from the water bag, and he reached into the flour sack and brought out a black string of jerky. His white teeth gnawed at the string until the tough meat parted. He chewed slowly and drank occasionally from the water bag. His little eyes were slumberous and tired, but the muscles of his face were hard-set. The earth of the trail was black now. It gave up a hollow sound under the walking hoofbeats.

The stream fell more sharply. Little waterfalls splashed on the stones. Five-fingered ferns hung over the water and dripped spray from their finger tips. Pepé rode half over his saddle, dangling one leg loosely. He picked a bay leaf from a tree beside the way and put

15. **cress:** watercress, an edible plant that grows in springs and in clear streams.

it into his mouth for a moment to flavor the dry jerky. He held the gun loosely across the pommel.[16]

Suddenly he squared in his saddle, swung the horse from the trail and kicked it hurriedly up behind a big redwood tree. He pulled up the reins tight against the bit to keep the horse from whinnying. His face was intent and his nostrils quivered a little.

A hollow pounding came down the trail, and a horseman rode by, a fat man with red cheeks and a white stubble beard. His horse put down his head and blubbered at the trail when it came to the place where Pepé had turned off. "Hold up!" said the man, and he pulled up his horse's head.

When the last sound of the hoofs died away, Pepé came back into the trail again. He did not relax in the saddle any more. He lifted the big rifle and swung the lever to throw a shell into the chamber, and then he let down the hammer to half cock.

The trail grew very steep. Now the redwood trees were smaller and their tops were dead, bitten dead where the wind reached them. The horse plodded on; the sun went slowly overhead and started down toward the afternoon.

Where the stream came out of a side canyon, the trail left it. Pepé dismounted and watered his horse and filled up his water bag. As soon as the trail had parted from the stream, the trees were gone and only the thick brittle sage and manzanita [17] and chaparral [18] edged the trail. And the soft black earth was gone, too, leaving only the light tan broken rock for the trail bed. Lizards scampered away into the brush as the horse rattled over the little stones.

Pepé turned in his saddle and looked back. He was in the open now: he could be seen from a distance. As he ascended the trail the country grew more rough and terrible and dry. The way wound about the bases of great square rocks. Little gray rabbits skittered in the brush. A bird made a monotonous high creaking. Eastward the bare rock mountaintops were pale and powder-dry under the dropping sun. The horse plodded up and up the trail toward a little V in the ridge which was the pass.

Pepé looked suspiciously back every minute or so, and his eyes

16. **pommel:** the knob at the front of a saddle.
17. **manzanita:** shrubs.
18. **chaparral:** a thicket of thorny shrubs.

sought the tops of the ridges ahead. Once, on a white barren spur, he saw a black figure for a moment; but he looked quickly away, for it was one of the dark watchers. No one knew who the watchers were, nor where they lived, but it was better to ignore them and never to show interest in them. They did not bother one who stayed on the trail and minded his own business.

The air was parched and full of light dust blown by the breeze from the eroding mountains. Pepé drank sparingly from his bag and corked it tightly and hung it on the horn again. The trail moved up the dry shale hillside, avoiding rocks, dropping under clefts, climbing in and out of old water scars. When he arrived at the little pass he stopped and looked back for a long time. No dark watchers were to be seen now. The trail behind was empty. Only the high tops of the redwoods indicated where the stream flowed.

Pepé rode on through the pass. His little eyes were nearly closed with weariness, but his face was stern, relentless, and manly. The high mountain wind coasted sighing through the pass and whistled on the edges of the big blocks of broken granite. In the air, a red-tailed hawk sailed over close to the ridge and screamed angrily. Pepé went slowly through the broken jagged pass and looked down on the other side.

The trail dropped quickly, staggering among broken rock. At the bottom of the slope there was a dark crease, thick with brush, and on the other side of the crease a little flat, in which a grove of oak trees grew. A scar of green grass cut across the flat. And behind the flat another mountain rose, desolate with dead rocks and starving little black bushes. Pepé drank from the bag again, for the air was so dry that it encrusted his nostrils and burned his lips. He put the horse down the trail. The hoofs slipped and struggled on the steep way, starting little stones that rolled off into the brush. The sun was gone behind the westward mountain now, but still it glowed brilliantly on the oaks and on the grassy flat. The rocks and the hillsides still sent up waves of the heat they had gathered from the day's sun.

Pepé looked up to the top of the next dry withered ridge. He saw a dark form against the sky, a man's figure standing on top of a rock, and he glanced away quickly not to appear curious. When a moment later he looked up again, the figure was gone.

Downward the trail was quickly covered. Sometimes the horse

floundered for footing, sometimes set his feet and slid a little way. They came at last to the bottom where the dark chaparral was higher than Pepé's head. He held up his rifle on one side and his arm on the other to shield his face from the sharp, brittle fingers of the brush.

Up and out of the crease he rode, and up a little cliff. The grassy flat was before him, and the round comfortable oaks. For a moment he studied the trail down which he had come, but there was no movement and no sound from it. Finally he rode out over the flat, to the green streak, and at the upper end of the damp he found a little spring welling out of the earth and dropping into a dug basin before it seeped out over the flat.

Pepé filled his bag first, and then he let the thirsty horse drink out of the pool. He led the horse to the clump of oaks, and in the middle of the grove, fairly protected from sight on all sides, he took off the saddle and the bridle and laid them on the ground. The horse stretched his jaws sideways and yawned. Pepé knotted the lead rope about the horse's neck and tied him to a sapling among the oaks, where he could graze in a fairly large circle.

When the horse was gnawing hungrily at the dry grass, Pepé went to the saddle and took a black string of jerky from the sack and strolled to an oak tree on the edge of the grove, from under which he could watch the trail. He sat down in the crisp dry oak leaves and automatically felt for his big black knife to cut the jerky, but he had no knife. He leaned back on his elbow and gnawed at the tough strong meat. His face was blank, but it was a man's face.

The bright evening light washed the eastern ridge, but the valley was darkening. Doves flew down from the hills to the spring, and the quail came running out of the brush and joined them, calling clearly to one another.

Out of the corner of his eye Pepé saw a shadow grow out of the bushy crease. He turned his head slowly. A big spotted wildcat was creeping toward the spring, belly to the ground, moving like thought.

Pepé cocked his rifle and edged the muzzle slowly around. Then he looked apprehensively up the trail and dropped the hammer again. From the ground beside him he picked an oak twig and threw it toward the spring. The quail flew up with a roar and the doves whistled away. The big cat stood up; for a long moment he looked at Pepé with cold yellow eyes, and then fearlessly walked back into the gulch.

The dusk gathered quickly in the deep valley. Pepé muttered his prayers, put his head down on his arm and went instantly to sleep.

The moon came up and filled the valley with cold blue light, and the wind swept rustling down from the peaks. The owls worked up and down the slopes looking for rabbits. Down in the brush of the gulch a coyote gabbled. The oak trees whispered softly in the night breeze.

Pepé started up, listening. His horse had whinnied. The moon was just slipping behind the western ridge, leaving the valley in darkness behind it. Pepé sat tensely gripping his rifle. From far up the trail he heard an answering whinny and the crash of shod hoofs on the broken rock. He jumped to his feet, ran to his horse and led it under the trees. He threw on the saddle and cinched it tight for the steep trail, caught the unwilling head and forced the bit into the mouth. He felt the saddle to make sure the water bag and the sack of jerky were there. Then he mounted and turned up the hill.

It was velvet-dark. The horse found the entrance to the trail where it left the flat, and started up, stumbling and slipping on the rocks. Pepé's hand rose up to his head. His hat was gone. He had left it under the oak tree.

The horse had struggled far up the trail when the first change of dawn came into the air, a steel grayness as light mixed thoroughly with dark. Gradually the sharp snaggled edge of the ridge stood out above them, rotten granite tortured and eaten by the winds of time. Pepé had dropped his reins on the horn, leaving direction to the horse. The brush grabbed at his legs in the dark until one knee of his jeans was ripped.

Gradually the light flowed down over the ridge. The starved brush and rocks stood out in the half-light, strange and lonely in high perspective. Then there came warmth into the light. Pepé drew up and looked back, but he could see nothing in the darker valley below. The sky turned blue over the coming sun. In the waste of the mountainside, the poor dry brush grew only three feet high. Here and there, big outcroppings of unrotted granite stood up like moldering houses. Pepé relaxed a little. He drank from his water bag and bit off a piece of jerky. A single eagle flew over, high in the light.

Without warning Pepé's horse screamed and fell on its side. He was almost down before the rifle crash echoed up from the valley. From a hole behind the struggling shoulder, a stream of bright crimson blood pumped and stopped and pumped and stopped. The hoofs threshed on the ground. Pepé lay half stunned beside the horse. He looked slowly down the hill. A piece of sage clipped off beside his head and another crash echoed up from side to side of the canyon. Pepé flung himself frantically behind a bush.

He crawled up the hill on his knees and one hand. His right hand held the rifle up off the ground and pushed it ahead of him. He moved with the instinctive care of an animal. Rapidly he wormed his way toward one of the big outcroppings of granite on the hill above him. Where the brush was high he doubled up and ran; but where the cover was slight he wriggled forward on his stomach, pushing the rifle ahead of him. In the last little distance there was no cover at all. Pepé poised and then he darted across the space and flashed around the corner of the rock.

He leaned panting against the stone. When his breath came easier he moved along behind the big rock until he came to a narrow split that offered a thin section of vision down the hill. Pepé lay on his stomach and pushed the rifle barrel through the slit and waited.

The sun reddened the western ridges now. Already the buzzards were settling down toward the place where the horse lay. A small brown bird scratched in the dead sage leaves directly in front of the rifle muzzle. The coasting eagle flew back toward the rising sun.

Pepé saw a little movement in the brush far below. His grip tightened on the gun. A little brown doe stepped daintily out on the trail and crossed it and disappeared into the brush again. For a long time Pepé waited. Far below he could see the little flat and the oak trees and the slash of green. Suddenly his eyes flashed back at the trail again. A quarter of a mile down there had been a quick movement in the chaparral. The rifle swung over. The front sight nestled in the V of the rear sight. Pepé studied for a moment and then raised the rear sight a notch. The little movement in the brush came again. The sight settled on it. Pepé squeezed the trigger. The explosion crashed down the mountain and up the other side, and came rattling back. The whole side of the slope grew still. No more movement. And then a white streak cut into the granite of the slit and a bullet whined away and a crash sounded up from below. Pepé felt a sharp pain in his right hand. A sliver of granite was sticking out from between his first and second knuckles and the point protruded from his palm. Carefully he pulled out the sliver of stone. The wound bled evenly and gently. No vein or artery was cut.

Pepé looked into a little dusty cave in the rock and gathered a handful of spider web, and he pressed the mass into the cut, plastering the soft web into the blood. The flow stopped almost at once.

The rifle was on the ground. Pepé picked it up, levered a new shell into the chamber. And then he slid into the brush on his stomach. Far to the right he crawled, and then up the hill, moving slowly and carefully, crawling to cover and resting and then crawling again.

In the mountains the sun is high in its arc before it penetrates the gorges. The hot face looked over the hill and brought instant heat with it. The white light beat on the rocks and reflected from them and rose up quivering from the earth again, and the rocks and bushes seemed to quiver behind the air.

Pepé crawled in the general direction of the ridge peak, zigzagging for cover. The deep cut between his knuckles began to throb. He crawled close to a rattlesnake before he saw it, and when it raised its dry head and made a soft beginning whir, he backed up and took another way. The quick gray lizards flashed in front of him, raising a tiny line of dust. He found another mass of spider web and pressed it against his throbbing hand.

Pepé was pushing the rifle with his left hand now. Little drops of sweat ran to the ends of his coarse black hair and rolled down his cheeks. His lips and tongue were growing thick and heavy. His lips writhed to draw saliva into his mouth. His little dark eyes were uneasy and suspicious. Once when a gray lizard paused in front of him on the parched ground and turned its head sideways, he crushed it flat with a stone.

When the sun slid past noon he had not gone a mile. He crawled exhaustedly a last hundred yards to a patch of high sharp manzanita, crawled desperately, and when the patch was reached he wriggled in among the tough gnarly trunks and dropped his head on his left arm. There was little shade in the meager brush, but there was cover and safety. Pepé went to sleep as he lay and the sun beat on his back. A few little birds hopped close to him and peered and hopped away. Pepé squirmed in his sleep and he raised and dropped his wounded hand again and again.

The sun went down behind the peaks and the cool evening came, and then the dark. A coyote yelled from the hillside. Pepé started awake and looked about with misty eyes. His hand was swollen and heavy; a little thread of pain ran up the inside of his arm and settled in a pocket in his armpit. He peered about and then stood up, for the mountains were black and the moon had not yet risen. Pepé stood up in the dark. The coat of his father pressed on his arm. His tongue was swollen until it nearly filled his mouth. He wriggled out of the coat and dropped it in the brush, and then he struggled up the hill, falling over rocks and tearing his way through the brush. The rifle knocked against stones as he went. Little dry avalanches of gravel and shattered stone went whispering down the hill behind him.

After a while the old moon came up and showed the jagged ridgetop ahead of him. By moonlight Pepé traveled more easily. He bent forward so that his throbbing arm hung away from his body. The journey uphill was made in dashes and rests, a frantic rush up a few yards and then a rest. The wind coasted down the slope, rattling the dry stems of the bushes.

The moon was at meridian when Pepé came at last to the sharp backbone of the ridgetop. On the last hundred yards of the rise no soil had clung under the wearing winds. The way was on solid rock. He clambered to the top and looked down on the other side. There was a draw like the last below him, misty with moonlight, brushed with dry struggling sage and chaparral. On the other side the hill rose up sharply and at the top the jagged rotten teeth of the mountain showed against the sky. At the bottom of the cut the brush was thick and dark.

Pepé stumbled down the hill. His throat was almost closed with thirst. At first he tried to run, but immediately he fell and rolled. After that he went more carefully. The moon was just disappearing behind the mountains when he came to the bottom. He crawled into the heavy brush, feeling with his fingers for water. There was no water in the bed of the stream, only damp earth. Pepé laid his gun down and scooped up a handful of mud and put it in his mouth, and then he spluttered and scraped the earth from his tongue with his finger, for the mud drew at his mouth like a poultice. He dug a hole in the stream bed with his fingers, dug a little basin to catch water; but before it was very deep his head fell forward on the damp ground and he slept.

The dawn came and the heat of the day fell on the earth, and still Pepé slept. Late in the afternoon his head jerked up. He looked slowly around. His eyes were slits of weariness. Twenty feet away in the heavy brush a big tawny mountain lion stood looking at him. Its long thick tail waved gracefully; its ears were erect with interest, not laid back dangerously. The lion squatted down on its stomach and watched him.

Pepé looked at the hole he had dug in the earth. A half inch of muddy water had collected in the bottom. He tore the sleeve from his hurt arm, with his teeth ripped out a little square, soaked it in the water and put it in his mouth. Over and over he filled the cloth and sucked it.

Still the lion sat and watched him. The evening came down but there was no movement on the hills. No birds visited the dry bottom of the cut. Pepé looked occasionally at the lion. The eyes of the yellow beast drooped as though he were about to sleep. He yawned and his long thin red tongue curled out. Suddenly his head jerked around and his nostrils quivered. His big tail lashed. He stood up and slunk like a tawny shadow into the thick brush.

A moment later Pepé heard the sound, the faint far crash of horses' hoofs on gravel. And he heard something else, a high whining yelp of a dog.

Pepé took his rifle in his left hand and he glided into the brush almost as quietly as the lion had. In the darkening evening he crouched up the hill toward the next ridge. Only when the dark came did he stand up. His energy was short. Once it was dark he fell over the rocks and slipped to his knees on the steep slope, but he moved on and on up the hill, climbing and scrambling over the broken hillside.

When he was far up toward the top, he lay down and slept for a little while. The withered moon, shining on his face, awakened him. He stood up and moved up the hill. Fifty yards away he stopped and turned back, for he had forgotten his rifle. He walked heavily down and poked about in the brush, but he could not find his gun. At last he lay down to rest. The pocket of pain in his armpit had grown more sharp. His arm seemed to swell out and fall with every heartbeat. There was no position lying down where the heavy arm did not press against his armpit.

With the effort of a hurt beast, Pepé got up and moved again toward the top of the ridge. He held his swollen arm away from his body with his left hand. Up the steep hill he dragged himself, a few steps and a rest, and a few more steps. At last he was nearing the top. The moon showed the uneven sharp back of it against the sky.

Pepé's brain spun in a big spiral up and away from him. He slumped to the ground and lay still. The rock ridgetop was only a hundred feet above him.

The moon moved over the sky. Pepé half turned on his back. His tongue tried to make words, but only a thick hissing came from between his lips.

When the dawn came, Pepé pulled himself up. His eyes were sane again. He drew his great puffed arm in front of him and looked at the angry wound. The black line ran up from his wrist to his armpit. Automatically he reached in his pocket for the big black knife, but it was not there. His eyes searched the ground. He picked up a sharp blade of stone and scraped at the wound, sawed at the proud flesh and then squeezed the green juice out in big drops. Instantly he threw back his head and whined like a dog. His whole right side shuddered at the pain, but the pain cleared his head.

In the gray light he struggled up the last slope to the ridge and crawled over and lay down behind a line of rocks. Below him lay a deep canyon exactly like the last, waterless and desolate. There was no flat, no oak trees, not even heavy brush in the bottom of it. And on the other side a sharp ridge stood up, thinly brushed with starving sage, littered with broken granite. Strewn over the hill there were giant outcroppings, and on the top the granite teeth stood out against the sky.

The new day was light now. The flame of the sun came over the ridge and fell on Pepé where he lay on the ground. His coarse black hair was littered with twigs and bits of spider web. His eyes had retreated back into his head. Between his lips the tip of his black tongue showed.

He sat up and dragged his great arm into his lap and nursed it, rocking his body and moaning in his throat. He threw back his head and looked up into the pale sky. A big black bird circled nearly out of sight, and far to the left another was sailing near.

He lifted his head to listen, for a familiar sound had come to him from the valley he had climbed out of; it was the crying yelp of hounds, excited and feverish, on a trail.

Pepé bowed his head quickly. He tried to speak rapid words but only a thick hiss came from his lips. He drew a shaky cross on his breast with his left hand. It was a long struggle to get to his feet. He crawled slowly and mehanically to the top of a big rock on the ridge peak. Once there, he arose slowly, swaying to his feet, and stood erect. Far below he could see the dark brush where he had slept. He braced his feet and stood there, black against the morning sky.

There came a ripping sound at his feet. A piece of stone flew up and a bullet droned off into the next gorge. The hollow crash echoed up from below. Pepé looked down for a moment and then pulled himself straight again.

His body jarred back. His left hand fluttered helplessly toward his breast. The second crash sounded from below. Pepé swung forward and toppled from the rock. His body struck and rolled over and over, starting a little avalanche. And when at last he stopped against a bush, the avalanche slid slowly down and covered up his head.

Meaning and Method

1. Characterize the Torres family. What elements in their environment and in their heritage seem to have conspired to keep them in poverty? What words and phrases in the opening paragraph create the impression that the environment is hostile?

2. When Pepé is preparing to go to town, he asks to wear his father's hatband and handkerchief. Why does he want to wear these clothes? What does his continual playing with the knife illustrate about his character?

3. The narrator says that the knife Pepé used to kill the man was inherited from his father. Why does this seem to support the contention that man is controlled by his heredity?

   Pepé's father died after tripping over a rock and falling on a poisonous snake. Is Pepé's act of murder an accident—like the death of his father? Do both these events seem to support the idea that man is dominated by forces he neither knows nor can control?

4. When Pepé begins his flight, the trail is gentle, with plenty of water and foliage. How does the landscape change during the flight? How does the change in the landscape and in his condition show the increasing hopelessness of his situation?

   Trace the steps by which Pepé is reduced to the animal level. For example, he loses possessions such as the horse, the gun, and the hat. In what order does he lose them? All the things he loses have been given to him by his family. Does his losing them indicate that he is gradually freeing himself from the control of his family in order to become a man? Or does it indicate that he is simply being reduced to the level of an animal?

5. As Pepé begins his trip, Mama warns him not to go near or to talk to the "dark watching men." Do these dark watchers represent those who never come into contact with the outside world because they know the outside world brings trouble? Or do they represent those who live at peace with nature unless threatened? Or do they represent the dark forces that come into every man's life? Why do they bother only those who leave the path? Is the path symbolic of life?

6. Throughout the story, nature is described in human terms—"the jagged, rotten teeth of the mountain showed against the sky" (page 153). On the other hand, Pepé is described in animal images —"he whined like a dog" (155).

   Do the animals Pepé meets treat him as an outsider, an enemy, or as just another animal? Are they indifferent to his plight?

   Reread the last paragraph. Does it seem that nature views his death with sympathy? with hostility? with indifference? How does the last sentence of the story clarify the role of nature? How is this role foreshadowed in the opening paragraph?

7. Does the narrator tell the story from an objective point of view or does he make comments on and interpret what is happening? Why is it necessary that the narrator use this point of view?

Language: Words from Other Languages

English is considered the most composite of languages, having borrowed for its vocabulary from virtually every language in the world. In fact, only about 25 percent of English words come from Anglo-Saxon, an old English tongue. The rest come from outside sources: Latin and Latin-based languages (French, Italian, Spanish, Portuguese), Greek, and other languages. For example, *chaparral*, meaning a thicket of low shrubs, is from Spanish *chaparro*, evergreen oak. Such words as *squaw*, *tepee*, and *hominy* are from North American Indian tongues; *ranch* and *canyon* come from Spanish; *yacht* and *boss* are from Dutch; *caravan* and *bazaar*, from Persian; *kimono*, from Japanese.

Find the words that follow in your dictionary and trace their origin. In each case, was the word borrowed directly from another language, or were there several borrowings and developments involved? How close are the word's present English meaning and form to those of the language(s) from which it was borrowed?

1. amen
2. bungalow
3. gong
4. moose
5. mustang
6. pecan
7. ski
8. sugar
9. tattoo
10. thug
11. tomato
12. zero

Composition and Discussion

1. Some critics, such as Chester Chapin of the University of Michigan, argue that Pepé, like some of Steinbeck's other characters (Lennie in *Of Mice and Men*, for example), is dull-witted. Chapin emphasizes that Steinbeck refers to Pepé's pointed head and that "a pointed or 'pinhead' is everywhere popularly understood as a sign of subnormal intelligence." Steinbeck's point in "Flight," Professor Chapin concludes, is that "man is *still* man even when defective in that part—intellect—which most clearly distinguishes him from the animals, a conclusion in harmony with Steinbeck's frequent insistence upon human worth."

Do you agree with this interpretation of Pepé? Do you agree that he "flees from responsible action, from reason, from order, from restraint"? Is he perhaps simply a victim of both his environment and the circumstances?

2. *Machismo*, a code of masculine behavior prevalent in Spanish cultures, attaches great value to "maleness," requiring a man to defend his honor immediately against anything he considers an affront, no

matter how slight. The word *honor* connotes everything which affects his self-respect as a man. Is it *machismo* to which Pepé refers when he says on page 143, "I am a man now, Mama. The man said names to me I could not allow"?

In a composition, define what you mean by "manhood." What characteristics make a person a man? Is the type of masculinity signified by *machismo* part of manhood?

State the definition generally in a topic sentence, and then develop it with facts, examples, and reasons.

Shirley Jackson

[1919–1965]

Like no other American writer since Nathaniel Hawthorne, Shirley Jackson was a writer fully aware of the dark and haunting shadows behind the seemingly normal and commonplace in life. In reviewing *Come Along with Me*, a posthumously published collection of Miss Jackson's last writings, one critic said, ". . . if we look carefully at her characters and plots we can see how subtly they suggest rites and mysteries."

This sort of comment came to Miss Jackson as early as 1948, when "The Lottery" was published in *The New Yorker*. The appearance of the story was followed immediately by a flood of letters—of shocked indignation, protest, consternation, and some praise. What many readers objected to was Miss Jackson's calm, objective presentation of a shocking act carried out by seemingly ordinary people against an all too familiar and real background. Moreover, her longtime refusal to discuss the story's symbolic meaning did little to quiet the situation. The situation, she felt, was clear enough and did not need her explanation. She eventually did offer an interpretation of the story by saying, "I would explain it as an attempt to define a present-day state of mind by a ritual of blood sacrifice still dormant in our minds."

In the years before her death, Shirley Jackson produced more of the same kind of fiction. Many stories and such novels as *The Bird's Nest* (1954), *The Haunting of Hill House* (1959), and *We Have Always Lived in the Castle* (1962), carried on her manner of depicting the haunted and the haunting against a homely backdrop.

One reader and critic who understood her fascination with the supernatural is her husband, Stanley Edgar Hyman. It is he who wrote shortly after her death, ". . . If she used the resources of supernatural terror, it was to provide metaphors for the all too real terrors of the natural." Mr. Hyman is the editor of *Come Along with Me* (1968), the collection of his wife's later writings —part of a novel, sixteen stories, and three lectures.

Shirley Jackson was born in San Francisco in 1919 and grew up there before going East to attend Syracuse University and, as it turned out, to marry and settle down. She met her husband-to-be at Syracuse and later established a home in Vermont near Bennington College, where her husband has taught English.

It is perhaps surprising to many readers that Miss Jackson enjoyed a happy existence as wife, mother of four children, and homemaker. A note of domestic happiness is clear in the two books she wrote about her family life. With titles as puckish as any that adorn the books of a James Thurber or an E. B. White, *Life Among the Savages* (1953) and *Raising Demons* (1957) are as bright and warm as Miss Jackson's fiction is dark and chilling. The titles are not completely lighthearted, however, for they allude to Miss Jackson's strong interest in ghosts, witchcraft, and sorcery.

The Lottery

The morning of June 27th was clear and sunny, with the fresh warmth of a full-summer day; the flowers were blossoming profusely, and the grass was richly green. The people of the village began to gather in the square, between the post office and the bank, around ten o'clock; in some towns there were so many people that the lottery took two days and had to be started on June 26th, but in this village, where there were only about three hundred people, the whole lottery took only about two hours, so it could begin at ten o'clock in the morning and still be through in time to allow the villagers to get home for noon dinner.

The children assembled first, of course. School was recently over for the summer, and the feeling of liberty sat uneasily on most of them; they tended to gather together quietly for a while before they broke into boisterous play, and their talk was still of the classroom and the teacher, of books and reprimands. Bobby Martin had already stuffed his pockets full of stones, and the other boys soon followed his example, selecting the smoothest and roundest stones; Bobby and Harry Jones and Dickie Delacroix—the villagers pronounced this name "Dellacroy"—eventually made a great pile of stones in one corner of the square and guarded it against the raids of the other boys. The girls stood aside, talking among themselves, looking over their shoulders at the boys, and the very small children rolled in the dust or clung to the hands of their older brothers or sisters.

Soon the men began to gather, surveying their own children, speaking of planting and rain, tractors and taxes. They stood together, away from the pile of stones in the corner, and their jokes were quiet, and they smiled rather than laughed. The women, wearing faded house dresses and sweaters, came shortly after their menfolk. They greeted one another and exchanged bits of gossip as they went to join their husbands. Soon the women, standing by their husbands, began to call to their children, and the children came reluctantly, having to be called four or five times. Bobby Martin ducked under his mother's grasping hand and ran, laughing, back to the pile of stones. His father spoke up sharply, and Bobby came quickly and took his place between his father and his oldest brother.

The lottery was conducted—as were the square dances, the teen-age club, the Halloween program—by Mr. Summers, who had time and energy to devote to civic activities. He was a round-faced, jovial man, and he ran the coal business; and people were sorry for him, because he had no children and his wife was a scold. When he arrived in the square, carrying the black wooden box, there was a murmur of conversation among the villagers, and he waved and called, "Little late today, folks." The postmaster, Mr. Graves, followed him, carrying a three-legged stool; and the stool was put in the center of the square, and Mr. Summers set the black box down on it. The villagers kept their distance, leaving a space between themselves and the stool, and when Mr. Summers said, "Some of you fellows want to give me a hand?" there was a hesitation before two men, Mr. Martin and his oldest son, Baxter, came forward to hold the box steady on the stool while Mr. Summers stirred up the papers inside it.

The original paraphernalia for the lottery had been lost long ago, and the black box now resting on the stool had been put into use even before Old Man Warner, the oldest man in town, was born. Mr. Summers spoke frequently to the villagers about making a new box, but no one liked to upset even as much tradition as was represented by the black box. There was a story that the present box had been made with some pieces of the box that had preceded it, the one that had been constructed when the first people settled down to make a village here. Every year, after the lottery, Mr. Summers began talking again about a new box, but every year the subject was allowed to fade off without anything's being done. The black box grew shabbier each year; by now it was no longer completely black but splintered badly along one side to show the original wood color, and in some places faded or stained.

Mr. Martin and his oldest son, Baxter, held the black box securely on the stool until Mr. Summers had stirred the papers thoroughly with his hand. Because so much of the ritual had been forgotten or discarded, Mr. Summers had been successful in having slips of paper substituted for the chips of wood that had been used for generations. Chips of wood, Mr. Summers had argued, had been all very well when the village was tiny, but now that the population was more than three hundred and likely to keep on growing, it was necessary to use something that would fit more easily into the black box. The night before the lottery, Mr. Summers and Mr. Graves made up the slips of paper and put them into the box, and it was then taken to the safe of Mr. Summers' coal company and locked up until Mr. Summers was ready to take it to the square next morning. The rest of the year, the box was put away, sometimes one place, sometimes another; it had spent one year in Mr. Graves's barn and another year underfoot in the post office, and sometimes it was set on a shelf in the Martin grocery and left there.

There was a great deal of fussing to be done before Mr. Summers declared the lottery open. There were the lists to make up— of heads of families, heads of households in each family, members of each household in each family. There was the proper swearing-in of Mr. Summers by the postmaster, as the official of the lottery; at one time, some people remembered, there had been a recital of some sort, performed by the official of the lottery, a perfunctory, tuneless chant that had been rattled off duly each year; some people believed that the official of the lottery used to stand just so when he said or sang it; others believed that he was supposed to walk among the people; but years and years ago this part of the ritual had been allowed to lapse. There had been, also, a ritual salute, which the official of the lottery had had to use in addressing each person who came up to draw from the box, but this also had changed with time, until now it was felt necessary only for the official to speak to each person approaching. Mr. Summers was very good at all this; in his clean white shirt and blue jeans, with one hand resting carelessly on the black box, he seemed very proper and important as he talked interminably to Mr. Graves and the Martins.

Just as Mr. Summers finally left off talking and turned to the assembled villagers, Mrs. Hutchinson came hurriedly along the path to the square, her sweater thrown over her shoulders, and slid into place in the back of the crowd. "Clean forgot what day it was," she said to Mrs. Delacroix, who stood next to her, and they both laughed softly. "Thought my old man was out back stacking wood," Mrs. Hutchinson went on, "and then I looked out the window and the kids was gone, and then I remembered it was the twenty-seventh and came a-running." She dried her hands on her apron, and Mrs. Delacroix said, "You're in time, though. They're still talking away up there."

Mrs. Hutchinson craned her neck to see through the crowd and found her husband and children standing near the front. She tapped Mrs. Delacroix on the arm as a farewell and began to make her way through the crowd. The people separated good-humoredly to let her through; two or three people said, in voices loud enough to be heard across the crowd, "Here comes your Mrs., Hutchinson," and "Bill, she made it after all." Mrs. Hutchinson reached her husband, and Mr. Summers, who had been waiting, said cheerfully, "Thought we were going to have to get on without you, Tessie." Mrs. Hutchinson said, grinning, "Wouldn't have me leave m'dishes in the sink, now, would you, Joe?" and soft laughter ran through the crowd as the people stirred back into position after Mrs. Hutchinson's arrival.

"Well, now," Mr. Summers said soberly, "guess we better get started, get this over with, so's we can go back to work. Anybody ain't here?"

"Dunbar," several people said. "Dunbar, Dunbar."

Mr. Summers consulted his list. "Clyde Dunbar," he said. "That's right. He's broke his leg, hasn't he? Who's drawing for him?"

"Me, I guess," a woman said, and Mr. Summers turned to look at her. "Wife draws for her husband," Mr. Summers said.

"Don't you have a grown boy to do it for you, Janey?" Although Mr. Summers and everyone else in the village knew the answer perfectly well, it was the business of the official of the lottery to ask such questions formally. Mr. Summers waited with an expression of polite interest while Mrs. Dunbar answered.

"Horace's not but sixteen yet," Mrs. Dunbar said regretfully. "Guess I gotta fill in for the old man this year."

"Right," Mr. Summers said. He made a note on the list he was holding. Then he asked, "Watson boy drawing this year?"

A tall boy in the crowd raised his hand. "Here," he said. "I'm drawing for m'mother and me." He blinked his eyes nervously and ducked his head as several voices in the crowd said things like "Good fellow, Jack," and "Glad to see your mother's got a man to do it."

"Well," Mr. Summers said, "guess that's everyone. Old Man Warner make it?"

"Here," a voice said, and Mr. Summers nodded.

A sudden hush fell on the crowd as Mr. Summers cleared his throat and looked at the list. "All ready?" he called. "Now, I'll read the names—heads of families first—and the men come up and take a paper out of the box. Keep the paper folded in your hand without looking at it until everyone has had a turn. Everything clear?"

The people had done it so many times that they only half listened to the directions; most of them were quiet, wetting their lips, not looking around. Then Mr. Summers raised one hand high and said, "Adams." A man disengaged himself from the crowd and came forward. "Hi, Steve," Mr. Summers said, and Mr. Adams said, "Hi, Joe." They grinned at one another humorlessly and nervously. Then Mr. Adams reached into the black box and took out a folded paper. He held it firmly by one corner as he turned and went hastily back to his place in the crowd, where he stood a little apart from his family, not looking down at his hand.

"Allen," Mr. Summers said. "Anderson. . . . Bentham."

"Seems like there's no time at all between lotteries any more," Mrs. Delacroix said to Mrs. Graves in the back row. "Seems like we got through with the last one only last week."

"Time sure goes fast," Mrs. Graves said.

"Clark. . . . Delacroix."

"There goes my old man," Mrs. Delacroix said. She held her breath while her husband went forward.

"Dunbar," Mr. Summers said, and Mrs. Dunbar went steadily to the box while one of the women said, "Go on, Janey," and another said, "There she goes."

"We're next," Mrs. Graves said. She watched while Mr. Graves came around from the side of the box, greeted Mr. Summers gravely, and selected a slip of paper from the box. By now, all through the crowd there were men holding the small folded papers in their large hands, turning them over and over nervously. Mrs. Dunbar and her two sons stood together, Mrs. Dunbar holding the slip of paper.

"Harburt. . . . Hutchinson."

"Get up there, Bill," Mrs. Hutchinson said, and the people near her laughed.

"Jones."

"They do say," Mr. Adams said to Old Man Warner, who stood next to him, "that over in the north village they're talking of giving up the lottery."

Old Man Warner snorted. "Pack of crazy fools," he said. "Listening to the young folks, nothing's good enough for them. Next thing you know, they'll be wanting to go back to living in caves, nobody work any more, live *that* way for a while. Used to be a saying about 'Lottery in June, corn be heavy soon.' First thing you know, we'd all be eating stewed chickweed and acorns. There's always been a lottery," he added petulantly. "Bad enough to see young Joe Summers up there joking with everybody."

"Some places have already quit lotteries," Mrs. Adams said.

"Nothing but trouble in that," Old Man Warner said stoutly. "Pack of young fools."

"Martin." And Bobby Martin watched his father go forward. "Overdyke. . . . Percy."

"I wish they'd hurry," Mrs. Dunbar said to her older son. "I wish they'd hurry."

"They're almost through," her son said.

"You get ready to run tell Dad," Mrs. Dunbar said.

Mr. Summers called his own name and then stepped forward precisely and selected a slip from the box. Then he called, "Warner."

"Seventy-seventh year I been in the lottery," Old Man Warner said as he went through the crowd. "Seventy-seventh time."

"Watson." The tall boy came awkwardly through the crowd. Someone said, "Don't be nervous, Jack," and Mr. Summers said, "Take your time, son."

"Zanini."

After that, there was a long pause, a breathless pause, until Mr. Summers, holding his slip of paper in the air, said, "All right, fellows." For a minute, no one moved, and then all the slips of paper were opened. Suddenly, all the women began to speak at once, saying, "Who is it?" "Who's got it?" "Is it the Dunbars?" "Is it the Watsons?" Then the voices began to say, "It's Hutchinson. It's Bill." "Bill Hutchinson's got it."

"Go tell your father," Mrs. Dunbar said to her older son.

People began to look around to see the Hutchinsons. Bill Hutchinson was standing quiet, staring down at the paper in his hand. Suddenly, Tessie Hutchinson shouted to Mr. Summers, "You didn't give him time enough to take any paper he wanted. I saw you. It wasn't fair!"

"Be a good sport, Tessie," Mrs. Delacroix called, and Mrs. Graves said, "All of us took the same chance."

"Shut up, Tessie," Bill Hutchinson said.

"Well, everyone," Mr. Summers said, "that was done pretty fast, and now we've got to be hurrying a little more to get done in time." He consulted his next list. "Bill," he said, "you draw for the Hutchinson family. You got any other households in the Hutchinsons?"

"There's Don and Eva," Mrs. Hutchinson yelled. "Make *them* take their chance!"

"Daughters draw with their husbands' families, Tessie," Mr. Summers said gently. "You know that as well as anyone else."

"It wasn't *fair*," Tessie said.

"I guess not, Joe," Bill Hutchinson said regretfully. "My daughter draws with her husband's family, that's only fair. And I've got no other family except the kids."

"Then, as far as drawing for families is concerned, it's you," Mr. Summers said in explanation, "and as far as drawing for households is concerned, that's you, too. Right?"

"Right," Bill Hutchinson said.

"How many kids, Bill?" Mr. Summers asked formally.

"Three," Bill Hutchinson said. "There's Bill, Jr., and Nancy, and little Dave. And Tessie and me."

"All right, then," Mr. Summers said. "Harry, you got their tickets back?"

Mr. Graves nodded and held up the slips of paper. "Put them in the box, then," Mr. Summers directed. "Take Bill's and put it in."

"I think we ought to start over," Mrs. Hutchinson said, as quietly as she could. "I tell you it wasn't *fair*. You didn't give him time enough to choose. *Every*body saw that."

Mr. Graves had selected the five slips and put them in the box, and he dropped all the papers but those onto the ground, where the breeze caught them and lifted them off.

"Listen, everybody," Mrs. Hutchinson was saying to the people around her.

"Ready, Bill?" Mr. Summers asked, and Bill Hutchinson, with one quick glance around at his wife and children, nodded.

"Remember," Mr. Summers said, "take the slips and keep them folded until each person has taken one. Harry, you help little Dave." Mr. Graves took the hand of the little boy, who came willingly with him up to the box. "Take a paper out of the box, Davy," Mr. Summers said. Davy put his hand into the box and laughed. "Take just one paper," Mr. Summers said. "Harry, you hold it for him." Mr. Graves took the child's hand and removed the folded paper from the tight fist and held it while little Dave stood next to him and looked up at him wonderingly.

"Nancy next," Mr. Summers said. Nancy was twelve, and her school friends breathed heavily as she went forward, switching her skirt, and took a slip daintily from the box. "Bill, Jr.," Mr. Summers said, and Billy, his face red and his feet overlarge, nearly knocked the box over as he got a paper out. "Tessie," Mr. Summers said. She hesitated for a minute, looking around defiantly, and then set her lips and went up to the box. She snatched a paper out and held it behind her.

"Bill," Mr. Summers said, and Bill Hutchinson reached into the box and felt around, bringing his hand out at last with the slip of paper in it.

The crowd was quiet. A girl whispered, "I hope it's not

Nancy," and the sound of the whisper reached the edges of the crowd.

"It's not the way it used to be," Old Man Warner said clearly. "People ain't the way they used to be."

"All right," Mr. Summers said. "Open the papers. Harry, you open little Dave's."

Mr. Graves opened the slip of paper, and there was a general sigh through the crowd as he held it up and everyone could see that it was blank. Nancy and Bill, Jr., opened theirs at the same time, and both beamed and laughed, turning around to the crowd and holding their slips of paper above their heads.

"Tessie," Mr. Summers said. There was a pause, and then Mr. Summers looked at Bill Hutchinson, and Bill unfolded his paper and showed it. It was blank.

"It's Tessie," Mr. Summers said, and his voice was hushed. "Show us her paper, Bill."

Bill Hutchinson went over to his wife and forced the slip of paper out of her hand. It had a black spot on it, the black spot Mr. Summers had made the night before with heavy pencil in the coal-company office. Bill Hutchinson held it up, and there was a stir in the crowd.

"All right, folks," Mr. Summers said. "Let's finish quickly."

Although the villagers had forgotten the ritual and lost the original black box, they still remembered to use stones. The pile of stones the boys had made earlier was ready; there were stones on the ground with the blowing scraps of paper that had come out of the box. Mrs. Delacroix selected a stone so large she had to pick it up with both hands and turned to Mrs. Dunbar. "Come on," she said. "Hurry up."

Mrs. Dunbar had small stones in both hands, and she said, gasping for breath, "I can't run at all. You'll have to go ahead and I'll catch up with you."

The children had stones already, and someone gave little Davy Hutchinson a few pebbles.

Tessie Hutchinson was in the center of a cleared space by now, and she held her hands out desperately as the villagers moved in on her. "It isn't fair," she said. A stone hit her on the side of the head.

Old Man Warner was saying, "Come on, come on, everyone." Steve Adams was in the front of the crowd of villagers, with Mrs. Graves beside him.

"It isn't fair, it isn't right," Mrs. Hutchinson screamed, and then they were upon her.

Meaning and Method

1. Shirley Jackson lets the horrific tension of the story build up in an atmosphere of peace and tranquillity. Nothing seems out of the ordinary as the townsfolk gather for the annual lottery.

   List the homely details in the story that contribute to an atmosphere of tranquillity. How do details of setting, in particular, contribute to the atmosphere? Can you tell the locale of the story from the details of setting the author supplies?

2. A *scapegoat* is an animal, person (or group of persons), or representation that is cast out or sacrificed in order to exorcise evil or atone for the sins of others. In the Bible, Leviticus 16 describes how the tribal leader Aaron selected a goat and symbolically placed upon its head the sins of his people, after which the goat was turned out to perish in the wilderness. And, many early or primitive societies used scapegoats for the periodic expulsion of evil.

   For example, every spring in ancient Rome, a man dubbed Mamurius Veturius (or "Old Mars," after Mars, who, besides being a god of war, was also the early Roman god of vegetation) was ritually beaten and chased from the city to make way for a "new" Mars, in order to ensure good crops for the year. And in many societies, the scapegoat was actually killed, as in "The Lottery."

   Why do you think the villagers in "The Lottery" carry out the annual ritual killing of a scapegoat chosen from among themselves? Do they seem to see a connection between the ritual and the tradition upon which it is based? Or do they simply blindly follow a tradition whose origins they do not know or understand?

3. What part does age play in regard to the villagers' varying attitudes toward the ritual of the lottery? What, for example, does the ritual mean to Old Man Warner? to Mr. Summers? to the children? Does the story offer any insights as to why people, especially community groups, cling to rituals about which they have little real knowledge other than the ritual acts themselves?

4. What do the disrepair and indistinct history of the drawing-box suggest about the moral state of repair of the society in which the lottery is conducted?

5. Much of the chill of the story comes from the author's use of

irony and paradox, separately or in combination. For example, the opening sentence in the story combines irony and paradox: irony, in the sense that it belies the real situation, and paradox, in the seeming contradiction of holding a murder on such a cheerful spring day. Pick out other passages in the story that, in review, seem ironic or paradoxical, or both.

6. Miss Jackson carefully describes how each member of the Hutchinson family went up during the second drawing to take a slip of paper from the lottery box. After they have all drawn, each reacts in a distinct manner to the outcome of his or her draw. How do the actions and reactions indicate the kind of person each is? Is it just too incredible that both older children laugh when they open their blank slips of paper? After all, don't they know that another family member, someone they love, will be the scapegoat? What is Shirley Jackson saying here about human nature? Do you agree with her, or do you think she is cynical?

7. As the villagers converge upon her at the end of the story, Mrs. Hutchinson cries out, "It isn't fair. It isn't right." What distinction is there, in the context of the story, between *fair* and *right*? Are fairness and rightness really important in the story? Do you think, for example, that Mrs. Hutchinson (or any villager) ever thought about what was fair and right about the lottery ritual stonings in earlier years? What point does the story make in this regard about individual guilt and collective guilt? What point is made about the relationship between victim and perpetrator?

8. A *parable* is a short, simple narrative that illustrates a moral lesson or a broad statement of truth. There are many parables in the New Testament in the Gospels, for example, in Matthew 13:18–23, 13:24–30, and 13:31–32; or in Luke 10:30–37. In parables, plot and characterization are minimal. They are kept simple so that the truth, lesson, or theme of the parable may be emphasized.

In what ways does "The Lottery" resemble a parable? What larger truth or lesson beyond the immediate narrative is suggested? How complicated are the plot and characterizations? Point to examples to support your answers. What is the theme or main point of the story?

Composition and Discussion

1. Although Shirley Jackson "localized" her story by setting it in a single rural village, she nonetheless gave the story a universal aspect by leaving open to question the exact locale of the village. In a two-part discussion explain (a) how the social criticisms in "The Lottery" can be applied to any relatively small group in a rural village, a small

suburban town, a neighborhood, or a city block; and (b) how the story provides a microcosmic view of society at large; that is, how its social criticisms can be taken by extension to represent the ills of society as a whole.

2. Scapegoats have played a part in the history of virtually every civilization. For example, in the ancient Greek city of Athens, a man and a woman were selected annually as scapegoats, paraded around the city, and finally led outside the city and stoned to death by the Athenian men and women.

Consult an encyclopedia of classical history, a history text, or an anthropological reference work such as Sir James Frazer's *The Golden Bough,* and prepare an oral report on an instance of the use of scapegoats in the history of a particular civilization. Describe the ritual ceremony and its background, explain its connection with mythology or demonology, if any, and trace its origin and development as a method of exorcising, or getting rid of, evil.

As an alternate assignment, develop a written or oral report on the evidence of scapegoats in recent history or in contemporary society.

Eudora Welty

Eudora Welty was born in 1909 in Jackson, Mississippi. Except for a few years at the University of Wisconsin and at Columbia University Business School, she has lived in her home town. After she returned from New York in 1931, she was in and out of jobs in advertising and on newspapers. For a time she was the publicity agent for the Works Progress Administration (WPA), a federal agency whose goal was to create jobs during the Depression, in the early and middle 1930's. This work took her throughout Mississippi and deepened her knowledge of its people and places; it also made her want to write about them. Thus, the state, especially the Delta region around the river, became the setting for most of her short stories and of her novels, *The Delta Wedding* (1946) and *The Ponder Heart* (1954).

Because so many of her stories are set in Mississippi, Miss Welty has been called a regional writer. This is only partly correct. It is true that one of her strengths is her ability to recreate and dissect the small southern community, and she can evoke strongly the atmosphere or mood of her settings, partly through her homey and colloquial diction and partly through her concrete descriptions. Yet she does more than merely narrate local customs and eccentricities. The characters in her collections of short stories—*The Wide Net* (1943), *The Golden Apples* (1949), and *The Bride of Innisfallen* (1955)—show the effects of isolation and loneliness on the human personality. By enlarging and distorting certain traits of a character, Miss Welty presents his interior or psychological condition rather than his external appearance.

Eudora Welty's personal interests and hobbies have also influenced her technique of storytelling. The air of fantasy that is often found in her works stems from her enjoyment of reading fairy tales and old legends, and of listening to the songs and stories of people who live in old communities. She also finds pleasure in oil painting, amateur photography, and painting in watercolor—interests which carry over into the artistically beautiful descriptions that characterize her writings.

A Worn Path

It was December—a bright frozen day in the early morning. Far out in the country there was an old Negro woman with her head tied in a red rag, coming along a path through the pinewoods. Her name was Phoenix [1] Jackson. She was very old and small and she walked slowly in the dark pine shadows, moving a little from side to side in her steps, with the balanced heaviness and lightness of a pendulum in a grandfather clock. She carried a thin, small cane made from an umbrella, and with this she kept tapping the frozen earth in front of her. This made a grave and persistent noise in the still air, that seemed meditative like the chirping of a solitary little bird.

She wore a dark striped dress reaching down to her shoe tops, and an equally long apron of bleached sugar sacks, with a full pocket: all neat and tidy, but every time she took a step she might have fallen over her shoelaces, which dragged from her unlaced shoes. She looked straight ahead. Her eyes were blue with age. Her skin had a pattern all its own of numberless branching wrinkles and as though a whole little tree stood in the middle of her forehead, but a golden color ran underneath, and the two knobs of her cheeks were illumined by a yellow burning under the dark. Under the red rag her hair came down on her neck in the frailest of ringlets, still black, and with an odor like copper.

Now and then there was a quivering in the thicket. Old Phoenix said, "Out of my way, all you foxes, owls, beetles, jack rabbits, coons, and wild animals! . . . Keep out from under these feet, little bobwhites. . . . Keep the big wild hogs out of my path. Don't let none of those come running my direction. I got a long way." Under her small black-freckled hand her cane, limber as a buggy whip, would switch at the brush as if to rouse up any hiding things.

1. **Phoenix:** in Egyptian mythology, a bird of great beauty said to live for 500 years in the desert, to burn and destroy itself by fire, to rise again from its ashes youthful and beautiful, and to live through another life cycle. The phoenix was supposedly the size of an eagle, with partly red and partly golden plumage. It is often used as a symbol of immortality.

"A Worn Path" by Eudora Welty, copyright 1941 by Eudora Welty, from her volume, *A Curtain of Green and Other Stories.* Reprinted by permission of Harcourt, Brace & World, Inc.

On she went. The woods were deep and still. The sun made the pine needles almost too bright to look at, up where the wind rocked. The cones dropped as light as feathers. Down in the hollow was the mourning dove [2]—it was not too late for him.

The path ran up a hill. "Seem like there is chains about my feet, time I get this far," she said, in the voice of argument old people keep to use with themselves. "Something always take a hold of me on this hill—pleads I should stay."

After she got to the top, she turned and gave a full, severe look behind her where she had come. "Up through pines," she said at length. "Now down through oaks."

Her eyes opened their widest and she started down gently. But before she got to the bottom of the hill a bush caught her dress.

Her fingers were busy and intent, but her skirts were full and long, so that before she could pull them free in one place they were caught in another. It was not possible to allow the dress to tear. "I in the thorny bush," she said. "Thorns, you doing your appointed work. Never want to let folks pass, no sir. Old eyes thought you was a pretty little *green* bush."

Finally, trembling all over, she stood free, and after a moment dared to stoop for her cane.

"Sun so high!" she cried, leaning back and looking, while the thick tears went over her eyes. "The time getting all gone here."

At the foot of this hill was a place where a log was laid across the creek.

"Now comes the trial," said Phoenix.

Putting her right foot out, she mounted the log and shut her eyes. Lifting her skirt, leveling her cane fiercely before her, like a festival figure in some parade, she began to march across. Then she opened her eyes and she was safe on the other side.

"I wasn't as old as I thought," she said.

But she sat down to rest. She spread her skirts on the bank around her and folded her hands over her knees. Up above her was a tree in a pearly cloud of mistletoe.[3] She did not dare to close her

2. **mourning dove:** the wild dove, which is known for its mournful cry.
3. **mistletoe:** the mistletoe and the tree to which it clings were held to be sacred by the Druids, the priests of the ancient Celtic religion. They believed that everything that grew on this clinging shrub had been sent from heaven as a proof that it was chosen by God.

eyes, and when a little boy brought her a plate with a slice of marble cake on it she spoke to him. "That would be acceptable," she said. But when she went to take it there was just her own hand in the air.

So she left that tree, and had to go through a barbed-wire fence. There she had to creep and crawl, spreading her knees and stretching her fingers like a baby trying to climb the steps. But she talked loudly to herself: she could not let her dress be torn now, so late in the day, and she could not pay for having her arm or her leg sawed off if she got caught fast where she was.

At last she was safe through the fence and risen up out in the clearing. Big dead trees, like black men with one arm, were standing in the purple stalks of the withered cotton field. There sat a buzzard.

"Who you watching?"

In the furrow she made her way along.

"Glad this not the season for bulls," she said, looking sideways, "and the good Lord made his snakes to curl up and sleep in the winter. A pleasure I don't see no two-headed snake coming around that tree, where it come once. It took a while to get by him, back in the summer."

She passed through the old cotton and went into a field of dead corn. It whispered and shook and was taller than her head. "Through the maze now," she said, for there was no path.

Then there was something tall, black, and skinny there, moving before her.

At first she took it for a man. It could have been a man dancing in the field. But she stood still and listened, and it did not make a sound. It was as silent as a ghost.

"Ghost," she said sharply, "who be you the ghost of? For I have heard of nary [4] death close by."

But there was no answer, only the ragged dancing in the wind.

She shut her eyes, reached out her hand, and touched a sleeve. She found a coat and inside that an emptiness, cold as ice.

"You scarecrow," she said. Her face lighted. "I ought to be shut up for good," she said with laughter. "My senses is gone. I too old. I the oldest people I ever know. Dance, old scarecrow," she said, "while I dancing with you."

---

4. **nary:** *dialect,* not one.

She kicked her foot over the furrow, and with mouth drawn down, shook her head once or twice in a little strutting way. Some husks blew down and whirled in streamers about her skirts.

Then she went on, parting her way from side to side with the cane, through the whispering field. At last she came to the end, to a wagon track where the silver grass blew between the red ruts. The quail were walking around like pullets,[5] seeming all dainty and unseen.

"Walk pretty," she said. "This the easy place. This the easy going."

She followed the track, swaying through the quiet bare fields, through the little strings of trees silver in their dead leaves, past cabins silver from weather, with the doors and windows boarded shut, all like old women under a spell sitting there. "I walking in their sleep," she said, nodding her head vigorously.

In a ravine she went where a spring was silently flowing through a hollow log. Old Phoenix bent and drank. "Sweet gum [6] makes the water sweet," she said, and drank more. "Nobody know who made this well, for it was here when I was born."

The track crossed a swampy part where the moss hung as white as lace from every limb. "Sleep on, alligators, and blow your bubbles." Then the track went into the road.

Deep, deep the road went down between the high green-colored banks. Overhead the live-oaks met, and it was as dark as a cave.

A black dog with a lolling [7] tongue came up out of the weeds by the ditch. She was meditating, and not ready, and when he came at her she only hit him a little with her cane. Over she went in the ditch, like a little puff of milkweed.

Down there, her senses drifted away. A dream visited her, and she reached her hand up, but nothing reached down and gave her a pull. So she lay there and presently went to talking. "Old woman," she said to herself, "that black dog come up out of the weeds to stall you off, and now there he sitting on his fine tail, smiling at you."

A white man finally came along and found her—a hunter, a young man, with his dog on a chain.

5. **pullets:** young hens.
6. **Sweet gum:** a tree that yields a sweet, gummy substance.
7. **lolling:** drooping.

"Well, Granny!" he laughed. "What are you doing there?"

"Lying on my back like a June bug waiting to be turned over, mister," she said, reaching up her hand.

He lifted her up, gave her a swing in the air, and set her down. "Anything broken, Granny?"

"No sir, them old dead weeds is springy enough," said Phoenix, when she had got her breath. "I thank you for your trouble."

"Where do you live, Granny?" he asked, while the two dogs were growling at each other.

"Away back yonder, sir, behind the ridge. You can't even see it from here."

"On your way home?"

"No sir, I going to town."

"Why, that's too far! That's as far as I walk when I come out myself, and I get something for my trouble." He patted the stuffed bag he carried, and there hung down a little closed claw. It was one of the bobwhites, with its beak hooked bitterly to show it was dead. "Now you go on home, Granny!"

"I bound to go to town, mister," said Phoenix. "The time come around."

He gave another laugh, filling the whole landscape. "I know you old colored people! Wouldn't miss going to town to see Santa Claus!"

But something held old Phoenix very still. The deep lines in her face went into a fierce and different radiation. Without warning, she had seen with her own eyes a flashing nickel fall out of the man's pocket onto the ground.

"How old are you, Granny?" he was saying.

"There is no telling, mister," she said, "no telling."

Then she gave a little cry and clapped her hands and said, "Git on away from here, dog! Look! Look at that dog!" She laughed as if in admiration. "He ain't scared of nobody. He a big black dog." She whispered, "Sic him!"

"Watch me get rid of that cur," said the man. "Sic him, Pete! Sic him!"

Phoenix heard the dogs fighting, and heard the man running and throwing sticks. She even heard a gunshot. But she was slowly bending forward by that time, further and further forward, the lids stretched down over her eyes, as if she were doing this in her sleep.

Her chin was lowered almost to her knees. The yellow palm of her hand came out from the fold of her apron. Her fingers slid down and along the ground under the piece of money with the grace and care they would have in lifting an egg from under a setting hen. Then she slowly straightened up, she stood erect, and the nickel was in her apron pocket. A bird flew by. Her lips moved. "God watching me the whole time. I come to stealing."

The man came back, and his own dog panted about them. "Well, I scared him off that time," he said, and then he laughed and lifted his gun and pointed it at Phoenix.

She stood straight and faced him.

"Doesn't the gun scare you?" he said, still pointing it.

"No, sir, I seen plenty go off closer by, in my day, and for less than what I done," she said, holding utterly still.

He smiled, and shouldered the gun. "Well, Granny," he said, "you must be a hundred years old, and scared of nothing. I'd give you a dime if I had any money with me. But you take my advice and stay home, and nothing will happen to you."

"I bound to go on my way, mister," said Phoenix. She inclined her head in the red rag. Then they went in different directions, but she could hear the gun shooting again and again over the hill.

She walked on. The shadows hung from the oak trees to the road like curtains. Then she smelled wood smoke, and smelled the river, and she saw a steeple and the cabins on their steep steps. Dozens of little black children whirled around her. There ahead was Natchez [8] shining. Bells were ringing. She walked on.

In the paved city it was Christmas time. There were red and green electric lights strung and crisscrossed everywhere, and all turned on in the daytime. Old Phoenix would have been lost if she had not distrusted her eyesight and depended on her feet to know where to take her.

She paused quietly on the sidewalk where people were passing by. A lady came along in the crowd, carrying an armful of red-, green- and silver-wrapped presents; she gave off perfume like the red roses in hot summer, and Phoenix stopped her.

"Please, missy, will you lace up my shoe?" She held up her foot.

8. **Natchez** (nach′iz): a port city in southwest Mississippi, located on the Mississippi River.

"What do you want, Grandma?"

"See my shoe," said Phoenix. "Do all right for out in the country, but wouldn't look right to go in a big building."

"Stand still then, Grandma," said the lady. She put her packages down on the sidewalk beside her and laced and tied both shoes tightly.

"Can't lace 'em with a cane," said Phoenix. "Thank you, missy. I doesn't mind asking a nice lady to tie up my shoe, when I gets out on the street."

Moving slowly and from side to side, she went into the big building, and into a tower of steps, where she walked up and around and around until her feet knew to stop.

She entered a door, and there she saw nailed up on the wall the document that had been stamped with the gold seal and framed in the gold frame, which matched the dream that was hung up in her head.

"Here I be," she said. There was a fixed and ceremonial stiffness over her body.

"A charity case, I suppose," said an attendant who sat at the desk before her.

But Phoenix only looked above her head. There was sweat on her face, the wrinkles in her skin shone like a bright net.

"Speak up, Grandma," the woman said. "What's your name? We must have your history, you know. Have you been here before? What seems to be the trouble with you?"

Old Phoenix only gave a twitch to her face as if a fly were bothering her.

"Are you deaf?" cried the attendant.

But then the nurse came in.

"Oh, that's just old Aunt Phoenix," she said. "She doesn't come for herself—she has a little grandson. She makes these trips just as regular as clockwork. She lives away back off the Old Natchez Trace." [9] She bent down. "Well, Aunt Phoenix, why don't you just take a seat? We won't keep you standing after your long trip." She pointed.

9. **Old Natchez Trace:** an old road, over 500 miles long, which runs from Nashville, Tennessee, to Natchez. It was built in the early nineteenth century for traders going to and from the river port. *Trace* means a path or trail through the woods.

The old woman sat down, bolt upright in the chair.

"Now, how is the boy?" asked the nurse.

Old Phoenix did not speak.

"I said, how is the boy?"

But Phoenix only waited and stared straight ahead, her face very solemn and withdrawn into rigidity.

"Is his throat any better?" asked the nurse. "Aunt Phoenix, don't you hear me? Is your grandson's throat any better since the last time you came for the medicine?"

With her hands on her knees, the old woman waited, silent, erect and motionless, just as if she were in armor.

"You mustn't take up our time this way, Aunt Phoenix," the nurse said. "Tell us quickly about your grandson, and get it over. He isn't dead, is he?"

At last there came a flicker and then a flame of comprehension across her face, and she spoke.

"My grandson. It was my memory had left me. There I sat and forgot why I made my long trip."

"Forgot?" The nurse frowned. "After you came so far?"

Then Phoenix was like an old woman begging a dignified forgiveness for waking up frightened in the night. "I never did go to school, I was too old at the Surrender," [10] she said in a soft voice. "I'm an old woman without an education. It was my memory fail me. My little grandson, he is just the same, and I forgot it in the coming."

"Throat never heals, does it?" said the nurse, speaking in a loud, sure voice to old Phoenix. By now she had a card with something written on it, a little list. "Yes. Swallowed lye. When was it? —January—two-three years ago—"

Phoenix spoke unasked now. "No, missy, he not dead, he just the same. Every little while his throat begin to close up again, and he not able to swallow. He not get his breath. He not able to help himself. So the time come around, and I go on another trip for the soothing medicine."

"All right. The doctor said as long as you came to get it, you could have it," said the nurse. "But it's an obstinate case."

"My little grandson, he sit up there in the house all wrapped

10. **Surrender:** that is, of the Confederate forces under General Lee on April 9, 1965, at Appomattox Courthouse, which virtually ended the Civil War.

up, waiting by himself," Phoenix went on. "We is the only two left in the world. He suffer and it don't seem to put him back at all. He got a sweet look. He going to last. He wear a little patch quilt and peep out holding his mouth open like a little bird. I remembers so plain now. I not going to forget him again, no, the whole enduring time. I could tell him from all the others in creation."

"All right." The nurse was trying to hush her now. She brought her a bottle of medicine. "Charity," she said, making a check mark in a book.

Old Phoenix held the bottle close to her eyes, and then carefully put it into her pocket.

"I thank you," she said.

"It's Christmas time, Grandma," said the attendant. "Could I give you a few pennies out of my purse?"

"Five pennies is a nickel," said Phoenix stiffly.

"Here's a nickel," said the attendant.

Phoenix rose carefully and held out her hand. She received the nickel and then fished the other nickel out of her pocket and laid it beside the new one. She stared at her palm closely, with her head on one side.

Then she gave a tap with her cane on the floor.

"This is what come to me to do," she said. "I going to the store and buy my child a little windmill they sells, made out of paper. He going to find it hard to believe there such a thing in the world. I'll march myself back where he waiting, holding it straight up in this hand."

She lifted her free hand, gave a little nod, turned around, and walked out of the doctor's office. Then her slow step began on the stairs, going down.

Meaning and Method

1. Reread footnote 1 on page 174. What words and phrases in the opening paragraph of the story connect Phoenix Jackson with the mythological bird?

2. How do the following facts and quotations from the story suggest parallels with the phoenix legend?
   (a) The grandson swallowed lye.
   (b) ". . . a golden color ran underneath, and the two knobs of

her cheeks were illumined by a yellow burning under the dark."

(c) "Under the red rag her hair came down on her neck . . . and with an odor like copper."

(d) "We is the only two left in the world."

(e) "He wear a little patch quilt and peep out holding his mouth open like a little bird."

(f) The time of the story is Christmas.

(g) Phoenix returns periodically to Natchez.

3. The critic Northrop Frye has noted that many myths throughout the world fall into similar narrative patterns. One such worldwide pattern is the quest myth. In a quest myth, the hero goes on a journey to gain a prize; on the journey he encounters severe hardships and faces great dangers, both from natural and supernatural enemies. *The Odyssey*, for example, is based on this narrative pattern, as are the exploits of King Arthur's knights, who go on journeys to save maidens or to defeat wrongdoers.

What is the prize Phoenix seeks? What hardships and dangers does she encounter? How does she show her courage in the meeting with the white man? with the scarecrow?

The white man who helps her from the ditch is also on a quest. Why is he traveling along the road? How does the quest of Phoenix contrast with that of the white man?

4. What is ironic, as well as condescending, about the hunter's comment: "I know you old colored people! Wouldn't miss going to town to see Santa Claus!"

5. When the hunter drops a nickel, Phoenix distracts him so that she can pocket the coin. Why did she take it? Is it actually stealing, or does her extreme poverty give her a right to the money? What is shown by her comment as she notices a bird flying by: "God watching me the whole time. I come to stealing"? And what note is added by the hunter's saying, "I'd give you a dime if I had any money with me"?

6. As Phoenix walks along the path (page 175), her dress becomes entangled in a thorn bush. While removing the thorns, she says, "Thorns, you doing your appointed work." How does her reaction illustrate her acceptance of life as it is? Does she ever complain about having to go on the journey? How do the hospital attendants' reactions when Phoenix's lapse of memory inconveniences them contrast with her attitude?

7. What are the connotations of a windmill, the gift that Phoenix buys for her grandson?

8. The hospital records will show that the medicine was given as

"charity." Contrast the idea of charity as exemplified by Phoenix with that of the hospital attendants and nurses. In what way does Phoenix exhibit the spirit of love inherent in Christmas?

9. Is there any similarity between Phoenix and the Magi? between the grandson and the Christ child? Why or why not?

10. Is Phoenix a symbol of immortality? of true love? of both? Is the theme of the story that self-sacrifice and love for others can help man renew himself and therefore endure? What might the worn path represent in Phoenix's life? in everyone's life? How do the title and the story have special significance regarding the history of the American Negro?

Language: Dialect

Dialect refers to a form of language that is spoken in a limited area or by a specific class of people. The word choice and the pronunciation, as well as the arrangement of the words in sentences, are different from standard English.

Examine the following sentences from "A Worn Path," and then decide how they would be written in standard English.

1. The time getting all gone here.
2. A pleasure I don't see no two-headed snake coming around that tree, where it come once.
3. I too old. I the oldest person I ever know.
4. It was my memory fail me.
5. I not going to forget him again, no, the whole enduring time.

How does this use of dialect help to characterize Phoenix?

Composition

Miss Welty believes people need such qualities as fortitude and courage, which she calls endurance, in order to survive in today's rapidly changing world. Write an essay in which you explain what virtues, traits, and qualities you feel are needed to live in twentieth-century America. Give specific examples to justify your opinions.

J. F. Powers

J[ames] F[arl] Powers was born in Jacksonville, Illinois, in 1917. He attended parochial schools in Rockford and Quincy, Illinois, and later the Quincy College Academy. After graduation, Powers drifted in and out of several jobs—at various times he was a door-to-door insurance salesman and a chauffeur. On one chauffering trip through the South and Southwest, he took a typewriter along and began to write in his spare time. By the time the trip ended, he had decided to be a writer.

Powers has enjoyed a successful career as a writer. His first published short story, "Lions, Harts, Leaping Does," won the O'Henry Memorial Award in 1943. A year later, "The Trouble" won the same award. In that year, his first collection of short stories, *The Prince of Darkness and Other Stories*, was published. In 1962, his second collection of stories, the *Presence of Grace*, and his first novel, *Morte d'Urban*, appeared.

His writing draws heavily on his Roman Catholic background. Many of his characters, such as Father Urban, are clerics faced with the conflicting demands of religion and the world. But no matter what their religion, Powers's characters are always concerned, consciously or unconsciously, with the spiritual challenge of life.

The Trouble

We watched at the window all that afternoon.

Old Gramma came out of her room and said, Now you kids get away from there this very minute, and we would until she went back to her room. We could hear her old rocking chair creak when she got up or sat down and so we always ran away from the window before she came into the room to see if we were minding her good or looking out. Except once she went back to her room and didn't sit down, or maybe she did and got up easy so the chair didn't creak, or maybe we got our signals mixed, because she caught us all there and shooed us away and pulled down the green shade. The next time we were very sure she wasn't foxing us before we went to the window and lifted the shade just enough to peek out.

It was like waiting for rats as big as cats to run out from under a tenement so you could pick them off with a .22. Rats are about the biggest live game you can find in ordinary times and you see more of them than white folks in our neighborhood—in ordinary times. But the rats we waited for today were white ones and they were doing most of the shooting themselves. Sometimes some coloreds would come by with guns, but not often; they mostly had clubs. This morning we'd seen the whites catch up with a shot-in-the-leg colored and throw bricks and stones at his black head till it got all red and he was dead. I could still see the wet places in the alley. That's why we kept looking out the window. We wanted to see some whites get killed for a change, but we didn't much think we would, and I guess what we really expected to see was nothing, or maybe them killing another colored.

There was a rumpus downstairs in front and I could hear a mess of people tramping up the stairs. They kept on coming after the second floor and my sister Carrie, my twin, said maybe they were whites come to get *us* because we saw what they did to the shot-in-the-leg colored in the alley. I was scared for a minute, I admit, but when I heard their voices plainer I knew they were coloreds and it was all right, only I didn't see why there were so many of them.

Then I got scared again, only different now, empty scared all over, when they came down the hall on our floor, not stopping at anybody else's door. And then there they were, banging on our door, of all the doors in the building. They tried to come right on in, but the door was locked.

Old Gramma was the one locked it and she said she'd clean house if one of us kids so much as looked at the knob even. She threw the key down her neck somewhere and I went and told her that was our door the people were pounding on and where was the key. She reached down her neck and there was the key all right. But she didn't act much like she intended to open the door. She just stood there staring at it like it was somebody alive, saying the litany to the Blessed Virgin: *Mère du Christ, priez pour nous;*

Secours des chrétiens, priez.[1] Then all the sudden she was crying, tears were blurry in her old yellow eyes, and she put the key in the lock, her veiny hands shaking, and unlocked the door.

They had Mama in their arms. I forgot all about Old Gramma but I guess she passed out. Anyway, she was on the floor and a couple of women were saying, Put her here, put her there. I wasn't worried as much about Old Gramma as I was about Mama.

A bone, God, it made me sick, had poked through the flesh of Mama's arm, all bloody like a sharp stick, and something terrible was wrong with her chest. I couldn't look any more and Carrie was screaming. That started me crying. Tears got in the way, but still I could see the baby, one-and-a-half, and brother George, four-and-a-half, and they had their eyes wide open at what they saw and weren't crying a bit, too young to know what the hell.

They put Old Gramma in her room on the cot and closed the door on her and some old woman friend of hers that kept dipping a handkerchief in cold water and laying it on Old Gramma's head. They put Mama on the bed in the room where everybody was standing around and talking lower and lower until pretty soon they were just whispering.

Somebody came in with a doctor, a colored one, and he had a little black bag like they have in the movies. I don't think our family ever had a doctor come to see us before. Maybe before I was born Mama and Daddy did. I heard the doctor tell Mr. Purvine, that works in the same mill Daddy does, only the night shift, that he ought to set the bone, but honest to God he thought he might as well wait as he didn't want to hurt Mama if it wasn't going to make any difference.

He wasn't nearly as brisk now with his little black bag as he had been when he came in. He touched Mama's forehead a couple of times and it didn't feel good to him, I guess, because he looked tired after he did it. He held his hand on her wrist of the good arm, but I couldn't tell what this meant from his face. It mustn't have been any worse than the forehead, or maybe his face had nothing to do with what he thought and I was imagining all

---

1. *Mère du Christ, priez pour nous; Secours des chrétiens, priez: French,* Mother of Christ, pray for us; Help of Christians, pray. The prayers are part of the litany, or the series of supplications and responses, said to the Virgin Mary.

this from seeing the shape Mama was in. Finally he said, I'll try, and he began calling for hot water and other things and pretty soon Mama was all bandaged up white.

The doctor stepped away from Mama and over to some men and women, six or seven of them now—a lot more had gone—and asked them what had happened. He didn't ask all the questions I wanted to ask—I guess he already knew some of the answers—but I did find out Mama was on a streetcar coming home from the plant—Mama works now and we're saving for a cranberry farm —when the riot broke out in that section. Mr. Purvine said he called the mill and told Daddy to come home. But Mr. Purvine said he wasn't going to work tonight himself, the way the riot was spreading and the way the coloreds were getting the worst of it.

As usual, said a man with glasses on, the Negroes ought to organize and fight the thing to a finish. The doctor frowned at that. Mr. Purvine said he didn't know. But one woman and another man said that was the right idea.

If we must die,[2] said the man with glasses on, let it not be like hogs hunted and penned in an inglorious spot! The doctor said, Yes, we all know that, but the man with glasses on went on, because the others were listening to him, and I was glad he did, because I was listening to him too: We must meet the common foe; though far outnumbered, let us show us brave, and for their thousand blows deal one deathblow! What though before us lies the open grave? Like men we'll face the murderous, cowardly pack, pressed to the wall, dying but—fighting back!

They all thought it was fine and a woman said that was poetry and I thought if that is what it is I know what I want to be now, a poetryman. I asked the man with glasses on if that was his poetry, though I did not think it was, for some reason, and the men and women all looked at me like they were surprised to see me there and like I ought not hear such things, except the man with glasses on, and he said, No, son, it was not his poetry, he wished it was, but it was Claude McKay's, a Negro, and I could find it in the public library. I decided I would go to the public library when the riot was over and it was the first time in my life I ever thought of the public library the way I did then.

2. From "If We Must Die" from *The Selected Poems of Claude McKay*. Reprinted by permission of Twayne Publishers, Inc.

They all left about this time, except the doctor and the old woman friend of Old Gramma's. She came out of Old Gramma's room, and when the door opened I saw Old Gramma lying on the cot with her eyes closed. The old woman asked me if I could work a can opener and I said, Yes, I can, and she handed me a can of vegetable soup from the shelf. She got a meal together and us kids sat down to eat. Not Carrie, though. She sat in our good chair with her legs under her and her eyes closed. Mama was sleeping and the doctor rolled up the shade of the window and looked out while we ate. I mean brother George and the baby. I couldn't eat. I just drank my glass of water. The old woman said, Here, here, I hadn't ought to let good food go to waste and was that any way to act at the table and I wasn't the first boy in the world to lose his mother.

I wondered was she crazy and I yelled I wasn't going to lose my mother and I looked to see and I was right. Mama was just sleeping and the doctor was there in case she needed him and everything was taken care of and—everything. The doctor didn't even turn away from the window when I yelled at the old woman and I thought at least he'd say I'd wake my mother up shouting that way, or maybe that I was right and the old woman was wrong. I got up from the table and stood by the doctor at the window. He only stayed there a minute more then and went over to feel Mama's wrist again. He did not touch her forehead this time.

Old Gramma came out of her room and said to me, Was that you raising so much Cain in here, boy? I said, Yes, it was, and just when I was going to tell her what the old woman said about losing Mama I couldn't. I didn't want to hear it out loud again. I didn't even want to think it in my mind. Old Gramma went over and gazed down at Mama. She turned away quickly and told the old woman, Please, I'll just have a cup of hot water, that's all, I'm so upset. Then she went over to the doctor by the window and whispered something to him and he whispered something back and it must've been only one or two words, because he was looking out the window the next moment.

Old Gramma said she'd be back in a minute and went out the door and slip-slapping down the hall. I went to the window; the evening sun was going down, and I saw Old Gramma come out the back entrance of our building. She crossed the alley and went in the back door of the grocery store.

A lot of racket cut loose about a block up the alley. It was still empty, though. Old Gramma came out of the grocery store with something in a brown bag. She stopped in the middle of the alley and seemed to be watching the orange evening sun going down behind the buildings. The sun got in her hair and somehow under her skin kind of and it did a wonderful thing to her. She looked so young for a moment that I saw Mama in her, both of them beautiful New Orleans ladies.

The racket cut loose again, nearer now, and a pack of men came running down the alley, about three dozen whites chasing two coloreds. One of the whites was blowing a bugle—*tan tivvy tan tivvy tan tivvy*—like the white folks do when they go fox-hunting in the movies or Virginia. I looked down, quick, to see if Old Gramma had enough sense to come inside and I guess she did because she wasn't there. The two coloreds ran between two buildings, the whites ran after them and then the alley was quiet again. Old Gramma stepped out and I watched her stoop and pick up the brown bag that she had dropped before.

Another big noise made her drop it again. A whole smear of men swarmed out of the used-car lot and came galloping down the alley like wild buffaloes. Old Gramma scooted inside our building and the brown bag stayed in the alley. This time I couldn't believe my eyes, I saw what I thought I'd never see, I saw what us kids had been waiting to see ever since the riot broke out—a white man fixing to get himself nice and killed. A white man running—running, God Almighty, from about a million coloreds. And he was the one with the tan-tivvy bugle too. I hoped the coloreds would do the job up right.

The closer the white man came the worse it got for him, because the alley comes to a dead end when it hits our building. All at once, I don't know why, I was praying for the fool white man with the bugle to get away. But I didn't think he had a Chinaman's chance, the way he was going now, and maybe that's what made me pray for him.

Then he did a smart thing. He whipped the bugle over his shoulder like you do with a horseshoe for good luck and it hit the first colored behind him smack in the head, knocking him out, and that slowed up the others. The white man turned into the junk-yard behind the furniture warehouse and the Victory Ballroom.

Another smart thing, if he used his head. The space between the warehouse and the Victory is just wide enough for a man to run through. It's a long piece to the street, but if he made it there he'd be safe probably.

The long passageway must've looked too narrow to him, though, because the fool came rushing around the garage next to our building. For a moment he was the only one in the alley. The coloreds had followed him through the junkyard and probably got themselves all tangled up in garbage cans and rusty bed springs and ashpiles. But the white man was a goner just the same. In a minute they'd be coming for him for real. He'd have to run the length of the alley again to get away and the coloreds have got the best legs.

Then Old Gramma opened our back door and saved him.

I was very glad for the white man until suddenly I remembered poor Mama all broken to pieces on the bed and then I was sorry Old Gramma did it. The next moment I was glad again that she did. I understood now I did not care one way or the other about the white man. Now I was thinking of Mama—not of myself. I did not see what difference it could make to Mama if the white man lived or died. It only had something to do with us and him.

Then I got hold of a very strange idea. I told myself the trouble is somebody gets cheated or insulted or killed and everybody else tries to make it come out even by cheating or insulting or killing the cheaters and insulters and killers. Only they never do. I did not think they ever would. I told myself that I had a very big idea there and when the riot was over I would go to the public library and sit in the reading room and think about it. Or I would speak to Old Gramma about it, because it seemed like she had the same big idea and like she had had it a long time too.

The doctor was standing by me at the window all the time. He said nothing about what Old Gramma did, and now he stepped away from the window and so did I. I guess he felt the same way I did about the white man and that's why he stepped away from the window. The big idea again. He was afraid the coloreds down below would yell up at us, did we see the white man pass by. The coloreds were crazy mad all right. One of them had the white man's bugle and he banged on our door with it. I was worried Old

Gramma had forgot to lock it and they might walk right in and that would be the end of the white man and the big idea.

But Old Gramma pulled another fast one. She ran out into the alley and pointed her yellow finger in about three wrong directions. In a second the alley was quiet and empty, except for Old Gramma. She walked slowly over against our building, where somebody had kicked the brown bag, and picked it up.

Old Gramma brought the white man right into our room, told him to sit down and poured herself a cup of hot water. She sipped it and said the white man could leave whenever he wanted to, but it might be better to wait a bit. The white man said he was much obliged, he hated to give us any trouble, and Oh, oh, is somebody sick over there, when he saw Mama, and that he'd just been passing by when a hundred nig—when he was attacked.

Old Gramma sipped her hot water. The doctor turned away from the window and said, Here they come again, take another look, and said, No, they're going back. He went over to Mama and held her wrist. I couldn't tell anything about her from his face. She was sleeping just the same. The doctor asked the white man, still standing, to sit down. Carrie only opened her eyes once and closed them. She hadn't changed her position in the good chair. Brother George and the baby stood in a corner with their eyes on the white man. The baby's legs buckled then—she'd only been walking about a week—and she collapsed softly to the floor. She worked her way up again without taking her eyes off the white man. He even looked funny and out of place to me in our room. I guess the man for the rent and Father Egan were the only white people come to see us since I could remember and now it was only the man for the rent since Father Egan died.

The doctor asked the white man did he work or own a business in this neighborhood. The white man said, No, glancing down at his feet, no, he just happened to be passing by when he was suddenly attacked like he said before. The doctor told Old Gramma she might wash Mama's face and neck again with warm water.

There was noise again in the alley, windows breaking and fences being pushed over. The doctor said, You could leave now, to the white man, it's a white mob this time, you'd be safe.

No, the white man said, I should say not, I wouldn't be seen with them, they're as bad as the others almost.

It is quite possible, the doctor said.

Old Gramma asked the white man if he would like a cup of tea.

Tea? No, he said, I don't drink tea, I didn't know you drank it.

I didn't know you knew her, the doctor said, looking at Old Gramma and the white man.

You colored folks, I mean, the white man said, Americans, I mean. Me, I don't drink tea, always considered it an English drink and bad for the kidneys.

The doctor did not answer. Old Gramma brought him a cup of tea.

And then Daddy came in. He ran over to Mama and fell down on his knees like he was dead, like seeing Mama with her arm broke and her chest so pushed in killed him on the spot. He lifted his face from the bed and kissed Mama on the lips; and then, Daddy, I could see, was crying, the strongest man in the world was crying with tears in his dark eyes and coming down the side of his big hard face. Mama called him her John Henry sometimes and there he was, her John Henry, the strongest man, black or white, in the whole damn world, crying.

He put his head down on the bed again. Nobody in the room moved until the baby toddled over to Daddy and patted him on the ear like she wanted to play the games those two make up with her little hands and his big ears and eyes and nose. But Daddy didn't move or say anything, if he even knew she was there, and the baby got a blank look in her eyes and walked away from Daddy and sat down, *plump*, on the floor across the room, staring at Daddy and the white man, back and forth, Daddy and the white man.

Daddy got up after a while and walked very slowly across the room and got himself a drink of water at the sink. For the first time he noticed the white man in the room. Who's he, he said, who's he? None of us said anything. Who the hell's he? Daddy wanted to know, thunder in his throat like there always is when he's extra mad or happy.

The doctor said the white man was Mr. Gorman and went over to Daddy and told him something in a low voice.

Innocent! What's he doing in this neighborhood then? Daddy said, loud as before. What's an *innocent* white man doing in this neighborhood now, answer me that! He looked at all of us in the room and none of us that knew what the white man was doing in this neighborhood wanted to explain to Daddy. Old Gramma and the doctor and me, none of us that knew, would tell.

I was just passing by, the white man said, as they can tell you.

The scared way he said it almost made me laugh. Was this a white man, I asked myself. Alongside Daddy's voice the white man's sounded plain foolish and weak, a little old pink tug squeaking at a big brown ocean liner about the right of way. Daddy seemed to forget all about him and began asking the doctor a lot of questions about Mama in a hoarse whisper I couldn't hear very well. Daddy's face got harder and harder and it didn't look like he'd ever crack a smile or shed a tear or anything soft again. Just hard, it got, hard as four spikes.

Old Gramma came and stood by Daddy's side and said she had called the priest when she was downstairs a while ago getting some candles. She was worried that the candles weren't blessed ones. She opened the brown bag then and that's what was inside, two white candles. I didn't know grocery stores carried them.

Old Gramma went to her room and took down the picture of the Sacred Heart all bleeding and put it on the little table by Mama's bed and set the candles in sticks on each side of it. She lit the candles and it made the Sacred Heart, punctured by the wreath of thorns, look bloodier than ever and made me think of that song, To Jesus' Heart All Burning, the kids sing at Our Saviour's on Sundays.

The white man went up to the doctor and said, I'm a Catholic too. But the doctor didn't say anything back, only nodded. He probably wasn't one himself, I thought, not many of the race are. Our family wouldn't be if Old Gramma and Mama didn't come from New Orleans, where Catholics are thicker than flies or Baptists.

Daddy got up from the table and said to the white man, So help me God, mister, I'll kill you in this room if my wife dies! The baby started crying and the doctor went to Daddy's side and turned him away from the white man and it wasn't hard to do because now Daddy was kind of limp and didn't look like he remembered anything about the white man or what he said he'd do to him if Mama . . . or anything.

I'll bet the priest won't show up, Daddy said.

The priest will come, Old Gramma said, the priest will always come when you need him, just wait. Her old lips were praying in French.

I hoped he would come like Old Gramma said, but I wasn't so sure. Some of the priests weren't much different from anybody else. They knew how to keep their necks in. Daddy said to Mama once if you only wanted to hear about social justice you could turn on the radio or go to the nearest stadium on the Fourth of July and there'd be an old white man in a new black suit saying it was a good thing and everybody ought to get some and if they'd just kick in more they might and anyway they'd be saved. One came to Our Saviour's last year and Father Egan said this is our new assistant and the next Sunday our new assistant was gone— poor health. But Daddy said he was transferred to a church in a white neighborhood because he couldn't stand to save black souls. Father Egan would've come a-flying, riot or no riot, but he was dead now and we didn't know much about the one that took his place.

Then he came, by God, the priest from Our Saviour's came to our room while the riot was going on. Old Gramma got all excited and said over and over she knew the priest would come. He was kind of young and skinny and pale, even for a white man, and he said, I'm Father Crowe, to everybody in the room and looked around to see who was who.

The doctor introduced himself and said Old Gramma was Old Gramma, Daddy was Daddy, we were the children, that was Mr. Gorman, who was just passing by, and over there was poor Mama. He missed Old Gramma's old woman friend; I guess he didn't know what to call her. The priest went over and took a look at Mama and nodded to the doctor and they went into Old Gramma's room together. The priest had a little black bag too and he took it with him. I suppose he was getting ready to give Mama Extreme Unction.[3] I didn't think they would wake her up for Confession or Holy Communion, she was so weak and needed the rest.

3. **Extreme Unction:** in the Roman Catholic Church, the sacrament ad-ministered to someone who is in danger of death or is dying. The narrator later describes the priest administering the sacrament, that is, anointing the person's five senses with holy oil.

Daddy got up mad as a bull from the table and said, Remember what I said, mister, to the white man.

But why me, the white man asked, just because I'm white?

Daddy looked over at Mama on the bed and said, Yeah, just because you're white, yeah that's why . . . Old Gramma took Daddy by the arm and steered him over to the table again and he sat down.

The priest and the doctor came out of Old Gramma's room and right away the priest faced the white man, like they'd been talking about him in Old Gramma's room, and asked him why he didn't go home. The white man said he'd heard some shouting in the alley a while ago that didn't sound so good to him and he didn't think it was safe yet and that was why.

I see, the priest said.

I am a Catholic too, Father, the white man said.

That's the trouble, the priest said.

The priest took some cotton from his little black bag, dipped his fingers in holy oil and made the sign of the cross on Mama's eyes, nose, ears, mouth, and hands, rubbing the oil off with the cotton, and said prayers in Latin all the time he was doing it.

I want you all to kneel down now, the priest said, and we'll say the rosary.[4] But we mustn't say it too loud because she is sleeping.

We all knelt down except the baby and Carrie. Carrie said she'd never kneel down to God again. Now Carrie, Old Gramma said, almost crying. She told Carrie it was for poor Mama and wouldn't Carrie kneel down if it was for poor Mama?

No! Carrie said, it must be a white God too! Then she began crying and she did kneel down after all.

Even the white man knelt down and the doctor and the old woman friend of Old Gramma's, a solid Baptist if I ever saw one, and we all said the rosary of the five sorrowful mysteries.[5]

---

4. rosary: a series of prayers consisting of the Lord's Prayer; ten prayers beginning, "Hail, Mary"; and a prayer beginning, "Glory be to the Father." Each series, called a decade, is repeated five times and is said while the person thinks about a specific event in the life of Christ or Christ's mother. The person may use a string of beads, also called a rosary, to keep count.
5. five sorrowful mysteries: the five decades of the rosary which pertain to the passion and death of Christ: the Agony in the Garden, the Scourging at the Pillar, the Crowning with Thorns, the Carrying of the Cross, and the Crucifixion and Death of the Lord.

Afterward the white man said to the priest, Do you mind if I leave when you do, Father? The priest didn't answer and the white man said, I think I'll be leaving now, Father. I wonder if you'd be going my way?

The priest finally said, All right, all right, come along, you won't be the first one to hide behind a Roman collar.

The white man said, I'm sure I don't know what you mean by that, Father. The priest didn't hear him, I guess, or want to explain, because he went over to Mama's bed.

The priest knelt once more by Mama and said a prayer in Latin out loud and made the sign of the cross over Mama: *In nomine Patris et Filii et Spiritus Sancti.*[6] He looked closer at Mama and motioned to the doctor. The doctor stepped over to the bed, felt Mama's wrist, put his head to her chest, where it wasn't pushed in, and stood up slowly.

Daddy and all of us had been watching the doctor when the priest motioned him over and now Daddy got up from the table kicking the chair over he got up so fast, and ran to the bed. He sank, shaking all over, to his knees, and I believe he must've been crying again, although I thought he never would again and his head was down and I couldn't see for sure.

I began to get an awful bulging pain in my stomach. The doctor left the bed and grabbed the white man by the arm and was taking him to the door when Daddy jumped up, like he knew where they were going and said, Wait a minute, mister!

The doctor and the white man stopped at the door. Daddy walked draggily over to them and stood in front of the white man, took a deep breath, and said in the stillest kind of whisper, I wouldn't touch you. That was all. He moved slowly back to Mama's bed and his big shoulders were sagged down like I never saw them before.

Old Gramma said *Jesus!* and stumbled down on her knees by Mama. Then the awful bulging pain in my stomach exploded and I knew that Mama wasn't just sleeping now and I couldn't breathe for a long while and then when I finally could I was crying like the baby and Brother George and so was Carrie.

---

6. *In nomine Patris et Filii et Spiritus Sancti: Latin,* In the name of the Father and of the Son and of the Holy Spirit.

Meaning and Method

1. Conflict, the opposition of two or more forces or people, can take place (a) between one character and some other person or group of persons; (b) between a character and his environment; (c) between various elements within his own nature.

   Which of these types of conflict are present in "The Trouble"? Which of these conflicts generates the most tension? Why?

2. The narrator of the story is a young person who, although he observes what is happening, doesn't always grasp the significance of what he sees.

   Does the narrator understand immediately the significance of the race riot? Or does he think of it as a game people play? Point out specific references in the text to justify your answer. How does the narrator's growing awareness of the effects of the riot build up the horror of the story?

3. Is the narrator pleased, excited, or disturbed when he sees the Negroes chasing the white man? How does Gramma help the white man to escape? Why is the child first sorry and then glad that the white man escaped?

4. Why don't they think the priest will come? What does Father Crowe mean when he says, "That's the trouble," in answer to the white man's statement that he too is a Catholic? What does Carrie mean when she cries that God must be white?

5. On page 191, the narrator says, "I told myself the trouble is somebody gets cheated or insulted or killed and everybody else tries to make it come out even by cheating or insulting or killing the cheaters and insulters and killers. Only they never do." How do the actions or reactions of Gramma and Daddy toward the white man illustrate the point the boy is making? Would killing the white man have helped?

6. An account of the race riot written for a newspaper would give the location of the riot, its immediate cause, when it took place, the number killed and wounded, what property damage was done, etc. Why does the short story have so much more impact? What does Powers add to a newspaper reporter's version of the riot?

7. Do you think the story is directed to an audience of whites? blacks? both? Why?

Language: Words and Expressions from the Bible

A number of commonly used words and expressions, such as "raising Cain," are derived from names found in the Bible. Use an unabridged dictionary to learn the meaning and origin of each of the following words or expressions. Use each in a sentence.

1. a Jonah
2. Adam's apple
3. as old as Methuselah
4. doubting Thomas
5. simony

Composition and Discussion

1. In *The Arrogance of Power*, Senator J. William Fulbright writes, "Another striking psychological phenomenon is the tendency of antagonists to dehumanize each other." In the Powers story, both the gang of whites and the gang of Negroes look upon each other as the abstract "enemy" and not as individual human beings.

How is this tendency for antagonists to dehumanize each other found in the story? For example, how does the white man's surprise that Negroes drink tea illustrate this? How does Powers's technique of showing scenes involving groups and scenes involving individuals illustrate Fulbright's point?

How does the same idea expressed in *The Arrogance of Power*—and in the phrase itself—apply to America's present racial strife? In what ways are both blacks and whites guilty of "the arrogance of power"? Cite recent examples that illustrate your answers.

2. Reread the passage from Claude McKay's poem "If We Must Die" (see page 188), and be prepared to defend or refute its argument or message in an open-class discussion. Use examples from contemporary situations to support your viewpoint.

Truman Capote

Truman Streckfus Persons (he later assumed his stepfather's name, Capote) was born in 1924 in New Orleans but grew up with relatives in rural Alabama. He detested school—especially the military schools to which he was sent—and was frequently truant, but managed to attend enough to earn a high-school diploma. After graduation, however, he carefully avoided any further contact with formal education. Besides, he already knew what he wanted to be, a writer, and had already had a short story published by the time he was seventeen. The story was "My Side of the Matter," and it appeared in *Story* Magazine.

Capote's first novel, *Other Voices, Other Rooms*, was published in 1948 and established its author as a bright, new writing talent. Since then, Capote's output has been steady. His works include a collection of stories, *Tree of Night* (1949); travel sketches, *Local Color* (1950); a musical play, *House of Flowers* (1954); the account of Capote's travels in Russia with the cast of *Porgy and Bess*, entitled *The Muses Are Heard* (1956); and a book Capote called a "nonfiction novel," *In Cold Blood* (1966), the meticulously detailed account of the murder of a family of four in Kansas in 1959. *In Cold Blood* took seven years to complete— one year for research and note taking (6,000 pages worth), and six for writing, rewriting, and final polishing.

One critic defines Capote's fiction as "romantic Gothic of a New American variety," but finds his penchant for incidental details too abundant and too elaborate, and considers many of Capote's characters overly passive—that is, reflecting the author's views and feelings more than their own.

Much of Capote's fiction is clearly autobiographical. The story that follows is an example, relating how a small boy named Buddy (Capote) and his "friend," an old maid favorite cousin (Miss Sook Falk), undertake their annual Christmas project.

A Christmas Memory

Imagine a morning in late November. A coming of winter morning more than twenty years ago. Consider the kitchen of a spreading old house in a country town. A great black stove is its main feature; but there are also a big round table and a fireplace with two rocking chairs placed in front of it. Just today the fireplace commenced its seasonal roar.

A woman with shorn white hair is standing at the kitchen window. She is wearing tennis shoes and a shapeless gray sweater over a summery calico dress. She is small and sprightly, like a bantam hen; but, due to a long youthful illness, her shoulders are pitifully hunched. Her face is remarkable—not unlike Lincoln's, craggy like that, and tinted by sun and wind; but it is delicate too, finely boned, and her eyes are sherry-colored and timid. "Oh my," she exclaims, her breath smoking the windowpane, "it's fruitcake weather!"

The person to whom she is speaking is myself. I am seven; she is sixty-something. We are cousins, very distant ones, and we have lived together—well, as long as I can remember. Other people inhabit the house, relatives; and though they have power over us, and frequently make us cry, we are not, on the whole, too much aware of them. We are each other's best friend. She calls me Buddy, in memory of a boy who was formerly her best friend. The other Buddy died in the 1880's, when she was still a child. She is still a child.

"I knew it before I got out of bed," she says, turning away from the window with a purposeful excitement in her eyes. "The courthouse bell sounded so cold and clear. And there were no birds singing; they've gone to warmer country, yes indeed. Oh, Buddy, stop stuffing biscuit and fetch our buggy. Help me find my hat. We've thirty cakes to bake."

It's always the same: a morning arrives in November, and my friend, as though officially inaugurating the Christmas time of year that exhilarates her imagination and fuels the blaze of her heart, announces: "It's fruitcake weather! Fetch our buggy. Help me find my hat."

The hat is found, a straw cartwheel corsaged with velvet roses out-of-doors has faded; it once belonged to a more fashionable relative. Together, we guide our buggy, a dilapidated baby carriage, out to the garden and into a grove of pecan trees. The buggy is mine; that is, it was bought for me when I was born. It is made of wicker, rather unraveled, and the wheels wobble like a drunkard's legs. But it is a faithful object; springtimes, we take it to the woods and fill it with flowers, herbs, wild fern for our porch pots; in the summer, we pile it with picnic paraphernalia and sugar-cane fishing poles and roll it down to the edge of a creek; it has its winter uses, too: as a truck for hauling firewood from the yard to the kitchen, as a warm bed for Queenie, our tough little orange and white rat terrier who has survived distemper and two rattlesnake bites. Queenie is trotting beside it now.

Three hours later we are back in the kitchen hulling a heaping buggyload of windfall pecans. Our backs hurt from gathering them: how hard they were to find (the main crop having been shaken off the trees and sold by the orchard's owners, who are not us) among the concealing leaves, the frosted, deceiving grass. Caarackle! A cheery crunch, scraps of miniature thunder sound as the shells collapse and the golden mound of sweet oily ivory meat mounts in the milk-glass bowl. Queenie begs to taste, and now and again my friend sneaks her a mite, though insisting we deprive ourselves. "We mustn't, Buddy. If we start, we won't stop. And there's scarcely enough as there is. For thirty cakes." The kitchen is growing dark. Dusk turns the window into a mirror: our reflections mingle with the rising moon as we work by the fireside in the firelight. At last, when the moon is quite high, we toss the final hull into the fire and, with joined sighs, watch it catch flame. The buggy is empty, the bowl is brimful.

We eat our supper (cold biscuits, bacon, blackberry jam) and discuss tomorrow. Tomorrow the kind of work I like best begins: buying. Cherries and citron, ginger and vanilla and canned Hawaiian pineapple, rinds and raisins and walnuts and whiskey and oh, so much flour, butter, so many eggs, spices, flavorings: why, we'll need a pony to pull the buggy home.

But before these purchases can be made, there is the question of money. Neither of us has any. Except for skinflint sums persons in the house occasionally provide (a dime is considered very big money); or what we earn ourselves from various activities: holding rummage sales, selling buckets of hand-picked blackberries, jars of homemade jam and apple jelly and peach preserves, rounding up flowers for funerals and weddings. Once we won seventy-ninth prize, five dollars, in a national football contest. Not that we know a fool thing about football. It's just that we enter any contest we hear about: at the moment our hopes are centered on the fifty-thousand-dollar Grand Prize being offered to name a new brand of coffee (we suggested "A.M."; and, after some hesitation, for my friend thought it perhaps sacrilegious, the slogan "A.M.! Amen!"). To tell the truth, our only really profitable enterprise was the Fun and Freak Museum we conducted in a back-yard woodshed two summers ago. The Fun was a stereopticon [1] with slide views of Washington and New York lent us by a relative who had been to those places (she was furious when she discovered why we'd borrowed it); the Freak was a three-legged biddy chicken hatched by one of our own hens. Everybody hereabouts wanted to see that biddy: we charged grownups a nickel, kids two cents. And took in a good twenty dollars before the museum shut down due to the decease of the main attraction.

But one way and another we do each year accumulate Christmas savings, a Fruitcake Fund. These moneys we keep hidden in an ancient bead purse under a loose board under the floor under a chamber pot under my friend's bed. The purse is seldom removed from this safe location except to make a deposit, or, as happens every Saturday, a withdrawal; for on Saturdays I am allowed ten cents to go to the picture show. My friend has never been to a picture show, nor does she intend to: "I'd rather hear you tell the story, Buddy. That way I can imagine it more. Besides, a person my age shouldn't squander their eyes. When the Lord comes, let me see him clear." In addition to never having seen a movie, she has never: eaten in a restaurant, traveled more than five miles from home, received or sent a telegram, read anything except funny papers and the Bible, worn cosmetics, cursed, wished someone harm, told a lie on purpose, let a hungry dog go hungry. Here are a few things she has done, does do: killed with a hoe the biggest rattlesnake ever seen in this county (sixteen rattles), dip snuff

1. **stereopticon** (ster'ē·op'ti·kon): a double "magic lantern" slide viewer that combines two images of the same scene to produce a three-dimensional effect.

(secretly), tame hummingbirds (just try it) till they balance on her finger, tell ghost stories (we both believe in ghosts) so tingling they chill you in July, talk to herself, take walks in the rain, grow the prettiest japonicas [2] in town, know the recipe for every sort of old-time Indian cure, including a magical wart-remover.

Now, with supper finished, we retire to the room in a faraway part of the house where my friend sleeps in a scrap-quilt-covered iron bed painted rose pink, her favorite color. Silently, wallowing in the pleasures of conspiracy, we take the bead purse from its secret place and spill its contents on the scrap quilt. Dollar bills, tightly rolled and green as May buds. Somber fifty-cent pieces, heavy enough to weight a dead man's eyes. [3] Lovely dimes, the liveliest coin, the one that really jingles. Nickels and quarters, worn smooth as creek pebbles. But mostly a hateful heap of bitter-odored pennies. Last summer others in the house contracted to pay us a penny for every twenty-five flies we killed. Oh, the carnage of August: the flies that flew to heaven! Yet it was not work in which we took pride. And, as we sit counting pennies, it is as though we were back tabulating dead flies. Neither of us has a head for figures; we count slowly, lose track, start again. According to her calculations, we have $12.73. According to mine, exactly $13. "I do hope you're wrong, Buddy. We can't mess around with thirteen. The cakes will fall. Or put somebody in the cemetery. Why, I wouldn't dream of getting out of bed on the thirteenth." This is true: she always spends thirteenths in bed. So, to be on the safe side, we subtract a penny and toss it out the window.

Of the ingredients that go into our fruitcakes, whiskey is the most expensive, as well as the hardest to obtain: State laws forbid its sale. But everybody knows you can buy a bottle from Mr. Haha Jones. And the next day, having completed our more prosaic shopping, we set out for Mr. Haha's business address, a "sinful" (to quote public opinion) fish-fry and dancing café down by the river. We've been there before, and on the same errand; but in previous years our dealings have been with Haha's wife, an iodine-dark Indian woman with brassy peroxided hair and a dead-tired

2. **japonicas:** shrubs with bright scarlet blossoms; Japanese quince.
3. **fifty-cent pieces . . . dead man's eyes:** it was a folk custom to put coins on the closed eyes of the dead in order to keep the lids from opening.

disposition. Actually, we've never laid eyes on her husband, though we've heard that he's an Indian too. A giant with razor scars across his cheeks. They call him Haha because he's so gloomy, a man who never laughs. As we approach his café (a large log cabin festooned inside and out with chains of garish-gay naked light bulbs and standing by the river's muddy edge under the shade of river trees where moss drifts through the branches like gray mist) our steps slow down. Even Queenie stops prancing and sticks close by. People have been murdered in Haha's café. Cut to pieces. Hit on the head. There's a case coming up in court next month. Naturally these goings-on happen at night when the colored lights cast crazy patterns and the victrola [4] wails. In the daytime Haha's is shabby and deserted. I knock at the door, Queenie barks, my friend calls: "Mrs. Haha, ma'am? Anyone to home?"

Footsteps. The door opens. Our hearts overturn. It's Mr. Haha Jones himself! And he *is* a giant; he *does* have scars; he *doesn't* smile. No, he glowers at us through Satan-tilted eyes and demands to know: "What you want with Haha?"

For a moment we are too paralyzed to tell. Presently my friend half-finds her voice, a whispery voice at best: "If you please, Mr. Haha, we'd like a quart of your finest whiskey."

His eyes tilt more. Would you believe it? Haha is smiling! Laughing, too. "Which one of you is a drinkin' man?"

"It's for making fruitcakes, Mr. Haha. Cooking."

This sobers him. He frowns. "That's no way to waste good whiskey." Nevertheless, he retreats into the shadowed café and seconds later appears carrying a bottle of daisy yellow unlabeled liquor. He demonstrates its sparkle in the sunlight and says: "Two dollars."

We pay him with nickels and dimes and pennies. Suddenly, jangling the coins in his hand like a fistful of dice, his face softens. "Tell you what," he proposes, pouring the money back into our bead purse, "just send me one of them fruitcakes instead."

"Well," my friend remarks on our way home, "there's a lovely man. We'll put an extra cup of raisins in his cake."

The black stove, stoked with coal and firewood, glows like a lighted pumpkin. Eggbeaters whirl, spoons spin round in bowls of butter and sugar, vanilla sweetens the air, ginger spices it; melting,

4. **victrola:** a record player, the forerunner of today's juke boxes and hi-fi's.

nose-tingling odors saturate the kitchen, suffuse the house, drift out to the world on puffs of chimney smoke. In four days our work is done. Thirty-one cakes, dampened with whiskey, bask on window sills and shelves.

Who are they for?

Friends. Not necessarily neighbor friends: indeed, the larger share are intended for persons we've met maybe once, perhaps not at all. People who've struck our fancy. Like President Roosevelt. Like the Reverend and Mrs. J. C. Lucey, Baptist missionaries to Borneo who lectured here last winter. Or the little knife grinder who comes through town twice a year. Or Abner Packer, the driver of the six o'clock bus from Mobile, who exchanges waves with us every day as he passes in a dust-cloud whoosh. Or the young Wistons, a California couple whose car one afternoon broke down outside the house and who spent a pleasant hour chatting with us on the porch (young Mr. Wiston snapped our picture, the only one we've ever had taken). Is it because my friend is shy with everyone *except* strangers that these strangers, and merest acquaintances, seem to us our truest friends? I think yes. Also, the scrapbooks we keep of thank-you's on White House stationery, time-to-time communications from California and Borneo, the knife grinder's penny post cards, make us feel connected to eventful worlds beyond the kitchen with its view of a sky that stops.

Now a nude December fig branch grates against the window. The kitchen is empty, the cakes are gone; yesterday we carted the last of them to the post office, where the cost of stamps turned our purse inside out. We're broke. That rather depresses me, but my friend insists on celebrating—with two inches of whiskey left in Haha's bottle. Queenie has a spoonful in a bowl of coffee (she likes her coffee chicory-flavored and strong). The rest we divide between a pair of jelly glasses. We're both quite awed at the prospect of drinking straight whiskey; the taste of it brings screwed-up expressions and sour shudders. But by and by we begin to sing, the two of us singing different songs simultaneously. I don't know the words to mine, just: *Come on along, come on along, to the dark-town strutters' ball.* But I can dance: that's what I mean to be, a tap dancer in the movies. My dancing shadow rollicks on the walls; our voices rock the chinaware; we giggle: as if unseen hands were tickling us. Queenie rolls on her back, her paws plow the air, something like a grin stretches her black lips. Inside myself, I feel warm and sparky as those crumbling logs, carefree as the wind in the chimney. My friend waltzes round the stove, the hem of her poor calico skirt pinched between her fingers as though it were a party dress: *Show me the way to go home*, she sings, her tennis shoes squeaking on the floor. *Show me the way to go home.*

Enter: two relatives. Very angry. Potent with eyes that scold, tongues that scald. Listen to what they have to say, the words tumbling together into a wrathful tune: "A child of seven! whiskey on his breath! are you out of your mind? feeding a child of seven! must be loony! road to ruination! remember Cousin Kate? Uncle Charlie? Uncle Charlie's brother-in-law? shame! scandal! humiliation! kneel, pray, beg the Lord!"

Queenie sneaks under the stove. My friend gazes at her shoes, her chin quivers, she lifts her skirt and blows her nose and runs to her room. Long after the town has gone to sleep and the house is silent except for the chimings of clocks and the sputter of fading fires, she is weeping into a pillow already as wet as a widow's handkerchief.

"Don't cry," I say, sitting at the bottom of her bed and shivering despite my flannel nightgown that smells of last winter's cough syrup, "don't cry," I beg, teasing her toes, tickling her feet, "you're too old for that."

"It's because," she hiccups, "I *am* too old. Old and funny."

"Not funny. Fun. More fun than anybody. Listen. If you don't stop crying you'll be so tired tomorrow we can't go cut a tree."

She straightens up. Queenie jumps on the bed (where Queenie is not allowed) to lick her cheeks. "I know where we'll find real pretty trees, Buddy. And holly, too. With berries big as your eyes. It's way off in the woods. Farther than we've ever been. Papa used to bring us Christmas trees from there: carry them on his shoulder. That's fifty years ago. Well, now: I can't wait for morning."

Morning. Frozen rime [5] lusters the grass; the sun, round as an orange and orange as hot-weather moons, balances on the horizon, burnishes the silvered winter woods. A wild turkey calls. A renegade hog grunts in the undergrowth. Soon, by the edge of

5. **rime:** a type of granular frost that forms on objects by the accumulation of frozen fog or mist.

knee-deep, rapid-running water, we have to abandon the buggy. Queenie wades the stream first, paddles across barking complaints at the swiftness of the current, the pneumonia-making coldness of it. We follow, holding our shoes and equipment (a hatchet, a burlap sack) above our heads. A mile more: of chastising thorns, burrs, and briers that catch at our clothes; of rusty pine needles brilliant with gaudy fungus and molted feathers. Here, there, a flash, a flutter, an ecstasy of shrillings remind us that not all the birds have flown south. Always, the path unwinds through lemony sun pools and pitch vine tunnels. Another creek to cross: a disturbed armada of speckled trout froths the water round us, and frogs the size of plates practice belly flops; beaver workmen are building a dam. On the farther shore, Queenie shakes herself and trembles. My friend shivers, too: not with cold but enthusiasm. One of her hat's ragged roses sheds a petal as she lifts her head and inhales the pine-heavy air. "We're almost there; can you smell it, Buddy?" she says, as though we were approaching an ocean.

And, indeed, it is a kind of ocean. Scented acres of holiday trees, prickly-leafed holly. Red berries shiny as Chinese bells: black crows swoop upon them screaming. Having stuffed our burlap sacks with enough greenery and crimson to garland a dozen windows, we set about choosing a tree. "It should be," muses my friend, "twice as tall as a boy. So a boy can't steal the star." The one we pick is twice as tall as me. A brave handsome brute that survives thirty hatchet strokes before it keels with a creaking rending cry. Lugging it like a kill, we commence the long trek out. Every few yards we abandon the struggle, sit down and pant. But we have the strength of triumphant huntsmen; that and the tree's virile, icy perfume revive us, goad us on. Many compliments accompany our sunset return along the red clay road to town; but my friend is sly and noncommittal when passers-by praise the treasure perched in our buggy: what a fine tree and where did it come from? "Yonderways," she murmurs vaguely. Once a car stops and the rich mill owner's lazy wife leans out and whines: "Giveya two-bits cash for that ol tree." Ordinarily my friend is afraid of saying no; but on this occasion she promptly shakes her head: "We wouldn't take a dollar." The mill owner's wife persists. "A dollar, my foot! Fifty cents. That's my last offer. Goodness, woman, you can get another one." In answer, my friend gently reflects: "I doubt it. There's never two of anything."

Home: Queenie slumps by the fire and sleeps till tomorrow, snoring loud as a human.

A trunk in the attic contains: a shoebox of ermine tails (off the opera cape of a curious lady who once rented a room in the house), coils of frazzled tinsel gone gold with age, one silver star, a brief rope of dilapidated, undoubtedly dangerous candy-like light bulbs. Excellent decorations, as far as they go, which isn't far enough: my friend wants our tree to blaze "like a Baptist window," droop with weighty snows of ornament. But we can't afford the made-in-Japan splendors at the five-and-dime. So we do what we've always done: sit for days at the kitchen table with scissors and crayons and stacks of colored paper. I make sketches and my friend cuts them out: lots of cats, fish too (because they're easy to draw), some apples, some watermelons, a few winged angels devised from saved-up sheets of Hershey-bar tin foil. We use safety pins to attach these creations to the tree; as a final touch, we sprinkle the branches with shredded cotton (picked in August for this purpose). My friend, surveying the effect, clasps her hands together. "Now honest, Buddy. Doesn't it look good enough to eat?" Queenie tries to eat an angel.

After weaving and ribboning holly wreaths for all the front windows, our next project is the fashioning of family gifts. Tie-dye scarves for the ladies, for the men a home-brewed lemon and licorice and aspirin syrup to be taken "at the first Symptoms of a Cold and after Hunting." But when it comes time for making each other's gift, my friend and I separate to work secretly. I would like to buy her a pearl-handled knife, a radio, a whole pound of choco-late-covered cherries (we tasted some once and she always swears: "I could live on them, Buddy, Lord yes I could—and that's not taking his name in vain"). Instead, I am building her a kite. She would like to give me a bicycle (she's said so on several million occasions: "If only I could, Buddy. It's bad enough in life to do without something *you* want; but confound it, what gets my goat is not being able to give somebody something you want *them* to have. Only one of these days I will, Buddy. Locate you a bike.

Don't ask how. Steal it, maybe"). Instead, I'm fairly certain that she is building me a kite—the same as last year, and the year before: the year before that we exchanged slingshots. All of which is fine by me. For we are champion kite-fliers who study the wind like sailors; my friend, more accomplished than I, can get a kite aloft when there isn't enough breeze to carry clouds.

Christmas Eve afternoon we scrape together a nickel and go to the butcher's to buy Queenie's traditional gift, a good gnawable beef bone. The bone, wrapped in funny paper, is placed high in the tree near the silver star. Queenie knows it's there. She squats at the foot of the tree staring up in a trance of greed: when bed-time arrives she refuses to budge. Her excitement is equaled by my own. I kick the covers and turn my pillow as though it were a scorching summer's night. Somewhere a rooster crows: falsely, for the sun is still on the other side of the world.

"Buddy, are you awake?" It is my friend, calling from her room, which is next to mine; and an instant later she is sitting on my bed holding a candle. "Well, I can't sleep a hoot," she declares. "My mind's jumping like a jack rabbit. Buddy, do you think Mrs. Roosevelt will serve our cake at dinner?" We huddle in the bed, and she squeezes my hand I-love-you. "Seems like your hands used to be so much smaller. I guess I hate to see you grow up. When you're grown up, will we still be friends?" I say always. "But I feel so bad, Buddy. I wanted so bad to give you a bike. I tried to sell my cameo Papa gave me. Buddy—" she hesitates, as though embarrassed—"I made you another kite." Then I confess that I made her one, too; and we laugh. The candle burns too short to hold. Out it goes, exposing the starlight, the stars spinning at the window like a visible caroling that slowly, slowly daybreak silences. Possibly we doze; but the beginnings of dawn splash us like cold water: we're up, wide-eyed and wandering while we wait for others to waken. Quite deliberately my friend drops a kettle on the kitchen floor. I tap-dance in front of closed doors. One by one the household emerges, looking as though they'd like to kill us both; but it's Christmas, so they can't. First, a gorgeous breakfast: just everything you can imagine—from flapjacks and fried squirrel to hominy grits and honey-in-the-comb. Which puts everyone in a good humor except my friend and I. Frankly, we're so impatient to get at the presents we can't eat a mouthful.

Well, I'm disappointed. Who wouldn't be? With socks, a

Sunday-school shirt, some handkerchiefs, a hand-me-down sweater and a year's subscription to a religious magazine for children. *The Little Shepherd*. It makes me boil. It really does.

My friend has a better haul. A sack of Satsumas,[6] that's her best present. She is proudest, however, of a white wool shawl knitted by her married sister. But she says her favorite gift is the kite I built her. And it is very beautiful; though not as beautiful as the one she made me, which is blue and scattered with gold and green Good Conduct stars; moreover, my name is painted on it, "Buddy."

"Buddy, the wind is blowing."

The wind is blowing, and nothing will do till we've run to a pasture below the house where Queenie has scooted to bury her bone (and where, a winter hence, Queenie will be buried, too). There, plunging through the healthy waist-high grass, we unreel our kites, feel them twitching at the string like sky fish as they swim into the wind. Satisfied, sun-warmed, we sprawl in the grass and peel Satsumas and watch our kites cavort. Soon I forget the socks and hand-me-down sweater. I'm as happy as if we'd already won the fifty-thousand-dollar Grand Prize in that coffee-naming contest.

"My, how foolish I am!" my friend cries, suddenly alert, like a woman remembering too late she has biscuits in the oven. "You know what I've always thought?" she asks in a tone of discovery, and not smiling at me but a point beyond. "I've always thought a body would have to be sick and dying before they saw the Lord. And I imagined that when he came it would be like looking at the Baptist window: pretty as colored glass with the sun pouring through, such a shine you don't know it's getting dark. And it's been a comfort: to think of that shine taking away all the spooky feeling. But I'll wager it never happens. I'll wager at the very end a body realizes the Lord has already shown himself. That things as they are"—her hand circles in a gesture that gathers clouds and kites and grass and Queenie pawing earth over her bone—"just what they've always seen, was seeing him. As for me, I could leave the world with today in my eyes."

6. **Satsumas** (sä·tsōō′mäz): the orangelike fruit—tart, seedless, and thin-skinned—of the satsuma tree, a type of mandarin tree first cultivated in Satsuma, a former province on the Japanese island of Kyushu.

This is our last Christmas together.

Life separates us. Those Who Know Best decide that I belong in a military school. And so follows a miserable succession of bugle-blowing prisons, grim reveille-ridden summer camps. I have a new home too. But it doesn't count. Home is where my friend is, and there I never go.

And there she remains, puttering around the kitchen. Alone with Queenie. Then alone. ("Buddy dear," she writes in her wild hard-to-read script, "yesterday Jim Macy's horse kicked Queenie bad. Be thankful she didn't feel much. I wrapped her in a Fine Linen sheet and rode her in the buggy down to Simpson's pasture where she can be with all her Bones. . . .") For a few Novembers she continues to bake her fruitcakes single-handed; not as many, but some: and, of course, she always sends me "the best of the batch." Also, in every letter she encloses a dime wadded in toilet paper: "See a picture show and write me the story." But gradually in her letters she tends to confuse me with her other friend, the Buddy who died in the 1880's; more and more thirteenths are not the only days she stays in bed; a morning arrives in November, a leafless birdless coming of winter morning, when she cannot rouse herself to exclaim: "Oh my, it's fruitcake weather!"

And when that happens, I know it. A message saying so merely confirms a piece of news some secret vein had already received, severing from me an irreplaceable part of myself, letting it loose like a kite on a broken string. That is why, walking across a school campus on this particular December morning, I keep searching the sky. As if I expected to see, rather like hearts, a lost pair of kites hurrying toward heaven.

Meaning and Method

1. The narrator is a high-school student recalling a Christmas memory from a time out of his childhood. How does the narrator achieve immediacy in his narrative? What are the characteristics of his style in relating the story?

2. How may the word *memory* in the title be interpreted to mean a recollection of a season, an atmosphere, an activity, a person? Refer to specific passages in the story to support or illustrate your answer.

3. The "persons in the house" are not shown as individuals but as a non-feeling, impersonal group. However, we do learn something

about them through their collective actions and their reactions to Buddy and his friend. What are the characteristics and attitudes of the others in the house? How do they regard and treat Buddy and his friend?

4. How would you characterize Buddy's friend? Why is the list of things she *never* did as important as the list of the things she "has done, does do"? (See page 203.) Which other methods of characterization (see Glossary) does Capote use to portray Buddy's friend. How does Buddy characterize himself?

5. How does the annual fruitcake-making bind Buddy and his friend in private friendship and at the same time bring them into friendly contact with the outside world? Who are their friends? Who are the people who receive the fruitcake, and how are they selected? Why did Buddy and his friend like Mr. Haha and promise to add an extra cup of raisins to *his* cake? Why do you think they would *not* have given a cake to Mrs. Haha?

6. On their last Christmas together, Buddy and his friend sail their kites in the pasture in an atmosphere of idyllic happiness and contentment. It is here that "Queenie has scooted to bury her bone (and where, a winter hence, Queenie will be buried, too)." (See page 211.)

   What are the connotations of the word *kite* in this context? What does Buddy's friend's statement, "As for me, I could leave the world with today in my eyes," tell you about what she learned about the real values in life? How does Capote tie in this scene with the ending of the story, beginning on page 212 with "This is our last Christmas together"?

7. Is the ending of the story sad? happy? bitter? ironic? hopeful? melancholy? all of these? none of these? something else?

   What would you say is the theme of the story?

Composition

1. There are many definitions of friendship, including these by Lord Byron and Oliver Goldsmith, respectively: "Friendship is Love without his wings!" and "Friendship is a disinterested commerce between equals." Write a paragraph explaining by definition your belief of what friendship is and, perhaps, what it *isn't*.

2. Write a brief, narrative composition on a Christmas or holiday memory—real or imagined—shared with another, perhaps an older, person. Adopt Capote's point of view in your narrative—that of a teen-ager looking back into his or her childhood.

Bernard Malamud

Most of Bernard Malamud's short stories are based on the life that surrounded him as he grew up in Brooklyn, where he was born in 1914. The stories reflect the culture and activities of a predominantly Jewish community, close-knit and slightly out of phase with the rest of the city and country.

After attending Brooklyn's Erasmus Hall High School, Malamud went on to the City College of New York, from which he was graduated in 1936, and later received a master's degree in literature from Columbia University. He has been a teacher of English since 1940 and is presently a professor at Bennington College in Vermont. During the academic year 1966–67 he was a guest lecturer at Harvard.

Malamud's output of fiction has been steady. His stories appear frequently in such magazines as *Partisan Review, The New Yorker, Harper's Bazaar,* and *Commentary.* His novels include *The Natural* (1952), *The Assistant* (1957), *The Fixer* (1966; winner that year of both the National Book Award and the Pulitzer prize for fiction), and *The Pictures of Fidelman* (1969).

Malamud's work has been described as "often both comic and sad, sometimes very realistic, sometimes very symbolic and fantastic, always moving and meaningful." He is at his best, perhaps, when writing about ordinary people with ordinary problems and pleasures. Many such people appear in the short stories collected in *The Magic Barrel* (1958) and *Idiots First* (1963). The story presented here is from *The Magic Barrel,* which won the 1958 National Book Award for fiction.

A Summer's Reading

George Stoyonovich was a neighborhood boy who had quit high school on an impulse when he was sixteen, run out of patience, and, though he was ashamed every time he went looking for a job, when people asked him if he had finished and he had to say no, he never went back to school. This summer was a hard time for jobs and he had none. Having so much time on his hands, George thought of going to summer school, but the kids in his classes would be too young. He also considered registering in a night high school, only he didn't like the idea of the teachers always telling him what to do. He felt they had not respected him. The result was he stayed off the streets and in his room most of the day. He was close to twenty and had needs with the neighborhood girls, but no money to spend, and he couldn't get more than an occasional few cents because his father was poor, and his sister Sophie, who resembled George, a tall, bony girl of twenty-three, earned very little, and what she had she kept for herself. Their mother was dead, and Sophie had to take care of the house.

Very early in the morning George's father got up to go to work in a fish market. Sophie left at about eight for her long ride in the subway to a cafeteria in the Bronx. George had his coffee by himself, then hung around in the house. When the house—a five-room railroad flat above a butcher store—got on his nerves, he cleaned it up, mopped the floors with a wet mop, and put things away. But most of the time he sat in his room. In the afternoons he listened to the ball game. Otherwise he had a couple of old copies of the *World Almanac* he had bought long ago, and he liked to read in them and also the magazines and newspapers that Sophie brought home, that had been left on the tables in the cafeteria. They were mostly picture magazines about movie stars and sports figures, also usually the *News* and *Mirror*. Sophie herself read whatever fell into her hands, although she sometimes read good books.

She once asked George what he did in his room all day and he said he read a lot, too.

"Of what besides what I bring home? Do you ever read any worthwhile books?"

"Some," George answered, although he really didn't. He had tried to read a book or two that Sophie had in the house but found he was in no mood for them. Lately he couldn't stand made-up stories, they got on his nerves. He wished he had some hobby to work at—as a kid he was good in carpentry, but where could he work at it? Sometimes during the day he went for walks, but mostly he did his walking after the hot sun had gone down and it was cooler in the streets.

In the evening after supper George left the house and

wandered in the neighborhood. During the sultry days some of the storekeepers and their wives sat in chairs on the thick, broken sidewalks in front of their shops, fanning themselves, and George walked past them and the guys hanging out on the candy store corner. A couple of them he had known his whole life, but nobody recognized each other. He had no place special to go, but generally, saving it till the last, he left the neighborhood and walked for blocks till he came to a darkly lit little park with benches and trees and an iron railing, giving it a feeling of privacy. He sat on a bench here, watching the leafy trees and the flowers blooming on the inside of the railing, thinking of a better life for himself. He thought of the jobs he had had since he had quit school—delivery boy, stock clerk, runner,[1] lately working in a factory—and he was dissatisfied with all of them. He felt he would someday like to have a good job and live in a private house with a porch, on a street with trees. He wanted to have some dough in his pocket to buy things with, and a girl to go with, so as not to be so lonely, especially on Saturday nights. He wanted people to like and respect him. He thought about these things often but mostly when he was alone at night. Around midnight he got up and drifted back to his hot and stony neighborhood.

One time while on his walk, George met Mr. Cattanzara coming home very late from work. He wondered if he was drunk but then could tell he wasn't. Mr. Cattanzara, a stocky, bald-headed man who worked in a change booth on an IRT station,[2] lived on the next block after George's, above a shoe repair store. Nights, during the hot weather, he sat on his stoop in an undershirt, reading *The New York Times* in the light of the shoemaker's window. He read it from the first page to the last, then went up to sleep. And all the time he was reading the paper, his wife, a fat woman with a white face, leaned out of the window, gazing into the street, her thick white arms folded under her loose breast, on the window ledge.

Once in a while Mr. Cattanzara came home drunk, but it was a quiet drunk. He never made any trouble, only walked stiffly up the street and slowly climbed the stairs into the hall. Though drunk, he looked the same as always, except for his tight walk, the

1. **runner:** messenger; one who runs errands for a business firm.
2. **IRT station:** Interborough Rapid Transit subway station.

quietness, and that his eyes were wet. George liked Mr. Cattanzara because he remembered him giving him nickels to buy lemon ice with when he was a squirt. Mr. Cattanzara was a different type than those in the neighborhood. He asked different questions than the others when he met you, and he seemed to know what went on in all the newspapers. He read them, as his fat sick wife watched from the window.

"What are you doing with yourself this summer, George?" Mr. Cattanzara asked. "I see you walkin' around at nights."

George felt embarrassed. "I like to walk."

"What are you doin' in the day now?"

"Nothing much just right now. I'm waiting for a job." Since it shamed him to admit he wasn't working, George said, "I'm staying home—but I'm reading a lot to pick up my education."

Mr. Cattanzara looked interested. He mopped his hot face with a red handkerchief.

"What are you readin'?"

George hesitated, then said, "I got a list of books in the library once, and now I'm gonna read them this summer." He felt strange and a little unhappy saying this, but he wanted Mr. Cattanzara to respect him.

"How many books are there on it?"

"I never counted them. Maybe around a hundred."

Mr. Cattanzara whistled through his teeth.

"I figure if I did that," George went on earnestly, "it would help me in my education. I don't mean the kind they give you in high school. I want to know different things than they learn there, if you know what I mean."

The change maker nodded. "Still and all, one hundred books is a pretty big load for one summer."

"It might take longer."

"After you're finished with some, maybe you and I can shoot the breeze about them?" said Mr. Cattanzara.

"When I'm finished," George answered.

Mr. Cattanzara went home and George continued on his walk. After that, though he had the urge to, George did nothing different from usual. He still took his walks at night, ending up in the little park. But one evening the shoemaker on the next block stopped George to say he was a good boy, and George figured that Mr. Cattanzara had told him all about the books he was reading. From the shoemaker it must have gone down the street, because George saw a couple of people smiling kindly at him, though nobody spoke to him personally. He felt a little better around the neighborhood and liked it more, though not so much he would want to live in it forever. He had never exactly disliked the people in it, yet he had never liked them very much either. It was the fault of the neighborhood. To his surprise, George found out that his father and Sophie knew about his reading too. His father was too shy to say anything about it—he was never much of a talker in his whole life—but Sophie was softer to George, and showed him in other ways she was proud of him.

As the summer went on George felt in a good mood about things. He cleaned the house every day, as a favor to Sophie, and he enjoyed the ball games more. Sophie gave him a buck a week allowance, and though it still wasn't enough and he had to use it carefully, it was a helluva lot better than just having two bits now and then. What he bought with the money—cigarettes mostly, an occasional beer or movie ticket—he got a big kick out of. Life wasn't so bad if you knew how to appreciate it. Occasionally he bought a paperback book from the newsstand, but he never got around to reading it, though he was glad to have a couple of books in his room. But he read thoroughly Sophie's magazines and newspapers. And at night was the most enjoyable time, because when he passed the storekeepers sitting outside their stores, he could tell they regarded him highly. He walked erect, and though he did not say much to them, or they to him, he could feel approval on all sides. A couple of nights he felt so good that he skipped the park at the end of the evening. He just wandered in the neighborhood, where people had known him from the time he was a kid playing punchball whenever there was a game of it going; he wandered there, then came home and got undressed for bed, feeling fine.

For a few weeks he had talked only once with Mr. Cattanzara, and though the change maker had said nothing more about the books, asked no questions, his silence made George a little uneasy. For a while George didn't pass in front of Mr. Cattanzara's house anymore, until one night, forgetting himself, he approached it from a different direction than he usually did when he did. It was already past midnight. The street, except for one or two people, was deserted, and George was surprised when he saw Mr. Cattanzara still reading his newspaper by the light of the street lamp overhead. His impulse was to stop at the stoop and talk to him. He wasn't sure what he wanted to say, though he felt the words would come when he began to talk; but the more he thought about it, the more the idea scared him, and he decided he'd better not. He even considered beating it home by another street, but he was too near Mr. Cattanzara, and the change maker might see him as he ran, and get annoyed. So George unobtrusively crossed the street, trying to make it seem as if he had to look in a store window on the other side, which he did, and then went on, uncomfortable at what he was doing. He feared Mr. Cattanzara would glance up from his paper and call him a dirty rat for walking on the other side of the street, but all he did was sit there, sweating through his undershirt, his bald head shining in the dim light as he read his *Times*, and upstairs his fat wife leaned out of the window, seeming to read the paper along with him. George thought she would spy him and yell out to Mr. Cattanzara, but she never moved her eyes off her husband.

George made up his mind to stay away from the change maker until he had got some of his softback books read, but when he started them and saw they were mostly story books, he lost his interest and didn't bother to finish them. He lost his interest in reading other things, too. Sophie's magazines and newspapers went unread. She saw them piling up on a chair in his room and asked why he was no longer looking at them, and George told her it was because of all the other reading he had to do. Sophie said she had guessed that was it. So for most of the day, George had the radio on, turning to music when he was sick of the human voice. He kept the house fairly neat, and Sophie said nothing on the days when he neglected it. She was still kind and gave him his extra buck, though things weren't so good for him as they had been before.

But they were good enough, considering. Also his night walks invariably picked him up, no matter how bad the day was. Then one night George saw Mr. Cattanzara coming down the street toward him. George was about to turn and run but he recognized from Mr. Cattanzara's walk that he was drunk, and if so, probably he would not even bother to notice him. So George kept on walking straight ahead until he came abreast of Mr. Cattanzara and though he felt wound up enough to pop into the sky, he was not surprised when Mr. Cattanzara passed him without a word, walking slowly, his face and body stiff. George drew a breath in relief at his narrow escape, when he heard his name called, and there stood Mr. Cattanzara at his elbow, smelling like the inside of a beer barrel. His eyes were sad as he gazed at George, and George felt so intensely uncomfortable he was tempted to shove the drunk aside and continue on his walk.

But he couldn't act that way to him, and, besides, Mr. Cattanzara took a nickel out of his pants pocket and handed it to him.

"Go buy yourself a lemon ice, Georgie."

"It's not that time anymore, Mr. Cattanzara," George said, "I am a big guy now."

"No, you ain't," said Mr. Cattanzara, to which George made no reply he could think of.

"How are all your books comin' along now?" Mr. Cattanzara asked. Though he tried to stand steady, he swayed a little.

"Fine, I guess," said George, feeling the red crawling up his face.

"You ain't sure?" The change maker smiled slyly, a way George had never seen him smile.

"Sure I'm sure. They're fine."

Though his head swayed in little arcs, Mr. Cattanzara's eyes were steady. He had small blue eyes which could hurt if you looked at them too long.

"George," he said, "name me one book on that list that you read this summer, and I will drink to your health."

"I don't want anybody drinking to me."

"Name me one so I can ask you a question on it. Who can tell, if it's a good book maybe I might wanna read it myself."

George knew he looked passable on the outside, but inside he was crumbling apart.

Unable to reply, he shut his eyes, but when—years later—he opened them, he saw that Mr. Cattanzara had, out of pity, gone away, but in his ears he still heard the words he had said when he left: "George, don't do what I did."

The next night he was afraid to leave his room, and though Sophie argued with him he wouldn't open the door.

"What are you doing in there?" she asked.

"Nothing."

"Aren't you reading?"

"No."

She was silent a minute, then asked, "Where do you keep the books you read? I never see any in your room outside of a few cheap trashy ones."

He wouldn't tell her.

"In that case you're not worth a buck of my hard earned money. Why should I break my back for you? Go on out, you bum, and get a job."

He stayed in his room for almost a week, except to sneak into the kitchen when nobody was home. Sophie railed at him, then begged him to come out, and his old father wept, but George wouldn't budge, though the weather was terrible and his small room stifling. He found it very hard to breathe, each breath was like drawing a flame into his lungs.

One night, unable to stand the heat anymore, he burst into the street at 1:00 A.M., a shadow of himself. He hoped to sneak to the park without being seen, but there were people all over the block, wilted and listless, waiting for a breeze. George lowered his eyes and walked, in disgrace, away from them, but before long he discovered they were still friendly to him. He figured Mr. Cattanzara hadn't told on him. Maybe when he woke up out of his drunk the next morning, he had forgotten all about meeting George. George felt his confidence slowly come back to him.

That same night a man on a street corner asked him if it was true that he had finished reading so many books, and George admitted he had. The man said it was a wonderful thing for a boy his age to read so much.

"Yeah," George said, but he felt relieved. He hoped nobody would mention the books anymore, and when, after a couple of days, he accidentally met Mr. Cattanzara again, he didn't, though

George had the idea he was the one who had started the rumor that he had finished all the books.

One evening in the fall, George ran out of his house to the library, where he hadn't been in years. There were books all over the place, wherever he looked, and though he was struggling to control an inward trembling, he easily counted off a hundred, then sat down at a table to read.

Meaning

1. George Stoyonovich's ambitions are simple enough: "He felt he would someday like to have a good job and live in a private house with a porch, on a street with trees. He wanted to have some dough in his pocket. . . . He wanted people to like and respect him." (See page 216.)

   How are these goals the opposite of what now surrounds him in his home and neighborhood? What sort of job do you think George would consider a "good" one? Explain.

2. Malamud tells us that George was a high-school dropout from a poor family, and that he had no skills apart from an early interest in carpentry. What do the following statements add to George's characterization:

   (a) George thought of going to summer school, but the kids in his classes would be too young. (page 215)

   (b) . . . he didn't like the idea of the teachers always telling him what to do. He felt they had not respected him. (215)

   (c) But most of the time he sat in his room. (215)

3. George's father and sister play minor roles in the story, yet we learn a lot about George by knowing what he thinks of them. What influence do the father and sister have on George? How does George regard their jobs and their ways of life? Do they have any understanding of George and his problems?

4. On his walk to the park (see page 216), George thinks about the past, present, and future. What has he had in life? What does he have in the story's present? What does he want to have? In what ways is this section of the story an indirect statement of its theme?

5. On page 217, Malamud says "Mr. Cattanzara was a different type than those in the neighborhood." How was Mr. Cattanzara different? Why did he live in the neighborhood? Was he satisfied or dissatisfied with his life there? How can you tell? What does he mean when he warns George, "Don't do what I did" (page 221)?

6. Why is it simultaneously easy and difficult for George to live his lie about the reading project? He lies to Mr. Cattanzara because

"he wanted Mr. Cattanzara to respect him." Why would Mr. Cattanzara respect him for reading books? Why do the attitudes of the others in the neighborhood change when they learn about George's reading?

As he fools the neighborhood and his family, does George fool himself as well? Or is he constantly aware of his deceit?

7. When he realizes that the whole neighborhood thinks he is reading the books on his list, George "felt in a good mood about things. He cleaned the house every day, as a favor to Sophie. . . ." Why are these changes a reflection of George's new self-respect?

8. When George is finally forced to confront Mr. Cattanzara, the latter gives him a nickel to buy "a lemon ice," and calls him "Georgie." George protests that he is "a big guy now," but Mr. Cattanzara disagrees. Why do you think he disagrees? How do you think he knows that George has been lying to him?

9. At the end of the story, George goes to the library, where "he easily counted off a hundred [books], then sat down at a table to read." Do you think the story ends here? That is, do you think the conflict between George's unrealized ambitions and his procrastination has been resolved? Do you think that George will stick to his reading and finish a hundred books?

Method

1. The style and diction in the story are simple and uncomplicated; even the occasional long sentences are not very complex. How do the diction and sentence structures in general reflect George Stoyonovich's personality? What words and expressions does the narrator use that George might use himself?

2. Notice how Malamud avoids describing George in specific detail. Do you think the author does this to make George a symbol, an "Everyman"? Or is Malamud simply trying to show how indirect and vague a person George is, as if to say that vagueness is George's main problem.

3. Notice that Malamud often refers to Mr. Cattanzara as "the change maker" (pages 217, 218, 219, and 220). The direct reference is to the man's job as a change maker in the subway. How is the name symbolic?

4. One interpretation of the story is that it is a story of indictment. Is the story an indictment of youth? of lack of initiative? lack of direction of the young by adults? the American way of life? city life? poverty? business? social pressures placed on the young? the education system? all of these? something else completely?

Modern
American
Nonfiction

C ONTEMPORARY AMERICAN nonfiction, particularly the essay, is even freer in form and content than its cousin the short story. By its open nature nonfiction defies strict definition; the only obvious definition is approximate—nonfiction includes all prose that is not fiction. For our purposes, *nonfiction* is the branch of literature that presents prose compositions on somewhat restricted topics having to do with some aspect of truth, fact, or theory.

The selections in this book make use of one or a combination of the basic forms of discourse: (1) description, (2) narration, (3) exposition, and (4) argumentation. The types of nonfiction presented include the essay, the biography and autobiography, and the speech. Tones range from the formal to the informal, the objective to the subjective; subjects are approached lightheartedly or seriously. In all, however, the voice of the writer is his or her own, and he speaks directly to his reader.

Like the short story, the modern essay may present or reflect the past while at the same time depicting and expressing values particularly relevant to the present. Today's writers of nonfiction select the topics that concern today's readers. Sometimes, the writers attempt to provide answers or solutions to the problems their readers are facing. At other times, they simply pose the questions in a way that, hopefully, will provoke the reader to work toward the answers on his own.

All of this means that the writer and the reader both get involved in the subject. An outgrowth has been the recent proliferation of interpretative journalism, in which a writer who, earlier, might have simply reported "the facts" in an objective way, now expresses his own thoughts and ideas about his topic. The result in modern magazines—such as *Time, Newsweek, Commentary, The Atlantic Monthly,* and *The New Yorker*—in biographies and even histories is a lively, thought-provoking type of prose.

Phyllis McGinley

Mrs. Charles Hayden, housewife on Grindstone Hill near Weston, Connecticut, is the Phyllis McGinley millions of readers know as poet and essayist. "In little strings of time," as she puts it, she has written two books of essays and nine of verse. She is also the author of fifteen children's books.

Upon publication of her first collection of essays, *The Province of the Heart* (1959), one critic wrote:

> "Gentle lectures on the joys of being all the things modern fiction deplores: married, feminine, suburban, maternal, adjusted, middle-aged, and unanalyzed. . . ."

The following essay, "I Knew Mrs. Tuttle," is taken from this collection.

I Knew Mrs. Tuttle

It must be that I lack a certain inner warmth possessed and exploited by my more spectacular friends. This refulgence [1] of the spirit is always leading them into little adventures, wittier and more human than mine. The strangest people confide in them. They are continually encountering a taxi-driver who reads Proust, a kindly and humorous laundress, a man who runs a newsstand and knew John Reed.[2] The boy who shines their shoes recites poetry of his own making, and their charwomen leave behind them misspelled notes amazing enough to make lovely dinner conversation. Somehow such characters elude me.

The shabby waiter who fetches my filet of sole may wear the lines of suffering in his patient face, but whether from nostalgia or bunions I will never learn. The utmost information I can pry

1. **refulgence:** brilliance; splendor.
2. **John Reed** (1887–1920): a radical American journalist, author of *Ten Days That Shook the World*, an account of the November Revolution in Russia, 1917.

"I Knew Mrs. Tuttle" from *The Province of the Heart* by Phyllis McGinley, copyright 1944 by Phyllis McGinley. Reprinted by permission of The Viking Press, Inc.

out of him concerns the fact that there's no more spumoni today and he doesn't know about the apple cake. My cleaning woman spells somewhat more confidently than I, and anyhow her *billets-doux* [3] are mere lists like, "Please order: 1 chamois,[4] 1 bottle ammonia."

Yet when I fall to brooding on this lack in me, this inability to discover the quaint and the unusual in the passing throng, I comfort myself with one reflection. After all, I knew Mrs. Tuttle.

Yes, I knew Mrs. Tuttle, and she was mine. Others were acquainted with her, could break her bread or pass the time of day; but it was in my presence alone that Mrs. Tuttle's extraordinary genius had its finest blooming.

Not that Mrs. Tuttle falls into any categories I have mentioned. On the contrary, Mrs. T. was landed gentry, the comfortable widow of a former feed-store proprietor in the Connecticut town where my husband and I once spent a summer. A placid and ample lady of late middle age, she owned a solid reputation in the village as a good if somewhat tight-fisted housekeeper, a member of the Ladies' Aid, a taxpayer. The village praised her spice cake annually at the Baked Bean Supper. So far as I know, her soul was untroubled by literary yearnings, and she had traveled extensively only between our village and West Hartford, where one of her daughters lived, happily married to a veterinarian. Yet great were her talents.

The square white house we rented that season stood across a shady lane from hers, and I used to see her moving, stately among the foxgloves in her small garden. At first we would nod amiably as we passed, but it was some time before our acquaintance took on a friendlier aspect. Then one lucky afternoon I ran across the lane to implore the use of her telephone. Ours was out of order. Mrs. Tuttle, coming to the door in a worn dressing gown, her hair clustered with bobby pins, graciously put me at my ease.

"You must excuse my appearance," she said with dignified po-

---

3. *billets-doux: French*, literally, "sweet notes"; love letters; (used here ironically).
4. chamois (sham′ē; *French* shä·mwä′): a soft leather used as a cleaning cloth; originally from only the chamois antelope of western Asia but now from the skins of goats, sheep, deer, etc.

liteness. "I have been decomposing." And, very *de rigueur mortis,*[5] she led me to the phone.

"You made it up," my husband accused me that night at dinner. "People simply don't say such things."

We passed it off, finally, as the solitary lapse of a confused elderly lady. I was to find, however, that Mrs. Tuttle could toss off such gems with the dexterity of a Chesterton composing paradoxes.[6] Provided, that is, I was the audience.

For Mrs. Tuttle was a Malaprop [7] of the first water, an inspired word-mangler, a lady in whom Dickens would have rejoiced. And the remarkable thing is that, during the months of our stay in the town, she improvised her enthralling sentences for my ears alone. My husband repeatedly egged her on. Nothing happened.

She called on me quite formally the following week, carrying an old-fashioned parasol and wearing a good deal of coral jewelry. I sat on the sofa, regaled her with tea and nut bread, and listened to her ponderous comments on the weather and the difficulty of getting real good service at the grocery store. It was as the talk veered to Mrs. Tuttle's contemplated visit to her daughter in West Hartford that she reared back and passed another miracle.

"I'm combining business with pleasure," she announced primly. "I plan to see the eye-noculist while I'm there."

The teacup wavered in my hand, but she swept on grandly.

"I've broken the glands of my spectacles," she said, "and I can't get them rightly repaired here. So I'm going to take them to the Hartford man—costive as he is."

Monday I ran across her at the post office and offered to

5. *de rigueur mortis:* a pun formed by combining two foreign expressions, French *de rigueur,* "according to the rule," required by good form; and Latin *rigor mortis,* "stiffness of death," the muscular rigidity that comes shortly after death.
6. **Chesterton . . . paradoxes:** G. K. Chesterton (1874–1936), British author, was renowned for his deft use of the paradox—a seemingly absurd or self-contradictory statement that nonetheless contains at least a partial truth; from Greek *paradoxos,* "incredible," itself a combination of Greek *para,* "contrary to," and *doxa,* "opinion."
7. **Malaprop** (mal′ə·prop): Mrs. Malaprop is a character in *The Rivals,* an English play by Richard Brinsley Sheridan (1751–1816). Her chief characteristic is the inadvertent substitution of one word for another similar in sound but quite different in meaning.

drive her home. She accepted with pleasure, volunteering that her ancient Ford "cupolo" was languishing in the village garage and no knowing when it would be running again, with the worthless help Mr. Hatfield employed in the place. Once when the radiator had leaked, she told me, he had kept her waiting three weeks.

"But this time," said Mrs. Tuttle, "I've told him he must have it done by Thursday, or he loses my business. I simply laid down my automaton."

My spouse grunted skeptically when he heard this. I could see the envy consuming his soul.

There was the time she beckoned me and asked me to come over to see her dining-room table, set for a Ladies' Aid meeting.

"I'm serving bologna sandwiches," she told me, "with men's dressing." And she went on to assure me that she was "diabolically opposed" to the view held by Mrs. Whitmark that the group members always should provide a three-course luncheon.

Once we walked down the lane together, pursued by a small black terrier, which yipped at our heels and shook even Mrs. Tuttle's monumental calm. At last she stopped and lifted her parasol threateningly.

"If that dog," she exclaimed, "doesn't stop following me, he'll simply have to suffer the contents!"

The tranquil summer passed. The leaf fell, the maple blazed, the cordwood [8] piled high in village sheds. One of Mrs. Tuttle's grandchildren spent a week with her and acquired as a pet a spirited white rabbit, which Mrs. T. described tolerantly to me as a cunning thing that "can do all sorts of tricks. You ought to see it jump through a person's arms and beg for carrots. Why, it's a regular maniac!" We supplied "acrobat," perhaps incorrectly.

Our neighbor was sorry to see us go back to town, she said. She would miss us, particularly my husband. "You have a fine man," she assured me privately not long before we left, "such a redundance of good humor."

I agreed, for his optimism *is* at times a little overwhelming.

We promised that we would be back if we could, though perhaps not next season, since we were planning to make a trip to California by way of the Panama Canal.

---

8. cordwood: firewood. Firewood is cut, split, and stacked into units of measure called cords.

Mrs. Tuttle pricked up her ears. "You won't like Panama," she warned me. "One of my nieces is married and living there, and she says the heat is something terrible."

"We won't be there long enough to mind," I reassured her vaguely, "although I expect it *is* a pretty warm place. It's only nine degrees above the equator, you know."

Mrs. Tuttle seemed surprised by this piece of information. She pondered, and then, as though she were providing me with a farewell token, she scaled new heights of language. "I hadn't realized that," she commented brightly. "Nine degrees above the equator, you say. All the year around?"

Meaning and Method

1. This essay is fleshed out on a skeleton of malapropisms (see footnote 7, page 229) such as Mrs. Tuttle's statement that she had "broken the glands of my spectacles." Here she has substituted *glands* for *lens*.

   List the other malapropisms Miss McGinley has recorded and then explain what you think Mrs. Tuttle had meant to say in each case. What similarities are there between the words Mrs. Tuttle uses and those she meant to use?

2. Phyllis McGinley has used several methods of characterization in her portrait of Mrs. Tuttle. (See Glossary.) The most obvious is her conversations and dialogue with the woman. Which of the other methods of characterization has she utilized?

3. The author makes a pun in relating how Mrs. Tuttle led her to the telephone "very *de rigueur mortis*." The pun comes from a playful combination of two expressions: *de rigueur*, from the French; and *rigor mortis*, a Latin medical term. How does each contribute to the pun, and how is their combination related to "decomposing," in the preceding sentence?

4. Is Miss McGinley serious when she claims to lack the "inner warmth" and "refulgence of the spirit" some of her friends seem to possess? Why? Why not? Why do you think she starts her essay with this sort of complaint? Compare her early claims with her theme statement: ". . . it was in my presence alone that Mrs. Tuttle's extraordinary genius had its finest blooming." Can you think of a reason why Mrs. Tuttle was a Malaprop in only the author's presence?

5. One reviewer of *The Province of the Heart*, from which this essay is taken, said the essays were "strung like luminous beads on a

thread of human understanding." One might apply the description to "I Knew Mrs. Tuttle" and say that it consists of anecdotes and incidents, strung like bright beads on a thread. Consider how Phyllis McGinley strings her beads—that is, show how she has used transitional devices to link anecdote to anecdote or paragraph to paragraph.

6. What is the author's attitude toward Mrs. Tuttle? Cite some specific illustrations. How do you think she regards her reader (*you*)? How can you tell? How would you characterize the tone of this essay?

7. The attitudes of the writer's husband are also important. What is his role in the essay? What does his presence add to it? How would his complete absence alter the essay?

Language: Foreign Expressions in English

One of Phyllis McGinley's puns involves the combination of two foreign expressions: *de rigueur* and *rigor mortis*. English is constantly absorbing and adopting foreign expressions as its own. Some of these, such as *bona fide* and *percent*, have been used long enough and frequently enough to be treated as any other English words—without italics, accent marks, or strict foreign pronunciation. Other expressions, such as *fin de siècle* (fàn də sye′kl; French, literally, "end of the century") and *objet d'art* (ôb·zhe′ dàr′; *French*, any artistic work), are a part of the specialized terminologies of science, medicine, law, literature, the arts, etc. Many of these have not been used long enough or widely enough to have been Anglicized, and are therefore treated, printed, and pronounced as distinctly foreign terms.

Good usage governs the function and appropriateness of the use of foreign expressions in our everyday speech and writing. For example, there are times when the use of a foreign word or phrase can and *should* be used in place of a longer and less clear English equivalent. Other times, however, a foreign expression would be out of place and its use would be pretentious.

Find each of the expressions in your dictionary. For each, indicate its pronunciation, origin, and literal meaning; use each of the expressions in a separate, original sentence.

1. ante-bellum	**6.** *de jure*	**11.** rendezvous
2. a priori	**7.** *esprit de corps*	**12.** sanctum sanctorum
3. bon mot	**8.** *faux pas*	**13.** tête-à-tête
4. carte blanche	**9.** laissez faire	**14.** tour de force
5. *de facto*	**10.** pro rata	**15.** vis-à-vis

Composition

Phyllis McGinley's narration of her initial encounter with Mrs. Tuttle is related in anecdote form, as are many of the subsequent encounters. Using "I Knew Mrs. Tuttle" as a guide, develop a humorous essay about malapropisms. Your essay may be based on actual experience or on a series of imaginary encounters—incidents that took place at a party, at the dinner table, in front of the class, etc. Relate the incidents as Phyllis McGinley relates her linguistic adventures with Mrs. Tuttle, that is, in the form of anecdotes.

S. J. Perelman

Life Magazine once called S. J. Perelman the Cranky Humorist. Perelman himself had furnished their lead: "I don't regard myself as a happy, laughing kid.* What I really am, you see, is a crank. I'm highly irritable and my senses bruise easily and when they are bruised, I write. It's a strange way for an adult to make a living, isn't it?"

Sidney Joseph Perelman was born in Brooklyn, New York, in 1904, the son of immigrant parents. He attended local public schools and then went on to study at Brown University. After being graduated in 1925, Perelman set about becoming what he is today: one of America's finest parodists and humorists. He began by contributing zany articles and stories to popular magazines, moved on to Hollywood as a screenwriter for the Marx Brothers comedies, collaborated on a few Broadway comedies, and then returned to writing for magazines, particularly for *The New Yorker*.

Armed with clichés, exaggerations, and improbabilities, Perelman aims volley after volley at any pompous, self-satisfied target in sight. Many of Perelman's targets would escape the ordinary reader's eye, but Perelman finds them in the form of isolated news items, "clever" advertisements, or tiny notices tucked away in the "Personals" columns of newspapers. Perelman will wrench one of these from context and, with vigorous shaking, fashion from it an adventure in words.

Many of Perelman's articles, stories, and parodies have been collected and published as books—books with such compelling titles as *Strictly from Hunger* (1937); *Crazy Like a Fox* (1944); *Acres and Pains* (1947); *The Road to Miltown, Or, Under the Spreading Atrophy* (1956; the source of our selection); and *Chicken Inspector No. 23* (1966). The Perelman family makes its home on a farm in Bucks County, Pennsylvania, but likes to travel about the globe. The accounts of two such jaunts are recorded in *Westward Ha! Or, Around the World in Eighty Clichés* (1948) † and *Swiss Family Perelman* (1950).

* **happy, laughing kid:** Perelman once characterized himself as "a thirty-five-year-old Spartan boy."
† Perelman was awarded the New York Film Critics Award in 1956 for his screenplay of Jules Verne's *Around the World in Eighty Days*.

No Starch in the Dhoti, S'il Vous Plaît *

Up until recently, I had always believed that nobody on earth could deliver a throwaway line with quite the sang-froid [1] of a certain comedian I worked for in Hollywood during the thirties. You probably don't recall the chap, but his hallmark was a big black mustache, a cigar, and a loping gait, and his three brothers, also in the act, impersonated with varying degrees of success a mute, an Italian, and a clean-cut boy. My respect for Julio (to cloak his identity partially) stemmed from a number of pearls that fell from his lips during our association, notably one inspired by an argument over dietary customs. We were having dinner at an off-Broadway hotel, in the noisiest locale imaginable outside the annual fair at Nizhnii Novgorod.[2] There were at least a dozen people in the party—lawyers, producers, agents, brokers, astrologers, tipsters, and various assorted sycophants [3]—for, like all celebrated theatrical personages, my man liked to travel with a retinue. The dining room was jammed, some paid-up ghoul from Local 802 [4] was interpreting the "Habanera" on an electric organ over the uproar, and, just to insure dyspepsia, a pair of adagio dancers were flinging themselves with abandon in and out of our food. I was seated next to Julio, who was discoursing learnedly to me on his favorite subject, anatomical deviations among showgirls. Halfway through the meal, we abruptly became aware of a dispute across the table between several of our companions.

"It is *not* just religious!" one was declaring hotly. "They knew a damn sight more about hygiene than you think in those biblical days!"

"That still don't answer my question!" shouted the man he addressed. "If they allow veal and mutton and beef, why do they forbid pork?"

---

* **Dhoti, S'il Vous Plaît** (dōtē; sēl·vōō·ple′): a dhoti is a kind of loin-cloth worn by Hindu men; *s'il vous plaît* is French for "please" (*literally,* if it pleases you").
1. **sang-froid** (sän·frwà′): *from French for "cold blood,"* coolness, composure.
2. **Nizhnii Novgorod** (nyēzh′nyē nôv′gə·rət): now Gorkiy, a city in central Russia, on the Volga River.
3. **sycophants** (sik′ə·fənts): parasites; flatterers; hangers-on.
4. **Local 802**: the musicians' union local.

"No Starch in the Dhoti, S'il Vous Plaît" from *The Road to Miltown* by S. J. Perelman, copyright © 1952, 1956 by S. J. Perelman. Reprinted by permission of Simon and Schuster, Inc. Originally appeared in *The New Yorker*.

"Because it's unclean, you dummy," the other rasped. "I'm trying to tell you—the pig is an unclean animal!"

"What's that?" demanded Julio, his voice slicing through the altercation. "The pig an unclean animal?" He rose from his chair and repeated the charge to be certain everyone within fifty feet was listening. "The pig an unclean animal? Why, the pig is the cleanest animal there is—except my father, of course." And dropped like a falcon back into his chow mein.

As I say, I'd gone along for years considering Julio preeminent in tossing off this kind of grenade, and then one Sunday a few weeks ago, in the *Times* Magazine, I stumbled across an item that leaves no doubt he has been deposed. The new champ is Robert Trumbull, the former Indian correspondent of the paper and a most affable bird with whom I once spent an afternoon crawling around the Qutb Minar, outside New Delhi. In the course of an article called "Portrait of a Symbol Named Nehru," [5] Mr. Trumbull had the following to say: "Nehru is accused of having a congenital distaste for Americans because of their all too frequent habit of bragging and of being patronizing when in unfamiliar surroundings. It is said that in the luxurious and gracious house of his father, the late Pandit Motilal Nehru—who sent his laundry to Paris—the young Jawaharlal's British nurse used to make caustic remarks to the impressionable boy about the table manners of his father's American guests."

It was, of course, the utter nonchalance of the phrase "who sent his laundry to Paris" that knocked me galley-west.[6] Obviously, Trumbull wasn't referring to one isolated occasion; he meant that the Pandit made a practice of consigning his laundry to the post, the way one used to under the academic elms. But this was no callow sophomore shipping his wash home to save money. A man willful and wealthy enough to have it shuttled from one hemisphere to another could hardly have been prompted by considerations of thrift. He must have been a consummate perfectionist, a fussbudget who wanted every last pleat in order, and, remember-

5. **Nehru** (nä′rōō): Jawaharlal (jə·wä′hər·läl) Nehru (1889–1964), Indian nationalist leader, served as India's first Prime Minister, from 1947 until his death.
6. **galley-west**: *U.S. informal*, completely out of position. The phrase is an idiom whose origins are probably in the English dialect phrase *collywest*, crooked, askew.

ing my own Homeric wrangles [7] with laundrymen just around the corner, I blanched at the complications his overseas dispatch must have entailed. Conducted long before there was any air service between India and Europe, it would have involved posting the stuff by sea—a minimum of three weeks in each direction, in addition to the time it took for processing. Each trip would have created problems of customs examination, valuation, duty (unless Nehru senior got friends to take it through for him, which was improbable; most people detest transporting laundry across the world, even their own). The old gentleman had evidently had a limitless wardrobe, to be able to dispense with portions of it for three months at a time.

The major headache, as I saw it, though, would have been coping with the *blanchisseur* [8] himself. How did Pandit Motilal get any service or redress out of him at such long range? There were the countless vexations that always arise: the missing sock, the half-pulverized button, the insistence on petrifying everything with starch despite the most detailed instructions. The more I thought about it, the clearer it became that he must have been enmeshed in an unending correspondence with the laundry owner. I suggest, accordingly, that while the exact nature of his letters can only be guessed at, it might be useful—or, by the same token, useless—to reconstruct a few, together with the replies they evoked. Even if they accomplish nothing else, they should help widen the breach between East and West.

Allahabad,
United Provinces,
June 7, 1903

Pleurniche et Cie.,
124, Avenue de la Grande Armée, Paris.
My Dear M. Pleurniche:

You may be interested to learn—though I doubt that anything would stir you out of your vegetable torpor—that your pom-

---

7. **Homeric wrangles:** heroic struggles; the reference being to the wrangles, or great struggles and disputes, related in the epic poems of the ancient Greek Homer (ninth century B.C.).
8. *blanchisseur: French,* laundryman.

pous, florid, and illiterate scrawl of the 27th arrived here with insufficient postage, forcing me to disgorge one rupee three annas to the mailman. How symbolic of your character, how magnificently consistent! Not content with impugning the quality of the cambric [9] in my drawers, you contrive to make me *pay* for the insult. That transcends mere nastiness, you know. If an international award for odium is ever projected, have no fear of the outcome as far as India is concerned. You can rely on my support.

And apropos of symbols, there is something approaching genius in the one that graces your letterhead, the golden fleece. Could any trademark be more apt for a type who charges six francs to wash a cummerbund? I realize that appealing to your sense of logic is like whistling an aria to the deaf, but I paid half that for it originally, and the Muslim who sold it to me was the worst thief in the bazaar. Enlighten me, my dear fellow, since I have never been a tradesman myself—what passes through your head when you mulct a customer in this outrageous fashion? Is it glee? Triumph? Self-approbation at the cunning with which you have swindled your betters? I ask altogether without malice, solely from a desire to fathom the dark intricacies of the human mind.

To revert now to the subject of the drawers. It will do you no good to bombinate endlessly about sleazy material, deterioration from pounding on stones, etc. That they were immersed in an acid bath powerful enough to corrode a zinc plate, that they were wrenched through a mangle with utmost ferocity, that they were deliberately spattered with grease and kicked about the floor of your establishment, and, finally, that a white-hot iron was appliquéd on their seat—the whole sordid tale of maltreatment is writ there for anybody to see. The motive, however, is far less apparent, and I have speculated for hours on why I should be the target of vandalism. Only one explanation fits the facts. Quite clearly, for all your extortionate rates, you underpay your workmen, and one of them, seeking to revenge himself, wreaked his spite on my undergarment. While I sympathize with the poor rascal's plight, I wish it understood that I hold you responsible to the very last sou. I therefore deduct from the enclosed draft

9. cambric: a fine, white linen.

nine francs fifty, which will hardly compensate me for the damage
to my raiment and my nerves, and remain, with the most transi-
tory assurances of my regard,

Sincerely yours,
Pandit Motilal Nehru

Paris,
July 18, 1903

Pandit Motilal Nehru,
Allahabad, U.P., India.
Dear Pandit Motilal:

I am desolated beyond words at the pique I sense between
the lines in your recent letter, and I affirm to you on my wife's
honor that in the six generations the family has conducted this
business, yours is the first complaint we have ever received. Were
I to list the illustrious clients we have satisfied—Robespierre, the
Duc d'Enghien, Saint-Saëns, Coquelin, Mérimée, Bouguereau,
and Dr. Pasteur, to name but a handful—it would read like a roll
call of the immortals. Only yesterday, Marcel Proust, an author
you will hear more of one of these days,[10] called at our *établisse-
ment* (establishment) to felicitate us in person. The work we do
for him is peculiarly exacting; due to his penchant for making
notes on his cuffs, we must observe the greatest discretion in selecting which to launder. In fine, our function is as much editorial
as sanitary, and he stated unreservedly that he holds our literary
judgment in the highest esteem. I ask you, could a firm with traditions like these stoop to the pettifoggery you imply?

You can be sure, however, that if our staff has been guilty of
any oversight, it will not be repeated. Between ourselves, we have
been zealously weeding out a Socialist element among the employees, malcontents who seek to inflame them with vicious nonsense about an eleven-hour day and compulsory ventilation. Our
firm refusal to compromise one iota has borne fruit; we now have
a hard core of loyal and spiritless drudges, many of them so lack-
luster that they do not even pause for lunch, which means a sub-

---

10. **Marcel Proust . . . days:** Proust (1871–1922) was a French novelist.
The first volume of his multi-volume novel, *Remembrance of Things Past*,
was published in 1913.

stantial time saving and consequently much speedier service for the customer. As you see, my dear Pandit Motilal, efficiency and devotion to our clientele dominate every waking thought at Pleur-niche.

As regards your last consignment, all seems to be in order; I ask leave, though, to beg one trifling favor that will help us execute your work more rapidly in future. Would you request whoever mails the laundry to make certain it contains no living organisms? When the current order was unpacked, a small yellow-black serpent, scarcely larger than a pencil but quite dynamic, wriggled out of one of your *dhotis* and spread terror in the workroom. We succeeded in decapitating it after a modicum of trouble and bore it to the Jardin d'Acclimatation,[11] where the curator identified it as a krait,[12] the most lethal of your indigenous snakes. Mind you, I personally thought M. Ratisbon an alarmist—the little émigré impressed me as a rather cunning fellow, vivacious, intelligent, and capable of transformation into a household pet if one had leisure. Unfortunately, we have none, so fervent is our desire to accelerate your shipments, and you will aid us materially by a hint in the right quarter, if you will. Accept, I implore of you, my salutations the most distinguished.

Yours cordially,
Octave-Hippolyte Pleurniche

Allahabad, U.P.,
September 11, 1903

Dear M. Pleurniche:

If I were a hothead, I might be tempted to horsewhip a Yahoo [13] who has the effrontery to set himself up as a patron of letters; if a humanitarian, to garrote him and earn the gratitude of the miserable wretches under his heel. As I am neither, but

11. Jardin d'Acclimatation: *French,* zoo.
12. krait (krīt).
13. Yahoo: any crude, vulgar person. The term was introduced by the British satirist Jonathan Swift (1667–1745) in *Gulliver's Travels,* a satiric novel whose fourth and last part deals with Gulliver's visit to the land of the Houyhnhnms, intelligent, horse-like creatures, who rule over the Yahoos, a race of humanoid brutes.

simply an idealist fatuous enough to believe he is entitled to what he pays for, I have a favor to ask of you, in turn. Spare me, I pray, your turgid rhetoric and bootlicking protestations, and be equally sparing of the bleach you use on my shirts. After a single baptism in your vats, my sky-blue *jibbahs* [14] faded to a ghastly greenish-white and the fabric evaporates under one's touch. Merciful God, whence springs this compulsion to eliminate every trace of color from my dress? Have you now become arbiters of fashion as well as littérateurs?

In your anxiety to ingratiate yourselves, incidentally, you have exposed me to as repugnant an experience as I can remember. Five or six days ago, a verminous individual named Champignon [15] arrived here from Pondichéry,[16] asserting that he was your nephew, delegated by you to expedite my household laundry problems. The blend of unction and cheek he displayed, reminiscent of a process server, should have warned me to beware, but, tenderhearted ninny that I am, I obeyed our Brahmin laws of hospitality and permitted him to remain the night. Needless to say, he distinguished himself. After a show of gluttony to dismay Falstaff,[17] he proceeded to regale the dinner table with a disquisition on the art of love, bolstering it with quotations from the Kamasutra [18] so coarse that one of the ladies present fainted dead away. Somewhat later, I surprised him in the kitchen tickling a female servant, and when I demurred, he rudely advised me to stick to my rope trick and stay out of matters that did not concern me. He was gone before daylight, accompanied by a Jaipur [19] enamel necklace of incalculable value and all our spoons. I felt it was a trivial price to be rid of him. Nevertheless, I question your wisdom, from a commercial standpoint, in employing such emissaries. Is it not safer

14. *jibbahs* (jĭb′ăz): smocks; long garments cut like shirts and with wide sleeves.
15. **Champignon:** in French, the name means "mushroom."
16. **Pondichéry:** a former French settlement in the Indian state of Madras.
17. **Falstaff:** one of Shakespeare's most famous comic characters, first appearing in *Henry IV*, Part I. A roguish fellow, Falstaff ate and drank to excess.
18. **Kamasutra:** a notoriously graphic Indian love manual written in the fourth century A.D.
19. **Jaipur** (jī·pŏŏr′): a former principality in India's Rajputana (räj′pŏŏ· tä′nə) States.

to rob the customer in the old humdrum fashion, a franc here and a franc there, than to stake everything on a youth's judgment and risk possible disaster? I subscribe myself, as always,

> Your well-wisher,
> Pandit Motilal Nehru

Paris,
October 25, 1903

Dear Pandit Motilal:

We trust that you have received the bundle shipped five weeks since and that our work continues to gratify. It is also pleasing to learn that our relative M. Champignon called on you and managed to be of assistance. If there is any further way he can serve you, do not hesitate to notify him.

I enclose herewith a cutting [20] which possibly needs a brief explanation. As you see, it is a newspaper advertisement embodying your photograph and a text woven out of laudatory remarks culled from your letters to us. Knowing you would gladly concur, I took the liberty of altering a word or two in places to clarify the meaning and underline the regard you hold us in. This dramatic license, so to speak, in no way vitiates [21] the sense of what you wrote; it is quite usual in theatrical advertising to touch up critical opinion, and to judge from comment I have already heard, you will enjoy publicity throughout the continent of Europe for years to come. Believe us, dear Pandit, your eternal debtor, and allow me to remain

> Yours fraternally,
> Octave-Hippolyte Pleurniche

Allahabad,
November 14, 1903

Dear M. Pleurniche:

The barristers I retained immediately on perusing your letter —Messrs. Bulstrode & Hawfinch, of Covent Garden,[22] a firm you will hear more of one of these days—have cautioned me not to

20. **cutting**: *chiefly British*, newspaper clipping.
21. **vitiates** (vish′ē·āts): corrupts; invalidates.
22. **Covent Garden**: a district in central London.

communicate with you henceforth, but the urge to speak one final word is irresistible. After all, when their suit for a million francs breaks over you like a thunderclap, when the bailiffs seize your business and you are reduced to sleeping along the *quais* [23] and subsisting on the carrot greens you pick up around Les Halles,[24] you may mistakenly attribute your predicament to my malignity, to voodoo, djinns,[25] etc. Nothing of the sort, my dear chap. Using me to publicize your filthy little concern is only a secondary factor in your downfall. What doomed you from the start was the bumbling incompetence, the ingrained slovenliness, that characterizes everyone in your calling. A man too indolent to replace the snaps he tears from a waistcoat or expunge the rust he sprinkles on a brand-new Kashmiri [26] shawl is obviously capable of any infamy, and it ill becomes him to snivel when retribution overtakes him in the end.

Adieu then, *mon brave,*[27] and try to exhibit in the dock [28] at least the dignity you have failed to heretofore. With every good wish and the certainty that nothing I have said has made the slightest possible impression on a brain addled by steam, I am,

Compassionately,
Pandit Motilal Nehru

23. *quais* (kā): *French,* quays, or embankments, such as those along the Seine in Paris.
24. Les Halles (lā häl): *French,* Paris's old covered market-place, where all of the city's food was brought in and distributed daily.
25. djinns (jinz): jinnis or genies; in Moslem mythology, supernatural beings capable of assuming human or animal form and capable of granting wishes for people.
26. Kashmiri shawl: cashmere shawl, from the district of Jammu and Kashmir, a disputed border area between India and Pakistan.
27. mon brave: *French,* the equivalent of "my friend," or "my good man" (*brave* in French means "worthy," "honest," "brave").
28. dock: an enclosed space for the defendant in a criminal court.

Meaning

1. Perelman bases his exchange of letters on what he calls a *throwaway line.* From his introductory paragraphs and the examples they contain, arrive at a definition of *throwaway line.* If you can, supply an example or two of your own—ones you think up or have heard.
2. In his opening letter to his Paris laundryman, Pandit Motilal Nehru describes the latter's "scrawl of the 27th" as *pompous* and *florid.* Basing your answer on M. Pleurniche's subsequent replies, and

quoting examples from them, explain whether you think Nehru's criticism is an accurate one.

3. Notice Pandit Nehru's sarcastic remarks about the symbol of M. Pleurniche's concern, the golden fleece. Find *Golden Fleece* in the dictionary. What meaning is given there? Why would it be correct to say that Pleurniche's use of the symbol is both pretentious and appropriate? What double meaning has Perelman (through Nehru) given the term? Look for the verb *fleece* in the dictionary if you are not sure.

Method

1. Tone is easy to recognize in letters of the sort Perelman has reconstructed here. Compare and contrast the letters' tones: how, for example, do the letters of Pandit Nehru differ in tone from those of M. Pleurniche? Does the tone in Nehru's letters remain constant throughout the correspondence? Point out specific words and phrases that reveal the tone of individual letters. What is the tone of the final lines and complimentary closing in Pandit Nehru's letters?

2. Emphasis can be achieved many ways; two of them are through the use of hyperbole and understatement (when used for humor, understatement is called *meiosis*). In his first reply to Pandit Nehru, for example, M. Pleurniche writes, "I am desolated beyond words at the pique I sense between the lines of your recent letter. . . ." Why is this statement an example of both hyperbole and understatement, and how much of its effect depends on our knowing what Nehru has said in his first letter?

3. Which method of characterization has Perelman used to portray Pandit Motilal Nehru and Octave-Hippolyte Pleurniche? Would you agree that the two correspondents have characterized themselves and each other as much as Perelman has characterized them? Why or why not?

4. Some readers feel that the humor in Perelman's writing, because of its overabundance, wears itself out in large portions. Would you have enjoyed reading more of the Pleurniche-Nehru letters, or do you think Perelman chose a good point to stop?

5. How has Perelman made it clear that Pandit Nehru looks down on M. Pleurniche? Cite specific words and details that characterize his attitudes. Is Nehru bearing a kind of white-man's-burden-in-reverse? How does Pleurniche indicate that he feels superior to Nehru?

6. Perelman has used distance in both time and place as a means of achieving humor in this selection. How, for example, does the

distance between the correspondents create a humorous breakdown of communications? Why would contemporary readers find humor in such references as Pleurniche's about certain "malcontents" in his laundry who seek to inflame others "with nonsense about an eleven-hour day and compulsory ventilation"?

Language: Words from Proper Nouns

In one of his letters to his laundryman, Pandit Motilal Nehru speculates on why he is the object of *vandalism*. The words *vandal* and *vandalism* are derived from the fierce Germanic people who overran and plundered much of western Europe in the early fifth century and who sacked Rome in 455.

Find each of the following terms in the dictionary and explain its meaning (or meanings) as well as its origin.

1. doll
2. gothic
3. maverick
4. spoonerism (give an example)
5. maudlin
6. mausoleum
7. daguerreotype
8. dollar
9. music
10. mosaic
11. sandwich
12. macadam

Composition: Three Letters

Compose a humorous letter of complaint to the customer-relations manager of a department store, mail-order house, or service company. In your letter, explain the exact nature of your complaint, indicate what you feel are its causes, and suggest what you think should be done about it. To create humor in your letter, use the same sort of burlesque and humorous exaggeration Perelman has in his letters.

In another letter, write a burlesque, or satire, of the manager's reply. Follow either of two courses: (a) you agree that the customer has been inconvenienced, you agree as well that your company is mostly to blame, you wish to regain the customer's good will and possible future business, and you therefore are going to offer what you believe is a reasonable settlement; or (b) you do not feel that the complaint is valid or that the company was at fault, and therefore cannot offer any settlement—but hope that the customer can appreciate your position.

In a third letter, again from the point of view of the customer, accept or reject the customer-relations manager's reply. If you reject it, be sure to give good reasons for your decision and indicate the next step you plan to take toward solving the problem.

Alfred Kazin *

For most of his life, Alfred Kazin has lived in Brooklyn, New York. Recently, he has lived in the borough's Brooklyn Heights, with its splendid view of lower Manhattan and New York Harbor. His prospects as a child, however, were not quite so fine. He was born in 1915 in a section called Brownsville, which he describes as "a raw, poor, fascinating immigrant quarter, settled mainly by Russian and Polish Jews. I spent the first twenty-three years of my life in a world whose poverty and fierce pieties opened up so many other worlds for me that I am still amazed by my good fortune—and by how long it took me to realize it."

Some of Kazin's other worlds are those of the teacher, editor, critic, and author. In a way, the last of these has governed the other worlds, for Kazin had early made up his mind that in order to be a good teacher, editor, or critic, he must first be a good writer. So he set about reading and studying those critics he recognized as good writers, men such as Matthew Arnold, Edmund Wilson, and Van Wyck Brooks.

Among his writings are three volumes of critical essays: *On Native Grounds* (1942), *The Inmost Leaf* (1955), and *Contemporaries* (1962). He has also written two volumes of memoirs: *A Walker in the City* (1951), from which the following selection is taken, and *Starting Out in the Thirties* (1965).

* Kazin (kā'zin).

The Kitchen

In Brownsville tenements, the kitchen is always the largest room and the center of the household. As a child I felt that we lived in a kitchen to which four other rooms were annexed. My mother, a "home" dressmaker, had her workshop in the kitchen. She told me once that she had begun dressmaking in Poland at thirteen; as far back as I can remember, she was always making dresses for the local women. She had an innate sense of design, a quick eye for all the subtleties in the latest fashions, even when she despised them, and great boldness. For three or four dollars she would study the fashion magazines with a customer, go with the customer to the remnants store on Belmont Avenue to pick out the material, argue the owner down—all remnants stores, for some reason, were supposed to be shady, as if the owners dealt in stolen goods—and then for days would patiently fit and baste and sew and fit again. Our apartment was always full of women in their housedresses sitting around the kitchen table waiting for a fitting. My little bedroom next to the kitchen was the fitting room. The sewing machine, an old nut-brown Singer with golden scrolls painted along the black arm and engraved along the two tiers of little drawers massed with needles and thread on each side of the treadle,[1] stood next to the window and the great coal-black stove which up to my last year in college was our main source of heat. By December the two outer bedrooms were closed off, and used to chill bottles of milk and cream, cold borscht,[2] and jellied calves' feet.

The kitchen held our lives together. My mother worked in it all day long, we ate in it almost all meals except the Passover seder,[3] I did my homework and first writing at the kitchen table, and in winter I often had a bed made up for me on three kitchen chairs near the stove. On the wall just over the table hung a long horizontal mirror that sloped to a ship's prow at each end and was lined in cherry wood. It took up the whole wall and drew every object in the kitchen to itself. The walls were a fiercely stippled whitewash, so often rewhitened by my father in slack seasons that the paint looked as if it had been squeezed and cracked into the walls. A large electric bulb hung down the center of the kitchen at the end of a chain that had been hooked into the ceiling; the old gas ring and key still jutted out of the wall like

1. **treadle** (tred′l): foot lever; working it caused the sewing machine's rotary motion.
2. **borscht** (bôrsht): a Russian soup made from beets and served either hot or cold, and often with a dab of sour cream.
3. **Passover** *seder* (sä′dər): Passover is a major Jewish festival, the first of the three Pilgrim festivals, and commemorates the "passing over" of the homes of the Jews by the Angel of Death during the plague of the first-born, described in the Bible in Exodus 12:13. The *seder* is a feast celebrated during Passover.

antlers. In the corner next to the toilet was the sink at which we washed, and the square tub in which my mother did our clothes. Above it, tacked to the shelf on which were pleasantly ranged square, blue-bordered white sugar and spice jars, hung calendars from the Public National Bank on Pitkin Avenue and the Minsker Progressive Branch of the Workman's Circle; receipts for the payment of insurance premiums and household bills on a spindle; two little boxes engraved with Hebrew letters. One of these was for the poor, the other to buy back the Land of Israel.[4] Each spring a bearded little man would suddenly appear in our kitchen, salute us with a hurried Hebrew blessing, empty the boxes (sometimes with a sidelong look of disdain if they were not full), hurriedly bless us again for remembering our less fortunate Jewish brothers and sisters, and so take his departure until the next spring, after vainly trying to persuade my mother to take still another box. We did occasionally remember to drop coins in the boxes, but this was usually only on the dreaded morning of "midterms" and final examinations, because my mother thought it would bring me luck. She was extremely superstitious, but embarrassed about it, and always laughed at herself whenever, on the morning of an examination, she counseled me to leave the house on my right foot. "I know it's silly," her smile seemed to say, "but what harm can it do? It may calm God down."

The kitchen gave a special character to our lives; my mother's character. All my memories of that kitchen are dominated by the nearness of my mother sitting all day long at her sewing machine, by the clacking of the treadle against the linoleum floor, by the patient twist of her right shoulder as she automatically pushed at the wheel with one hand or lifted the foot to free the needle where it had got stuck in a thick piece of material. The kitchen was her life. Year by year, as I began to take in her fantastic capacity for labor and her anxious zeal, I realized it was ourselves she kept stitched together. I can never remember a time when she was not working. She worked because the law of her life was work, work and anxiety; she worked because she would have found life meaningless without work. She read almost no English;

4. **buy back the Land of Israel**: a reference to the Zionist efforts to buy land in Palestine for Jewish settlement. The Jewish State of Israel was established officially and sanctioned by the United Nations in 1948.

she could read the Yiddish paper, but never felt she had time to. We were always talking of a time when I would teach her how to read, but somehow there was never time. When I awoke in the morning she was already at her machine, or conferring over *McCall's* with some neighborhood woman who had come in pointing hopefully to an illustration—"Mrs. Kazin! Mrs. Kazin! Make me a dress like it shows here in the picture!" When my father came home from work she had somehow mysteriously interrupted herself to make supper for us and, the dishes cleared and washed, was back at her machine. When I went to bed at night, often she was still there, pounding away at the treadle, hunched over the wheel, her hands steering a piece of gauze under the needle with a finesse that always contrasted sharply with her swollen hands and broken nails. Her left hand had been pierced through when as a girl she had worked in the infamous Triangle Shirtwaist Factory [5] on the East Side. A needle had gone straight through the palm, severing a large vein. They had sewn it up for her so clumsily that a tuft of flesh always lay folded over the palm.

The kitchen was the great machine that set our lives running; it whirred down a little only on Saturdays and holy days. From my mother's kitchen I gained my first picture of life as a white, overheated, starkly lit workshop redolent with Jewish cooking, crowded with women in housedresses, strewn with fashion magazines, patterns, dress material, spools of thread—and at whose center, so lashed to her machine that bolts of energy seemed to dance out of her hands and feet as she worked, my mother stamped the treadle hard against the floor, hard, hard, and silently, grimly at war, beat out the first rhythm of the world for me.

Every sound from the street roared and trembled at our windows—a mother feeding her child on the doorstep, the screech of the trolley cars on Rockaway Avenue, the eternal smash of a handball against the wall of our house, the clatter of *"der Italyéner"*'s [6] cart packed with watermelons, the sing-song of the old-clothes men walking Chester Street, the cries *"Arbes! Arbes!*

5. **Triangle Shirtwaist Factory**: a notorious "sweatshop" on New York's lower East Side, in 1911 the scene of a fire in which 149 workers, mostly girls, perished. Public outcries over the disaster led to legislation prohibiting the unsafe and oppressive working conditions in such factories.
6. **"der Italyéner"**: Yiddish for "the Italian."

Kinder! Kinder! Heyse gute arbes!" [7] All day long people streamed into our apartment as a matter of course—"customers," upstairs neighbors, downstairs neighbors, women who would stop in for a half-hour's talk, salesmen, relatives, insurance agents. Usually they came in without ringing the bell—everyone knew my mother was always at home. I would hear the front door opening, the wind whistling through our front hall, and then some familiar face would appear in our kitchen with the same bland, matter-of-fact inquiring look: no need to stand on ceremony; my mother and her kitchen were available to everyone all day long.

At night the kitchen contracted around the blaze of light on the cloth, the patterns, the ironing board where the iron had burned a black border around the tear in the muslin cover; the finished dresses looked so frilly as they jostled on their wire hangers after all the work my mother had put into them. And then I would get that strangely ominous smell of tension from the dress fabrics and the burn in the cover of the ironing board—as if each piece of cloth and paper crushed with light under the naked bulb might suddenly go up in flames. Whenever I pass some small tailoring shop still lit up at night and see the owner hunched over his steam press; whenever in some poorer neighborhood of the city I see through a window some small crowded kitchen naked under the harsh light glittering in the ceiling, I still smell that fiery breath, that warning of imminent fire. I was always holding my breath. What I must have felt most about ourselves, I see now, was that we ourselves were like kindling—that all the hard-pressed pieces of ourselves and all the hard-used objects in that kitchen were like so many slivers of wood that might go up in flames if we came too near the white-blazing filaments in that naked bulb. Our tension itself was fire, we ourselves were forever burning—to live, to get down the foreboding in our souls, to make good.

Twice a year, on the anniversaries of her parents' deaths, my mother placed on top of the icebox an ordinary kitchen glass packed with wax, the *yortsayt*,[8] and lit the candle in it. Sitting at

7. *"Arbes! Arbes! Kinder! Kinder! Heyse gute arbes!"*: Yiddish, literally, "Chickpeas! Chickpeas! Children! Children! Good hot chickpeas!"
8. *yortsayt*: Yiddish, literally, "year's end," in reference to memorial candles—wax and wick in a glass cup—lighted to commemorate the anniversary of the death of a relative or friend.

the kitchen table over my homework, I would look across the threshold to that mourning-glass, and sense that for my mother the distance from our kitchen to *der heym*,[9] from life to death, was only a flame's length away. Poor as we were, it was not poverty that drove my mother so hard; it was loneliness—some endless bitter brooding over all those left behind, dead or dying or soon to die; a loneliness locked up in her kitchen that dwelt every day on the hazardousness of life and the nearness of death, but still kept struggling in the lock, trying to get us through by endless labor.

With us, life started up again only on the last shore. There seemed to be no middle ground between despair and the fury of our ambition. Whenever my mother spoke of her hopes for us, it was with such unbelievingness that the likes of us would ever come to anything, such abashed hope and readiness for pain, that I finally came to see in the flame burning on top of the icebox death itself burning away the bones of poor Jews, burning out in us everything but courage, the blind resolution to live. In the light of that mourning-candle, there were ranged around me how many dead and dying—how many eras of pain, of exile, of dispersion, of cringing before the powers of this world!

It was always at dusk that my mother's loneliness came home most to me. Painfully alert to every shift in the light at her window, she would suddenly confess her fatigue by removing her pince-nez,[10] and then wearily pushing aside the great mound of fabrics on her machine, would stare at the street as if to warm herself in the last of the sun. "How sad it is!" I once heard her say. "It grips me! It grips me!" Twilight was the bottommost part of the day, the chilliest and loneliest time for her. Always so near to her moods, I knew she was fighting some deep inner dread, struggling against the returning tide of darkness along the streets that invariably assailed her heart with the same foreboding—Where? Where now? Where is the day taking us now?

Yet one good look at the street would revive her. I see her now, perched against the windowsill, with her face against the

---

9. *der heym:* *Yiddish,* the home. For the Kazins, the old country was Poland.
10. **pince-nez** (pans′nā′): eyeglasses or spectacles that clamp over the bridge of the nose. The term is from French, in which the literal meaning is "pinch-nose."

glass, her eyes almost asleep in enjoyment, just as she starts up with the guilty cry—"What foolishness is this in me!"—and goes to the stove to prepare supper for us: a moment, only a moment, watching the evening crowd of women gathering at the grocery for fresh bread and milk. But between my mother's pent-up face at the window and the winter sun dying in the fabrics—"Alfred, see how beautiful!"—she has drawn for me one single line of sentience.[11]

11. **sentience** (sen'shē·əns): the state of awareness; sensation as immediate experience, as distinguished from thought or perception.

Meaning and Method

1. So far as its interpretation is concerned, "The Kitchen" is both (a) specific or particular, and (b) general or universal.

    Specifically, the essay is an account of the life, home atmosphere, and attitudes of an immigrant Jewish family in the Brownsville section of Brooklyn. What are some of the details of their home life and of their home's atmosphere that relate to this specific interpretation?

    How is the essay also general or universal in its appeal and application? What are the qualities or details which contribute to the essay's universality?

2. How thorough is Kazin's characterization of his mother? Has he merely sketched her or has he given us a full, finished portrait? With examples from the text, enumerate some of the methods of characterization he has used. Does she come through as an individual, or does she represent a *type*?

3. Skim back over the essay and write a summary sentence—in your own words—for each of the nine paragraphs. Which of the paragraphs contains the statement closest to the essay's theme? Do your sentences, taken in sum,. summarize the essay as a whole? Is the essay unified; that is, are the paragraphs all related to the central theme? Why? Why not?

4. How can a kitchen wall (or any wall) be "a *fiercely* stippled whitewash"? Why is *fiercely* an apt modifier here, even though it is obviously not meant to be taken literally?

5. The impressions in "The Kitchen" are drawn from the author's memories—memories rich in vivid detail. How has Kazin used the details: for characterization? for description? for the development of larger, often abstract, considerations? Which details contribute most to your impression of the place? of the family life? Use direct references to the essay to support your answer.

6. Notice the *fire-burning* imagery in paragraph six (beginning on page 250). Through which particular words and details is the imagery extended? What is its cumulative effect? Does it fit in with the rest of the essay? Why do you think Kazin used it? How does it serve both literal and figurative purposes?

7. Contentment, coziness, tranquility. Nostalgia, foreboding, loneliness, yearning. Show how each of these is found in "The Kitchen." Would you agree that there is a current of near-despair underneath the essay's nostalgia? Why or why not?

8. How successful is Kazin at re-creating the atmosphere of the kitchen through a child's eyes? Which details of setting emphasize the child's point of view? Where does the adult point of view enter the essay? Does it change the tone of "The Kitchen"?

9. Kazin closes his essay with this sentence: "But between my mother's pent-up face at the window and the winter sun dying in the fabrics —'Alfred, see how beautiful!'—she has drawn for me one single line of sentience."

   Through her presence, he has arrived at a moment of complete, instantaneous awareness. How does this awareness, and Kazin's statement of it, sum up his attitudes toward his subject?

Composition and Discussion

1. Reread and then rewrite paragraph three, page 249 (or any other of the essay's paragraphs) but change the neighborhood, the houses and rooms, and the language. Use the same sort of "impressionistic" descriptives that Kazin has used to depict his neighborhood.

2. Be prepared for an open-class discussion of one of the following topics:

(a) Compare and contrast this essay with Truman Capote's story, "A Christmas Memory" (page 201). Consider their *content* rather than their *form*—what themes, details, feelings, etc. do they share? How do they differ in these regards? Is there much fiction in the essay and much fact in the story? Explain your answers, with examples from both texts.

(b) Both "Neighbor Rosicky" (page 23) and "The Kitchen" offer views of New York City. How are the views alike, and how do they differ? How do you account for the differences?

James Agee

James Rufus Agee was born in Knoxville, Tennessee, in 1909, and died of a heart attack in a New York taxicab forty-six years later. The years between were filled with frustration, self-doubt, hard work, and a share of literary success.

Agee had attended St. Andrew's School in Tennessee's Cumberland Mountain region and had then gone to Phillip's [Exeter] Academy in Exeter, New Hampshire. During the summers, he worked as a field hand in the rolling farmlands of Kansas and Nebraska before they became the parched "Dust Bowl" region of the thirties and forties. After Exeter, Agee entered Harvard and was graduated in 1932. While there, he won a coveted poetry prize and edited the Harvard *Advocate*, a student newspaper.

In 1934 *Permit Me Voyage*, a collection of his early poems, was published as part of Yale University's *Young Poets* Series. The same year he joined the editorial staff of *Fortune* Magazine. One of his assignments was to travel to the Alabama cotton country, where he lived for several weeks with a sharecropper's family. What he saw and learned there appalled him and ultimately led to the publication of *Let Us Now Praise Famous Men* (1941), for which he wrote a text accompanied by Walker Evans's stark photographs.

From 1939 to 1943, Agee worked as an editor for *Time* Magazine, which he left to become film critic for *The Nation*, a liberal monthly. He left *The Nation* five years later in order to concentrate full-time on his own creative writing.

Among his works are a short novel, *The Morning Watch* (1951), depicting a day in the life of an adolescent boy; several screenplays, including adaptations of two Stephen Crane stories, "The Bride Comes to Yellow Sky," and "The Blue Hotel"; and a screen version of C. S. Forester's novel *The African Queen*. Many of his screenplays and film criticisms are collected in *Agee on Film* (1958) and *Agee on Film II* (1960). There is also a collection of his letters to a favorite teacher and mentor at St. Andrew's School. These letters, which he signed Rufus, appear in *Letters to Father Flye* (1962).

Agee's most memorable work, although unfinished, is the

novel *A Death in the Family,* a partly autobiographical narrative about a Tennessee family whose happy life is shattered by the death of the father in an automobile accident. The novel was published posthumously in 1955 and won a Pulitzer prize for fiction. It was adapted for the stage by Tad Mosel with the title *All the Way Home;* the play also won a Pulitzer prize.

When the novel was published, its editors used as a prologue a brief essay they found among Agee's papers. The essay is presented here.

Knoxville: Summer 1915

We are talking now of summer evenings in Knoxville, Tennessee, in the time that I lived there so successfully disguised to myself as a child. It was a little bit mixed sort of block, fairly solidly lower middle class, with one or two juts apiece on either side of that. The houses corresponded: middle-sized gracefully fretted[1] wood houses built in the late nineties and early nineteen hundreds, with small front and side and more spacious back yards, and trees in the yards, and porches. These were softwooded trees, poplars, tulip trees, cottonwoods. There were fences around one or two of the houses, but mainly the yards ran into each other with only now and then a low hedge that wasn't doing very well. There were few good friends among the grown people, and they were not poor enough for the other sort of intimate acquaintance, but everyone nodded and spoke, and even might talk short times, trivially, and at the two extremes of the general or the particular, and ordinarily nextdoor neighbors talked quite a bit when they happened to run into each other, and never paid calls. The men were mostly small-business men, one or two very modestly executives, one or two worked with their hands, most of them clerical, and most of them between thirty and forty-five.

1. **fretted:** decorated with filigree borders in the Victorian "gingerbread" style. *Fret* is from Old French *frette,* lattice.

But it is of these evenings I speak.

Supper was at six and was over by half past. There was still daylight, shining softly and with a tarnish, like the lining of a shell; and the carbon lamps lifted [2] at the corners were on in the light, and the locusts were started, and the fireflies were out, and a few frogs were flopping in the dewy grass, by the time the fathers and the children came out. The children ran out first hell bent and yelling those names by which they were known; then the fathers sank out leisurely in crossed suspenders, their collars removed and their necks looking tall and shy. The mothers stayed back in the kitchen washing and drying, putting things away, recrossing their traceless footsteps like the lifetime journeys of bees, measuring out the dry cocoa for breakfast. When they came out they had taken off their aprons and their skirts were dampened and they sat in rockers on their porches quietly.

It is not of the games children play in the evening that I want to speak now, it is of a contemporaneous atmosphere that has little to do with them: that of the fathers of families, each in his space of lawn, his shirt fishlike pale in the unnatural light and his face nearly anonymous, hosing their lawns. The hoses were attached at spigots that stood out of the brick foundations of the houses. The nozzles were variously set but usually so there was a long sweet stream of spray, the nozzle wet in the hand, the water trickling the right forearm and the peeled-back cuff, and the water whishing out a long loose and low-curved cone, and so gentle a sound. First an insane noise of violence in the nozzle, then the still irregular sound of adjustment, then the smoothing into steadiness and a pitch as accurately tuned to the size and style of stream as any violin. So many qualities of sound out of one hose: so many choral differences out of those several hoses that were in earshot. Out of any one hose, the almost dead silence of the release, and the short still arch of the separate big drops, silent as a held breath, and the only noise the flattering noise on leaves and the slapped grass at the fall of each big drop. That, and the intense hiss with the intense stream; that, and that same intensity not growing less but growing more quiet and delicate with the turn of the nozzle, up to that extreme tender whisper when the water was just a wide bell of film. Chiefly, though, the hoses were set much alike, in a

2. **carbon lamps lifted:** carbon-arc lamps raised.

compromise between distance and tenderness of spray (and quite surely a sense of art behind this compromise, and a quiet deep joy, too real to recognize itself), and the sounds therefore were pitched much alike; pointed by the snorting start of a new hose; decorated by some man playful with the nozzle; left empty, like God by the sparrow's fall, when any single one of them desists: and all, though near alike, of various pitch; and in this unison. These sweet pale streamings in the light lift out their pallors and their voices all together, mothers hushing their children, the hushing unnaturally prolonged, the men gentle and silent and each snail-like withdrawn into the quietude of what he singly is doing, the urination of huge children stood loosely military against an invisible wall, and gentle happy and peaceful, tasting the mean goodness of their living like the last of their suppers in their mouths; while the locusts carry on this noise of hoses on their much higher and sharper key. The noise of the locust is dry, and it seems not to be rasped or vibrated but urged from him as if through a small orifice by a breath that can never give out. Also there is never one locust but an illusion of at least a thousand. The noise of each locust is pitched in some classic locust range out of which none of them varies more than two full tones; and yet you seem to hear each locust discrete from all the rest, and there is a long, slow pulse in their noise, like the scarcely defined arch of a long and high set bridge. They are all around in every tree, so that the noise seems to come from nowhere and everywhere at once, from the whole shell heaven, shivering in your flesh and teasing your eardrums, the boldest of all the sounds of night. And yet it is habitual to summer nights, and is of the great order of noises, like the noises of the sea and of the blood her precocious grandchild, which you realize you are hearing only when you catch yourself listening. Meantime from low in the dark, just outside the swaying horizons of the hoses, conveying always grass in the damp of dew and its strong green-black smear of smell, the regular yet spaced noises of the crickets, each a sweet cold silver noise three-noted, like the slipping each time of three matched links of a small chain.

But the men by now, one by one, have silenced their hoses and drained and coiled them. Now only two, and now only one, is left, and you see only ghostlike shirt with the sleeve garters, and sober mystery of his mild face like the lifted face of large cattle inquiring of your presence in a pitchdark pool of meadow; and now he too is gone; and it has become that time of evening when people sit on their porches, rocking gently and talking gently and watching the street and the standing up into their sphere of possession of the trees, of birds hung havens, hangars. People go by; things go by. A horse, drawing a buggy, breaking his hollow iron music on the asphalt; a loud auto; a quiet auto; people in pairs, not in a hurry, scuffling, switching their weight of aestival [3] body, talking casually, the taste hovering over them of vanilla, strawberry, pasteboard, and starched milk,[4] the image upon them of lovers and horsemen, squared with clowns in hueless amber. A street car raising its iron moan; stopping, belling, and starting; stertorous; [5] rousing and raising again its iron increasing moan and swimming its gold windows and straw seats on past and past and past, the bleak spark crackling and cursing above it like a small malignant spirit set to dog its tracks; the iron whine rises on rising speed; still risen, faints; halts; the faint stinging bell; rises again, still fainter; fainting, lifting, lifts, faints forgone: forgotten. Now is the night one blue dew.

Now is the night one blue dew, my father has drained, he has coiled the hose.
Low on the length of lawns, a frailing of fire who breathes.
Content, silver, like peeps of light, each cricket makes his comment over and over in the drowned grass.
A cold toad thumpily flounders.
Within the edges of damp shadows of side yards are hovering children nearly sick with joy of fear, who watch the unguarding of a telephone pole.
Around white carbon corner lamps bugs of all sizes are lifted elliptic, solar systems. Big hardshells bruise themselves, assailant; he is fallen on his back, legs squiggling.
Parents on porches: rock and rock. From damp strings morning glories hang their ancient faces.

3. aestival (es′tə·vəl) : *also estival; here,* summertime; of or pertaining to summer. The word is from the Latin word for summer, *aestas.*
4. starched milk: a kind of custard pudding.
5. stertorous (stûr′tər·əs) : snoring. From Latin *stertere,* to snore.

The dry and exalted noise of the locusts from all the air at once
enchants my eardrums.

On the rough wet grass of the back yard my father and mother
have spread quilts. We all lie there, my mother, my father, my
uncle, my aunt, and I too am lying there. First we were sitting
up, then one of us lay down, and then we all lay down, on our
stomachs, or on our sides, or on our backs, and they have kept on
talking. They are not talking much, and the talk is quiet, of nothing in particular, of nothing at all in particular, of nothing at all.
The stars are wide and alive, they seem each like a smile of great
sweetness, and they seem very near. All my people are larger bodies
than mine, quiet, with voices gentle and meaningless like the voices
of sleeping birds. One is an artist, he is living at home. One is a
musician, she is living at home. One is my mother, who is good
to me. One is my father, who is good to me. By some chance,
here they are, all on this earth; and who shall ever tell the sorrow
of being on this earth, lying, on quilts, on the grass, in a summer
evening, among the sounds of the night. May God bless my people, my uncle, my aunt, my mother, my good father, oh, remember
them kindly in their time of trouble; and in the hour of their taking away.

After a little I am taken in and put to bed. Sleep, soft smiling,
draws me unto her: and those receive me, who quietly treat me,
as one familiar and well-beloved in that home: but will not, oh,
will not, not now, not ever; but will not ever tell me who I am.

Meaning and Method

1. At the beginning of the essay, the author's tone is one of studied
objectivity, and his description and narration are those of a sensitive
writer with a sharp awareness of details. How does Agee manage to
become so intensely personal at the end of the selection without
introducing a jarring note? Where does the tone begin to change?
What do you think is the overall mood of the essay? How do the
setting and the details of setting Agee mentions help create the
overall mood?

2. Writers often use sentence length to reflect the kind of action or
situation being presented or described. Short, choppy sentences, for
example, can help give the impression of rapid action. Longer sen-

tences can do just the opposite and help create the impression of slow, deliberate action or of careful, thorough description or inspection. Long sentences may also be used to show a number of things happening or being seen at the same time.

What is the effect of the long, loosely constructed sentences in Agee's sketch of Knoxville? How does punctuation, especially the commas and semicolons, contribute to the pace of the sketch?

3. In "Knoxville: Summer 1915," prose verges on poetry and, in fact, is presented in poetic lines near the end of the sketch. What poetic qualities exist in the entire sketch? in the eight lines set as poetry in particular?

4. Agee was about six years old in the summer of 1915. Is this essay written from the point of view of a six-year-old child, or is it written from the point of view of a grown man looking back into his childhood? Explain your answer, with direct references to the text to illustrate it.

5. The essay abounds in sensory imagery. Explain how the imagery in each of the following excerpts is visual, auditory, gustatory, olfactory, thermal, tactile, or a combination of more than one of these:

   (a) There was still daylight, shining softly and with a tarnish, like the lining of a shell. . . . (page 256)

   (b) . . . there was a long sweet stream of spray, the nozzle wet in the hand, the water trickling the right forearm and the peeled-back cuff, and the water whishing out a long loose and low-curved cone, and so gentle a sound. (256)

   (c) Meantime from low in the dark, just outside the swaying horizons of the hoses, conveying always grass in the damp of dew and its strong green-black smear of smell, the regular yet spaced noises of the crickets, each a sweet cold silver noise three-noted, like the slipping each time of three matched links of a small chain. (257)

   (d) A street car raising its iron moan; stopping, belling and starting; stertorous; rousing and raising again its iron increasing moan and swimming its gold windows and straw seats on past and past and past, the bleak spark crackling and cursing above it like a small malignant spirit set to dog its tracks. . . . (258)

   (e) Now is the night one blue dew. (258)

   (f) A cold toad thumpily flounders. (258)

6. What are Agee's attitudes toward Knoxville and his childhood home? Has he succeeded in conveying his feelings to you, the reader?

7. Agee's title, "Knoxville: Summer 1915," is a bit prosaic. Suggest a new title for the sketch, one that expresses what you think is the theme or main impression of the essay.

8. What is Agee trying to express in the closing paragraph? Who, in particular, are "those who receive" him? Having reread the closing paragraph, would you agree that "Knoxville: Summer 1915" is an attempt to show that no matter how comfortable one is in one's environment, no matter how well loved and cared for, one's self-knowledge must be gained in loneliness?

Composition

In a sense, America is a nation of many worlds. In this book, for example, we have seen two vastly different childhood worlds: that of Alfred Kazin, in Brooklyn's Brownsville section; and that of James Agee, in Knoxville, Tennessee.

Write your own essay about childhood in America, describing the place where you grew up or the place where you wish you could have grown up. If you wish to follow Agee's approach of detail and impression to create an emotional effect, do so.

John Updike

Critics and readers share the same general feeling about John Updike—that he is one of America's finest contemporary essayists and short-story writers and that he might become one of its finest novelists. All of Updike's writing is marked by a precise, ornately figurative style (one critic refers to his "baroque metaphors" and "sparkling similes"), but he has so far lacked the power to write a truly memorable novel. His writing seems best suited to the short story and essay, for which, because of his clarity and sharp focus, he has been called a modern miniaturist.

John Hoyer Updike began writing seriously at Harvard University, to which he had come from a childhood and youth in Shillington, Pennsylvania, the small town where he was born in 1932. At Harvard, Updike wrote for campus publications and began sending stories, poems, and essays to *The New Yorker*—just as thousands of other would-be writers have done and continue to do. Unlike the many others, however, Updike found that some of his material was accepted and published.

After leaving Harvard—he was graduated *summa cum laude* in 1954—Updike spent a year in England, studying as a Knox Fellow at the Ruskin School of Drawing and Fine Art, Oxford. He returned to America in 1955 and worked as a reporter and staff writer for *The New Yorker*, which continued to publish his assorted poems, essays, and stories.

Updike's first book of prose is the short novel *Poorhouse Fair*, published in 1959. His other novels include *Rabbit, Run* (1960), *The Centaur* (1963; winner of the National Book Award for fiction that year), *Of the Farm* (1965), and *Couples* (1968). His short stories are collected in. *The Same Door* (1959), *Pigeon Feathers* (1962), and *The Music School* (1966). His poems appear in *The Carpentered Hen and Other Tame Creatures* (1958) and *Telephone Poles* (1963), and his essays in *Assorted Prose* (1965).

Updike and his young family now live in Ipswich, Massachusetts, in a large rambling house he bought in 1957. He also rents office space in the center of town, where he does his writing. He is no longer on the staff of *The New Yorker* but does continue to contribute poems and short stories to the magazine.

The following essay first appeared in *The New Yorker* and was later collected in *Assorted Prose*. It is about the baseball hero Ted Williams, who for a generation was the grudging idol of Boston's rabid Red Sox fans. Updike was there with the other "Hub" fans in late September 1960, when Williams played his last game in Fenway Park.

Hub Fans Bid Kid Adieu

Fenway Park, in Boston, is a lyric little bandbox of a ballpark. Everything is painted green and seems in curiously sharp focus, like the inside of an old-fashioned peeping-type Easter egg. It was built in 1912 and rebuilt in 1934, and offers, as do most Boston artifacts, a compromise between Man's Euclidean determinations [1] and Nature's beguiling irregularities. Its right field is one of the deepest in the American League, while its left field is the shortest; the high left-field wall, three hundred and fifteen feet from home plate along the foul line, virtually thrusts its surface at right-handed hitters. On the afternoon of Wednesday, September 28, 1960, as I took a seat behind third base, a uniformed groundkeeper was treading the top of this wall, picking batting-practice home runs out of the screen, like a mushroom gatherer seen in Wordsworthian perspective [2] on the verge of a cliff. The day was overcast, chill, and uninspirational. The Boston team was the worst in twenty-seven seasons. A jangling medley of incompetent youth and aging competence, the Red Sox were finishing in seventh place only because the Kansas City Athletics had locked them out of the cellar. They were scheduled to play the Baltimore Orioles, a much nimbler blend of May and December, who had been dumped from pennant contention a week before by the in-

1. **Euclidean determinations:** that is, geometrical limitations. Euclid (who lived during the third century B.C.) was a Greek mathematician, and is credited with developing the basic principles of geometry.
2. **mushroom gatherer . . . Wordsworthian perspective:** of the many poems by the English romanticist William Wordsworth (1770–1850), one of the most famous is "Tintern Abbey," in which the poet expresses satisfaction in beholding once more "these steep and lofty cliffs" on which the ruins of the abbey rested.

satiable Yankees. I, and 10,453 others, had shown up primarily because this was the Red Sox's last home game of the season, and therefore the last time in all eternity that their regular left fielder, known to the headlines as TED, KID, SPLINTER, THUMPER, TW, and, most cloyingly, MISTER WONDERFUL, would play in Boston. "WHAT WILL WE DO WITHOUT TED? HUB FANS ASK" ran the headline on a newspaper being read by a bulb-nosed cigar smoker a few rows away. Willams's retirement had been announced, doubted (he had been threatening retirement for years), confirmed by Tom Yawkey, the Red Sox owner, and at last widely accepted as the sad but probable truth. He was forty-two and had redeemed his abysmal season of 1959 with a—considering his advanced age—fine one. He had been giving away his gloves and bats and had grudgingly consented to a sentimental ceremony today. This was not necessarily his last game; the Red Sox were scheduled to travel to New York and wind up the season with three games there.

I arrived early. The Orioles were hitting fungos [3] on the field. The day before, they had spitefully smothered the Red Sox, 17–4, and neither their faces nor their drab gray visiting-team uniforms seemed very gracious. I wondered who had invited them to the party. Between our heads and the lowering clouds a frenzied organ was thundering through, with an appositeness [4] perhaps accidental, "You *maaaade* me love you, I didn't wanna do it, I didn't wanna do it. . . ."

The affair between Boston and Ted Williams was no mere summer romance; it was a marriage composed of spats, mutual disappointments, and, toward the end, a mellowing hoard of shared memories. It fell into three stages, which may be termed Youth, Maturity, and Age; or Thesis, Antithesis, and Synthesis; [5] or Jason, Achilles, and Nestor.[6]

3. fungos: practice hits—ground balls to infielders, fly balls to outfielders—from a batter who throws the ball up himself and hits it as it falls.
4. appositeness (ap′pə·zit·nes): appropriateness.
5. Thesis, Antithesis, and Synthesis: elements in dialectical materialism, a philosophy combining materialism and logic, in which the conflicts of two opposing forces or ideas (thesis and antithesis) are resolved by forming from them a new force or idea (synthesis).
6. Jason, Achilles, and Nestor: ancient Greek heroes who were, respectively, young, mature, and old when most prominent in literature and myths. Jason, a youthful prince of Ioclus, was captain of the ship *Argo* and leader of its

First, there was the by now legendary epoch [7] when the young bridegroom came out of the West and announced "All I want out of life is that when I walk down the street folks will say 'There goes the greatest hitter who ever lived.'" The dowagers of local journalism attempted to give elementary deportment lessons to

---

Argonauts; he sailed in quest of the Golden Fleece. **Achilles,** son of Peleus (King of Phthiotis) and Thetis (a sea-deity), was a Greek hero who in the Trojan War killed the Trojan leader Hector; Achilles was a favored warrior, according to mythology, because his mother had dipped him in the River Styx, which rendered all of his body invulnerable except for the heel by which she held him and, ultimately, in which he was fatally wounded by the Trojan prince Paris. **Nestor,** an aged king of Pylos, was among the Argonauts.

7. **epoch** (ep′ək): an important memorable span or interval of time. [*Author's note*] This piece was written with no research materials save an outdated record book and the Boston newspapers of the day, and Williams's early career preceded the dawning of my *Schlagballewusstsein* (Baseball-consciousness). Also for reasons of perspective was my account of his beginnings skimped. Williams first attracted the notice of a major-league scout—Bill Essick of the Yankees—when he was a fifteen-year-old pitcher with the San Diego American Legion Post team. As a pitcher-outfielder for the San Diego's Herbert Hoover High School, Williams recorded averages of .586 and .403. Essick balked at signing Williams for the $1,000 his mother asked; he was signed instead, for $150 a month, by the local Pacific Coast League franchise, the newly created San Diego Padres. In his two seasons with this team, Williams hit merely .271 and .291, but his style and slugging (23 home runs the second year) caught the eye of, among others, Casey Stengel, then with the Boston Braves, and Eddie Collins, the Red Sox general manager. Collins bought him from the Padres for $25,000 in cash and $25,000 in players. Williams was then nineteen. Collins's fond confidence in the boy's potential matched Williams's own. Williams reported to the Red Sox training camp in Sarasota in 1938 and, after showing more volubility than skill, was shipped down to the Minneapolis Millers, the top Sox farm team. It should be said, perhaps, that the parent club was equipped with an excellent, if mature, outfield, mostly purchased from Connie Mack's dismantled A's. Upon leaving Sarasota, Williams is supposed to have told the regular outfield of Joe Vosmik, Doc Cramer, and Ben Chapman that he would be back and would make more money than the three of them put together. At Minneapolis he hit .366, batted in 142 runs, scored 130, and hit 43 home runs. He also loafed in the field, jabbered at the fans, and smashed a water cooler with his fist. In 1939 he came north with the Red Sox. On the way, in Atlanta, he dropped a foul fly, accidentally kicked it away in trying to pick it up, and threw it out of the park. It would be nice if, his first time up in Fenway Park, he had hit a home run. Actually, in his first Massachusetts appearance, the first inning of an exhibition game against Holy Cross at Worcester, he did hit a home run, a grand slam. The Red Sox season opened in Yankee Stadium. Facing Red Ruffing, Williams struck out and, the next time up, doubled for his first major-league hit. In the Fenway Park opener, against Philadelphia, he had a single in five trips. His first home run came on April 23, in that same series with the A's. Williams was then twenty, and played *right* field. In his rookie season he hit .327; in 1940, .344.

this child who spake as a god, and to their horror were themselves
rebuked. Thus began the long exchange of backbiting, bat-flip-
ping, booing, and spitting that has distinguished Williams's public
relations.[8] The spitting incidents of 1957 and 1958 and the similar
dockside courtesies that Williams has now and then extended to
the grandstand should be judged against this background: the
left-field stands at Fenway for twenty years have held a large number of customers who have bought their way in primarily for the
privilege of showering abuse on Williams. Greatness necessarily
attracts debunkers, but in Williams's case the hostility has been
systematic and unappeasable. His basic offense against the fans
has been to wish that they weren't there. Seeking a perfectionist's
vacuum, he has quixotically desired to sever the game from the
ground of paid spectatorship and publicity that supports it. Hence
his refusal to tip his cap [9] to the crowd or turn the other cheek to
newsmen. It has been a costly theory—it has probably cost him,
among other evidences of good will, two Most Valuable Player

8. **Williams's public relations:** [*Author's note*] See *Ted Williams*, by Ed Linn
(Sport Magazine Library), Chapter 6, "Williams vs. the Press." It is Linn's
suggestion that Williams walked into a circulation war among the seven Boston newspapers, who in their competitive zeal headlined incidents that the
New York papers, say, would have minimized, just as they minimized the less
genial side of the moody and aloof DiMaggio and smoothed Babe Ruth into a
folk hero. It is also Linn's thought, and an interesting one, that Williams
thrived on even adverse publicity, and needed a hostile press to elicit, contrari-
wise, his defiant best. The statistics (especially of the 1958 season, when he
snapped a slump by spitting in all directions, and inadvertently conked an
elderly female fan with a tossed bat) seem to corroborate this. Certainly Williams could have had a truce for the asking, and his industrious perpetuation
of the war, down to his last day in uniform, implies its usefulness to him. The
actual and intimate anatomy of the matter resides in locker rooms and hotel
corridors fading from memory. When my admiring account was printed, I received a letter from a sports reporter who hated Williams with a bitter and
explicit immediacy. And even Linn's hagiology (saint's life) permits some
glimpses of Williams's locker-room manners that are not pleasant.
9. **refusal to tip his hat:** [*Author's note*] But he did tip his cap, high off his
head, in at least his first season, as cartoons from that period verify. He also
was extravagantly cordial to taxi-drivers and stray children. See Linn, Chapter
4, "The Kid Comes to Boston": "There has never been a ballplayer—anywhere, anytime—more popular than Ted Williams in his first season in Boston." To this epoch belong Williams's prankish use of the Fenway scoreboard
lights for rifle practice, his celebrated expressed preference for the life of a
fireman, and his determined designation of himself as "The Kid."

awards, which are voted by reporters [10]—but he has held to it. While his critics, oral and literary, remained beyond the reach of his discipline, the opposing pitchers were accessible, and he spanked them to the tune of .406 in 1941.[11] He slumped to .356 in 1942 and went off to war.

In 1946, Williams returned from three years as a Marine pilot to the second of his baseball avatars,[12] that of Achilles, the hero of incomparable prowess and beauty who nevertheless was to be found sulking in his tent while the Trojans (mostly Yankees) fought through to the ships. Yawkey, a timber and mining maharajah, had surrounded his central jewel with many gems of slightly lesser water, such as Bobby Doerr, Dom DiMaggio, Rudy York, Birdie Tebbetts, and Johnny Pesky. Throughout the late forties, the Red Sox were the best paper team in baseball, yet they had little three-dimensional to show for it, and if this was a tragedy, Williams was Hamlet. A succinct review of the indictment—and a fair sample of appreciative sports-page prose—appeared the very day of Williams's valedictory,[13] in a column by Huck Finnegan in the Boston *American* (no sentimentalist, Huck):

10. **Most Valuable Player awards . . . reporters:** [*Author's note*] In 1947 Joe DiMaggio and in 1957 Mickey Mantle, with seasons inferior to Williams's, won the MVP award because sportswriters, who vote on ballots with ten places, had vengefully placed Williams ninth, tenth, or nowhere at all. The 1941 award to Joe DiMaggio, even though this was Williams's .406 year, is more understandable, since this was also the *annus miraculorum* when DiMaggio hit safely in 56 consecutive games.

11. **.406 in 1941:** [*Author's note*] The sweet saga of this beautiful decimal must be sung once more. Williams, after hitting above .400 all season, had cooled to .39955 with one doubleheader left to play, in Philadelphia. Joe Cronin, then managing the Red Sox, offered to bench him to safeguard his average, which was exactly .400 when rounded to the third decimal place. Williams said (I forget where I read this) that he did not want to become the .400 hitter with just his toenails over the line. He played the first game and singled, homered, singled, and singled. With less to gain than to lose, he elected to play the second game and got two more hits, including a double that dented a loudspeaker horn on the top of the right-field wall, giving him six-for-eight on the day and a season's average that, in the forty years between Rogers Hornsby's .403 (1925) and the present, stands as unique.

12. **avatars** (avʹə·tärz): incarnations of gods or, in this context, the great heroes Jason, Achilles, and Nestor. The word is from Hindu mythology.

13. **valedictory** (valʹə·dikʹtər·ē): a parting address. The term is from Latin *valedictus*, a combination of *vale*, "well," and *dicere*, "to say."

Williams's career, in contrast [to Babe Ruth's], has been a series of failures except for his averages. He flopped in the only World Series he ever played in (1946) when he batted only .200. He flopped in the playoff game with Cleveland in 1948. He flopped in the final game of the 1949 season with the pennant hinging on the outcome (Yanks 5, Sox 3). He flopped in 1950 when he returned to the lineup after a two-month absence and ruined the morale of a club that seemed pennant-bound under Steve O'Neill. It has always been Williams's records first, the team second, and the Sox non-winning record is proof enough of that.

There are answers to all this, of course. The fatal weakness of the great Sox slugging teams was not-quite-good-enough pitching rather than Williams's failure to hit a home run every time he came to bat. Again, Williams's depressing effect on his teammates has never been proved. Despite ample coaching to the contrary, most insisted that they *liked* him. He has been generous with advice to any player who asked for it. In an increasingly combative baseball atmosphere, he continued to duck beanballs docilely. With umpires he was gracious to a fault. This courtesy itself annoyed his critics, whom there was no pleasing. And against the ten crucial games (the seven World Series games with the St. Louis Cardinals, the 1948 playoff with the Cleveland Indians, and the two-game series with the Yankees at the end of the 1949 season, when one victory would have given the Red Sox the pennant) that make up the Achilles's heel of Williams's record, a mass of statistics can be set showing that day in and day out he was no slouch in the clutch.[14] The correspondence columns of the Boston papers now and then suffer a sharp flurry of arithmetic on this score; indeed, for Williams to have distributed all his hits so they did nobody else any good would constitute a feat of placement unparalleled in the annals of selfishness.

14. no slouch in the clutch: [*Author's note*] For example: In 1948, the Sox came from behind to tie the Indians by winning three straight; in those games Williams went two for two, two for two; and two for four. In 1949, the Sox overtook the Yankees by winning nine in a row; in that streak, Williams won four games with home runs.

Whatever residue of truth remains of the Finnegan charge, those of us who love Williams must transmute [15] as best we can, in our own personal crucibles. My personal memories of Williams began when I was a boy in Pennsylvania, with two last-place teams in Philadelphia to keep me company. For me, "W'ms, lf" [16] was a figment of the box scores who always seemed to be going 3-for-5. He radiated, from afar, the hard blue glow of high purpose. I remember listening over the radio to the All-Star Game of 1946, in which Williams hit two singles and two home runs, the second one off a Rip Sewell "blooper" pitch; it was like hitting a balloon out of the park. I remember watching one of his home runs from the bleachers of Shibe Park; it went over the first baseman's head and rose methodically along a straight line and was still rising when it cleared the fence. The trajectory seemed qualitatively different from anything anyone else might hit. For me, Williams is the classic ballplayer of the game on a hot August weekday, before a small crowd, when the only thing at stake is the tissue-thin difference between a thing done well and a thing done ill. Baseball is a game of the long season, of relentless and gradual averaging-out. Irrelevance—since the reference point of most individual contests is remote and statistical—always threatens its interest, which can be maintained not by the occasional heroics that sportswriters feed upon but by players who always *care*; who care, that is to say, about themselves and their art. Insofar as the clutch hitter is not a sportswriter's myth, he is a vulgarity, like a writer who writes only for money. It may be that, compared to such managers' dreams as the manifestly classy Joe DiMaggio and the always helpful Stan Musial, Williams was an icy star. But of all team sports, baseball, with its graceful intermittences of action, its immense and tranquil field sparsely settled with poised men in white, its dispassionate mathematics, seems to me best suited to accommodate, and be ornamented by, a loner. It is an essentially lonely game. No other player visible to my generation concentrated within himself so much of the sport's poignance, so assiduously refined his natural skills, so constantly brought to the plate that intensity of competence that crowds the throat with joy.

15. transmute: transform; change in form.
16. "W'ms, lf": that is, "Williams, left field"—the shortened form would be used in the box scores that appear in the newspapers.

By the time I went to college, near Boston, the lesser stars Yawkey had assembled around Williams had faded, and his rigorous pride of craftsmanship had become itself a kind of heroism. This brittle and temperamental player developed an unexpected quality of persistence. He was always coming back—back from Korea, back from a broken collarbone, a shattered elbow, a bruised heel, back from drastic bouts of flu and ptomaine poisoning. Hardly a season went by without some enfeebling mishap, yet he always came back, and always looked like himself. The delicate mechanism of timing and power seemed sealed, shockproof, in some case deep within his frame.[17] In addition to injuries, there was a heavily publicized divorce, and the usual storms with the press, and the Williams Shift—the maneuver, custom-built by Lou Boudreau of the Cleveland Indians, whereby three infielders were concentrated on the right side of the infield.[18] Williams could easily have learned to punch singles through the vacancy on his left and fattened his average hugely. This was what Ty Cobb, the Einstein of average, told him to do. But the game had changed since Cobb; Williams believed that his value to the club and to the league was as a slugger, so he went on pulling the ball, trying to blast it through three men, and paid the price of perhaps fifteen points of lifetime average. Like Ruth before him, he bought the

17. delicate mechanism . . . frame: [Author's note] Two reasons for his durability may be adduced. A non-smoker, non-drinker, habitual walker, and year-round outdoorsman, Williams spared his body the vicissitudes of the seasonal athlete. And his hitting was in large part a mental process; the amount of cerebration he devoted to such details as pitchers' patterns, prevailing winds, and the muscular mechanics of swinging a bat would seem ridiculous, if it had not paid off. His intellectuality, as it were, perhaps explains the quickness with which he adjusted, after the war, to the changed conditions—the night games, the addition of the slider to the standard pitching repertoire, the new cry for the long ball. His reaction to the Williams Shift, then, cannot be dismissed as unconsidered.
18. Williams Shift . . . infield: [Author's note] Invented, or perpetrated (as a joke?) by Boudreau on July 14, 1946, between games of a doubleheader. In the first game of the doubleheader, Williams had hit three homers and batted in eight runs. The shift was not used when men were on base and, had Williams bunted or hit late against it immediately, it might not have spread, in all its variations, throughout the league. The Cardinals used it in the lamented World Series of that year. Toward the end, in 1959 and 1960, rather sadly, it had faded from use, or degenerated to the mere clockwise twitching of the infield customary against pull hitters.

occasional home run at the cost of many directed singles—a calculated sacrifice certainly not, in the case of a hitter as average-minded as Williams, entirely selfish.

After a prime so harassed and hobbled, Williams was granted by the relenting fates a golden twilight. He became at the end of his career perhaps the best *old* hitter of the century. The dividing line falls between the 1956 and the 1957 seasons. In September of the first year, he and Mickey Mantle were contending for the batting championship. Both were hitting around .350, and there was no one else near them. The season ended with a three-game series between the Yankees and the Sox, and, living in New York then, I went up to the Stadium. Williams was slightly shy of the four hundred at-bats needed to qualify; the fear was expressed that the Yankee pitchers would walk him to protect Mantle. Instead, they pitched to him. It was wise. He looked terrible at the plate, tired and discouraged and unconvincing. He never looked very good to me in the Stadium.[19] The final outcome in 1956 was Mantle .353, Williams .345.

The next year, I moved from New York to New England, and it made all the difference. For in September of 1957, in the same situation, the story was reversed. Mantle finally hit .365; it was the best season of his career. But Williams, though sick and old, had run away from him. A bout of flu had laid him low in September. He emerged from his cave in the Hotel Somerset haggard but irresistible; he hit four successive pinch-hit home runs. "I feel terrible," he confessed, "but every time I take a swing at the ball it goes out of the park." He ended the season with thirty-eight home runs and an average of .388, the highest in either league since his own .406, and, coming from a decrepit man of thirty-nine, an even more supernal[20] figure. With eight or so of the "leg hits" that a younger man would have beaten out, it would have been .400. And the next year, Williams, who in 1949 and 1953 had

19. **He never looked . . . in the Stadium:** [*Author's note*] Shortly after his retirement, Williams, in *Life*, wrote gloomily of the Staduim, "There's the bigness of it. There are those high stands and all those people smoking—and, of course, the shadows. . . . It takes at least one series to get accustomed to the Stadium and even then you're not sure." Yet his lifetime batting average there is .340, only four points under his median average.
20. **supernal:** celestial; towering.

lost batting championships by decimal whiskers to George Kell and Mickey Vernon, sneaked in behind his teammate Pete Runnels and filched his sixth title, a bargain at .328.

In 1959, it seemed all over. The dinosaur thrashed around in the .200 swamp for the first half of the season, and was even benched ("rested," Manager Mike Higgins tactfully said). Old foes like the late Bill Cunningham began to offer batting tips. Cunningham thought Williams was jiggling his elbows; [21] in truth, Williams's neck was so stiff he could hardly turn his head to look at the pitcher. When he swung, it looked like a Calder mobile with one thread cut; [22] it reminded you that since 1954 William's shoulders had been wired together. A solicitous pall settled over the sports pages. In the two decades since Williams had come to Boston, his status had imperceptibly shifted from that of a naughty prodigy to that of a municipal monument. As his shadow in the record books lengthened, the Red Sox teams around him declined, and the entire American League seemed to be losing life and color to the National. The inconsistency of the new super-stars—Mantle, Colavito, and Kaline—served to make Williams appear all the more singular. And off the field, his private philanthropy—in particular, his zealous chairmanship of the Jimmy Fund, a charity for children with cancer—gave him a civic presence matched only by that of Richard Cardinal Cushing. In religion, Williams appears to be a humanist,[23] and a selective one at that, but he and the abrasive-voiced Cardinal, when their good works intersect and they appear in the public eye together, make a handsome pair of seraphim.[24]

21. **Cunningham . . . elbows:** [*Author's note*] It was Cunningham who, when Williams first appeared in a Red Sox uniform at the 1938 spring training camp, wrote with melodious prescience: "The Sox seem to think Williams is just cocky enough and gabby enough to make a great and colorful outfielder, possibly the Babe Herman type. Me? I don't like the way he stands at the plate. He bends his front knee inward and moves his foot just before he takes a swing. That's exactly what I do just before I drive a golf ball and knowing what happens to the golf balls I drive, I don't believe this kid will ever hit half a singer midget's weight in a bathing suit."

22. **Calder mobile with one thread cut:** the American sculptor Alexander Calder is famous for his mobiles—sculptures consisting of movable parts hung or balanced on rods, wires, or threads and subject to motion from air currents; a cut thread would destroy the mobile's delicate balance.

23. **humanist:** one who believes in a system that focuses on human ideals and human perfection rather than on theological or strictly religious principles.

24. **seraphim** (plural form of *seraph*): angels of a high order.

Humiliated by his '59 season, Williams determined, once more, to come back. I, as a specimen Williams partisan, was both glad and fearful. All baseball fans believe in miracles; the question is, how *many* do you believe in? He looked like a ghost in spring training. Manager Jurges warned us ahead of time that if Williams didn't come through he would be benched, just like anybody else. As it turned out, it was Jurges who was benched. Williams entered the 1960 season needing eight home runs to have a lifetime total of 500; after one time at bat in Washington, he needed seven. For a stretch, he was hitting a home run every second game that he played. He passed Lou Gehrig's lifetime total [of 512], and finished with 521, thirteen behind Jimmy Foxx, who alone stands between Williams and Babe Ruth's unapproachable 714.[25] The summer was a statistician's picnic. His two-thousandth walk came and went, his eighteen-hundredth run batted in, his sixteenth All-Star Game. At one point, he hit a home run off a pitcher, Don Lee, off whose father, Thornton Lee, he had hit a home run a generation before. The only comparable season for a forty-two-year-old man was Ty Cobb's in 1928. Cobb batted .323 and hit one homer. Williams batted .316 but hit twenty-nine homers.

In sum, though generally conceded to be the greatest hitter of his era, he did not establish himself as "the greatest hitter who ever lived." Cobb, for average, and Ruth, for power, remain supreme. Cobb, Rogers Hornsby, Joe Jackson, and Lefty O'Doul, among players since 1900, have higher lifetime averages than Williams's .344. Unlike Foxx, Gehrig, Hack Wilson, Hank Greenberg, and Ralph Kiner, Williams never came close to matching Babe Ruth's season home-run total of sixty.[26] In the list of major-league batting records, not one is held by Williams. He is second in walks drawn, third in home runs, fifth in lifetime average, sixth in runs batted in, eighth in runs scored and in total bases, fourteenth in doubles, and thirtieth in hits.[27] But if we allow him merely average seasons for the four-plus seasons he lost to two

25. Jimmy Foxx . . . between Williams and Babe Ruth's unapproachable 714: in the 1968 season, Mickey Mantle passed both Williams's and Foxx's home-run totals.
26. home-run total of sixty: [Author's note] Written before Roger Maris's fluky, phenomenal sixty-one.
27. He is second . . . thirtieth in hits: [Author's note] Again, as of 1960. Since then Musial may have surpassed him in some statistical areas. [Editor's note:] Mantle and Willy Mays and Henry Aaron may have, too.

wars,[28] and add another season for the months he lost to injuries, we get a man who in all the power totals would be second, and not a very distant second, to Ruth. And if we further allow that these years would have been not merely average but prime years, if we allow for all the months when Williams was playing in sub-par condition, if we permit his early and later years in baseball to be some sort of index of what the middle years could have been, if we give him a right-field fence that is not, like Fenway's, one of the most distant in the league, and if—the least excusable "if"—we imagine him condescending to outsmart the Williams Shift, we can defensibly assemble, like a colossus induced from the sizable fragments that do remain,[29] a statistical figure not incommensurate with his grandiose ambition. From the statistics that are on the books, a good case can be made that in the *combination* of power and average Williams is first; nobody else ranks so high in both categories. Finally, there is the witness of the eyes; men whose memories go back to Shoeless Joe Jackson—another unlucky natural—rank him and Williams together as the best-looking hitters they have seen. It was for our last look that ten thousand of us had come.

Two girls, one of them with pert buckteeth and eyes as black as vest buttons, the other with white skin and flesh-colored hair, like an underdeveloped photograph of a redhead, came and sat on my right. On my other side was one of those frowning chestless young-old men who can frequently be seen, often wearing sailor hats, attending ball games alone. He did not once open his program but instead tapped it, rolled up, on his knee as he gave the game his disconsolate attention. A young lady, with freckles and a depressed, dainty nose that by an optical illusion seemed to thrust her lips forward for a kiss, sauntered down into the box seat

28. **two wars:** World War II (1939–1945) and the Korean War (1950–1952).

29. **colossus . . . remain:** a colossus is any statue of great size. The most famous colossus was the Giant of Rhodes (considered one of the Seven Wonders of the [ancient] World), a gigantic bronze statue that straddled the entrance to the harbor of Rhodes. Built around 285 B.C., it was toppled fifty-six years later by an earthquake which left only its feet intact. It lay in ruins until its fragments were sold by Arabs in the seventh century A.D. From the fragments, modern archaeologists determined that the colossus' original height was somewhere between 90 and 120 feet.

right behind the roof of the Oriole dugout. She wore a blue coat with a Northeastern University emblem sewed to it. The girls beside me took it into their heads that this was Williams's daughter. She looked too old to me, and why would she be sitting behind the visitors' dugout? On the other hand, from the way she sat there, staring at the sky and French-inhaling, she clearly was *somebody*. Other fans came and eclipsed her from view. The crowd looked less like a weekday ballpark crowd than like the folks you might find in Yellowstone National Park, or emerging from automobiles at the top of scenic Mount Mansfield. There were a lot of competitively well-dressed couples of tourist age, and not a few babes in arms. A row of five seats in front of me was abruptly filled with a woman and four children, the youngest of them two years old, if that. Someday, presumably, he could tell his grandchildren that he saw Williams play. Along with these tots and second-honeymooners, there were Harvard freshmen, giving off that peculiar nervous glow created when a sufficient quantity of insouciance is saturated with enough insecurity; thick-necked Army officers with brass on their shoulders and steel in their stares; pepperings of priests; perfumed bouquets of Roxbury Fabian fans; shiny salesmen from Albany and Fall River; and those gray, hoarse men—taxi drivers, slaughterers, and bartenders—who will continue to click through the turnstiles long after everyone else has deserted to television and tramporamas.[30] Behind me, two young male voices blossomed, cracking a joke about God's five proofs that Thomas Aquinas exists [31]—typical Boston College levity.

The batting cage was trundled away. The Orioles fluttered to the sidelines. Diagonally across the field, by the Red Sox dugout, a cluster of men in overcoats were festering like maggots. I could see a splinter of white uniform, and Williams's head, held at a self-deprecating and evasive tilt. Williams's conversational stance is that of a six-foot-three-inch man under a six-foot ceiling. He moved away to the patter of flash bulbs, and began playing catch with a young Negro outfielder named Willie Tasby. His arm, never

30. **tramporamas:** trampoline centers, which proliferated and then faded away, (as fads do) in America during the early 1960's.
31. **God's five proofs that Thomas Aquinas exists:** St. Thomas Aquinas (1225?–1274) was a Dominican monk who through rational analysis offered five proofs that God exists. His system is known as Thomism or Scholastic philosophy.

very powerful, had grown lax with the years, and his throwing motion was a kind of muscular drawl. To catch the ball, he flicked his glove hand onto his left shoulder (he batted left but threw right, as every schoolboy ought to know) and let the ball plop into it comically. This catch session with Tasby was the only time all afternoon I saw him grin.

A tight little flock of human sparrows who, from the lambent [32] and pampered pink of their faces, could only have been Boston politicians moved toward the plate. The loudspeakers mammothly coughed as someone huffed on the microphone. The ceremonies began. Curt Gowdy, the Red Sox radio and television announcer, who sounds like everybody's brother-in-law, delivered a brief sermon, taking the two words "pride" and "champion" as his text. It began. "Twenty-one years ago, a skinny kid from San Diego, California . . ." and ended, "I don't think we'll ever see another like him." Robert Tibolt, chairman of the board of the Greater Boston Chamber of Commerce, presented Williams with a big Paul Revere silver bowl. Harry Carlson, a member of the sports committee of the Boston Chamber, gave him a plaque, whose inscription he did not read in its entirety, out of deference to Williams's distaste for this sort of fuss. Mayor Collins, seated in a wheelchair, presented the Jimmy Fund with a thousand-dollar check.

Then the occasion himself stooped to the microphone, and his voice sounded, after the others, very Californian; it seemed to be coming, excellently amplified, from a great distance, adolescently young and as smooth as a butternut. His thanks for the gifts had not died from our ears before he glided, as if helplessly, into "In spite of all the terrible things that have been said about me by the knights of the keyboard up there. . . ." He glanced up at the press rows suspended behind home plate. The crowd tittered, appalled. A frightful vision flashed upon me, of the press gallery pelting Williams with erasers, of Williams clambering up the foul screen to slug journalists, of a riot, of Mayor Collins being crushed. ". . . And they *were* terrible things," Williams insisted, with level melancholy, into the mike. "I'd like to forget them, but I can't." He paused, swallowed his memories, and went on, "I want to say that my years in Boston have been the greatest thing

32. **lambent:** softly radiant; bright; high-colored.

in my life." The crowd, like an immense sail going limp in a change of wind, sighed with relief. Taking all the parts himself, Williams then acted out a vivacious little morality drama in which an imaginary tempter came to him at the beginning of his career and said, "Ted, you can play anywhere you like." Leaping nimbly into the role of his younger self (who in biographical actuality had yearned to be a Yankee), Williams gallantly chose Boston over all the other cities, and told us that Tom Yawkey was the greatest owner in baseball and we were the greatest fans. We applauded ourselves lustily. The umpire came out and dusted the plate. The voice of doom announced over the loudspeakers that after Williams's retirement his uniform number, 9, would be permanently retired—the first time the Red Sox had so honored a player. We cheered. The national anthem was played. We cheered. The game began.

Williams was third in the batting order, so he came up in the bottom of the first inning, and Steve Barber, a young pitcher born two months before Williams began playing in the major leagues, offered him four pitches, at all of which he disdained to swing, since none of them were within the strike zone. This demonstrated simultaneously that Williams's eyes were razor-sharp and that Barber's control wasn't. Shortly, the bases were full, with Williams on second. "Oh, I hope he gets held up at third! That would be wonderful," the girl beside me moaned, and, sure enough, the man at bat walked and Williams was delivered into our foreground. He struck the pose of Donatello's David, the third-base bag being Goliath's head.[33] Fiddling with his cap, swapping small talk with the Oriole third baseman (who seemed delighted to have him drop in), swinging his arms with a sort of prancing nervousness, he looked fine—flexible, hard, and not unbecomingly substantial through the middle. The long neck, the small head, the knickers whose cuffs were worn down near his ankles—all these clichés of sports cartoon iconography[34] were rendered in the flesh.

33. pose of Donatello's David . . . Goliath's head: a pose similar to that of the biblical hero David in the statue by the Florentine artist Donatello (1386?–1466). The statue depicts David, having just slain the Philistine giant Goliath, standing in victory with one foot resting on the fallen giant's head.
34. iconography (ī'kə·nog'rə·fē): portraiture, particularly that adorned with symbolic details.

With each pitch, Williams danced down the baseline, waving his arms and stirring dust, ponderous but menacing, like an attacking goose. It occurred to about a dozen humorists at once to shout "Steal home! Go, go!" Williams's speed afoot was never legendary. Lou Clinton, a young Sox outfielder, hit a fairly deep fly to center field. Williams tagged up and ran home. As he slid across the plate, the ball, thrown with unusual heft by Jackie Brandt, the Oriole center fielder, hit him on the back.

"Boy, he was really loafing, wasn't he?" one of the collegiate voices behind me said.

"It's cold," the other voice explained. "He doesn't play well when it's cold. He likes heat. He's a hedonist."

The run that Williams scored was the second and last of the inning. Gus Triandos, of the Orioles, quickly evened the score by plunking a home run over the handy left-field wall. Williams, who had had this wall at his back for twenty years,[35] played the ball flawlessly. He didn't budge. He just stood still, in the center of the little patch of grass that his patient footsteps had worn brown, and, limp with lack of interest, watched the ball pass overhead. It was not a very interesting game. Mike Higgins, the Red Sox manager, with nothing to lose, had restricted his major-league players to the left-field line—along with Williams, Frank Malzone, a first-rate third baseman, played the game—and had peopled the rest of the terrain with unpredictable youngsters fresh, or not so fresh, off the farms. Other than Williams's recurrent appearances at the plate, the *maladresse* [36] of the Sox infield was the sole focus of suspense; the second baseman turned every grounder into a juggling act, while the shortstop did a breath-taking impersonation of an open window. With this sort of assistance, the Orioles wheedled their way into a 4–2 lead. They had early replaced Barber with another young pitcher, Jack Fisher. Fortunately (as it turned out), Fisher is no cutie; he is willing to burn the ball through the strike zone, and inning after inning this tactic punctured Higgins's string of test balloons.

Whenever Williams appeared at the plate—pounding the dirt from his cleats, gouging a pit in the batter's box with his left

35. **this wall . . . twenty years:** [*Author's note*] In his second season (1940), he was switched to left field, to protect his eyes from the right-field sun.
36. *maladresse:* clumsiness.

foot, wringing resin out of the bat handle with his vehement grip, switching the stick at the pitcher with an electric ferocity—it was like having a familiar Leonardo [37] appear in a shuffle of *Saturday Evening Post* covers. This man, you realized—and here, perhaps, was the difference, greater than the difference in gifts—really desired to hit the ball. In the third inning, he hoisted a high fly to deep center. In the fifth, we thought he had it; he smacked the ball hard and high into the heart of his power zone, but the deep right field in Fenway and the heavy air and a casual east wind defeated him. The ball died. Al Pilarcik leaned his back against the big "380" painted on the right-field wall and caught it. On another day, in another park, it would have been gone. (After the game, Williams said, "I didn't think I could hit one any harder than that. The conditions weren't good.")

The afternoon grew so glowering that in the sixth inning the arc lights were turned on—always a wan sight in the daytime, like the burning headlights of a funeral procession. Aided by the gloom, Fisher was slicing through the Sox rookies, and Williams did not come to bat in the seventh. He was second up in the eighth. This was almost certainly his last time to come to the plate in Fenway Park, and instead of merely cheering, as we had at his three previous appearances, we stood, all of us, and applauded. I had never before heard pure applause in a ballpark. No calling, no whistling, just an ocean of handclaps, minute after minute, burst after burst, crowding and running together in continuous succession like the pushes of surf at the edge of the sand. It was a somber and considered tumult. There was not a boo in it. It seemed to renew itself out of a shifting set of memories as the Kid, the Marine, the veteran of feuds and failures and injuries, the friend of children, and the enduring old pro evolved down the bright tunnel of twenty-two summers toward this moment. At last, the umpire signalled for Fisher to pitch; with the other players, he had been frozen in position. Only Williams had moved during the ovation, switching his bat impatiently, ignoring everything except his cherished task. Fisher wound up, and the applause sank into a hush.

37. **a familiar Leonardo:** a painting by the Florentine master Leonardo da Vinci (1452–1519).

Understand that we were a crowd of rational people. We knew that a home run cannot be produced at will; the right pitch must be perfectly met and luck must ride with the ball. Three innings before, we had seen a brave effort fail. The air was soggy, the season was exhausted. Nevertheless, there will always lurk, around the corner in a pocket of our knowledge of the odds, an indefensible hope, and this was one of the times, which you now and then find in sports, when a density of expectation hangs in the air and plucks an event out of the future.

Fisher, after his unsettling wait, was low with the first pitch. He put the second one over, and Williams swung mightily and missed. The crowd grunted, seeing that classic swing, so long and smooth and quick, exposed. Fisher threw the third time, Williams swung again, and there it was. The ball climbed on a diagonal line into the vast volume of air over center field. From my angle, behind third base, the ball seemed less an object in flight than the tip of a towering, motionless construct, like the Eiffel Tower or the Tappan Zee Bridge. It was in the books while it was still in the sky. Brandt ran back to the deepest corner of the outfield grass, the ball descended beyond his reach and struck in the crotch where the bullpen met the wall, bounced chunkily, and vanished.

Like a feather caught in a vortex, Williams ran around the square of bases at the center of our beseeching screaming. He ran as he always ran out home runs—hurriedly, unsmiling, head down, as if our praise were a storm of rain to get out of. He didn't tip his cap. Though we thumped, wept, and chanted "We want Ted" for minutes after he hid in the dugout, he did not come back. Our noise for some seconds passed beyond excitement into a kind of immense open anguish, a wailing, a cry to be saved. But immortality is nontransferable. The papers said that the other players, and even the umpires on the field, begged him to come out and acknowledge us in some way, but he refused. Gods do not answer letters.

Every true story has an anticlimax. The men on the field refused to disappear, as would have seemed decent, in the smoke of Williams's miracle. Fisher continued to pitch, and escaped further harm. At the end of the inning, Higgins sent Williams out to his left-field position, then instantly replaced him with Carrol Hardy, so we had a long last look at Williams as he ran out there and then back, his uniform jogging, his eyes steadfast on the ground. It was nice, and we were grateful, but it left a funny taste.

One of the scholasticists behind me said, "Let's go. We've seen everything. I don't want to spoil it." This seemed a sound aesthetic decision. Williams's last word had been so exquisitely chosen, such a perfect fusion of expectation, intention, and execution, that already it felt a little unreal in my head, and I wanted to get out before the castle collapsed. But the game, though played by clumsy midgets under the feeble glow of the arc lights, began to tug at my attention, and I loitered in the runway until it was over. Williams's homer had, quite incidentally, made the score 4–3. In the bottom of the ninth inning, with one out, Marlin Coughtry, the second-base juggler, singled. Vic Wertz, pinch-hitting, doubled off the left-field wall, Coughtry advancing to third. Pumpsie Green walked, to load the bases. Willie Tasby hit a double-play ball to the third baseman, but in making the pivot throw Billy Klaus, an ex-Red Sox infielder, reverted to form and threw the ball past the first baseman and into the Red Sox dugout. The Sox won, 5–4. On the car radio as I drove home I heard that Williams, his own man to the end, had decided not to accompany the team to New York. He had met the little death that awaits athletes. He had quit.

Meaning

1. Updike's title is modeled after the type of headlines, especially sports headlines, that appear in tabloid newspapers. Why is the title puzzling, amusing, striking, and accurate? What connotations does *Adieu* add that *good-bye* or *farewell* might not have added?
2. To judge from what Updike has written, what seemed to be Williams's attitudes toward (a) baseball in general, (b) baseball's spectators, especially the "Hub fans," (c) sportswriters? What, in turn, were the fans' and the sportswriters' respective attitudes toward Williams?
3. Updike's eulogy considers both Williams's strong points and his weaknesses. What are some of the weaknesses he mentions? What evidence does he offer that Williams was truly one of baseball's great heroes? How does he counter others' arguments against Williams as a great player?

4. On page 269 Updike begins a somewhat philosophical statement about the quality of players and their individual contests: "Baseball is a game of the long season, of relentless and gradual averaging out. Irrelevance . . . always threatens its interest. . . ."

   Does the philosophizing add to or detract from the essay? What is Updike's attitude toward baseball in general? Why does he admire Williams particularly?

Method

1. John Updike chooses to dispense with providing much biographical detail and background information about his subject. Does the lack of such information leave gaps in Updike's portrait of Ted Williams?
2. This essay was originally published in *The New Yorker* with a number of author's notes; more of them were added when the essay appeared a few years later in *Assorted Prose*. How effectively has Updike used his notes? Do they complement and add to the essay, or are they merely interesting in themselves, without making any real contribution to the essay as a whole? Is it both of these, depending on the individual notes? Explain, giving examples and reasons from the text. Does the reaction to these notes depend in part on the reader's understanding of and attitude toward baseball?
3. On page 264 Updike says that Williams's career in Boston "fell into three stages, which may be termed Youth, Maturity, and Age; or Thesis, Antithesis, and Synthesis; or Jason, Achilles, and Nestor." Why do you think Updike has offered three alternative ways of showing the stages in Williams's career; wouldn't one of them have served amply? What is gained, for example, by comparing Williams to Jason, Achilles, and Nestor? How has Updike developed this triple classical *allusion* into an *analogy*? What, for example, was Williams's "Achilles' heel"?
4. Updike is an acknowledged master stylist. Much of his style's power is in the way he handles two basic figures of speech, simile and metaphor. At one point, for example, he says that a particular home run of Williams's was "like hitting a balloon out of the park" (page 269); later, he describes how an inept shortstop "did a breathtaking impersonation of an open window" (page 278).

   His prose also abounds in direct comparisons and contrasts, literary, historical, biblical, and mythological allusions, and sensory images. Reread the excerpts that follow (in context, if you wish) and identify the technique being used. Try to explain how each adds to the essay in general or to the characterization of Ted Williams in particular.

(a) Fenway Park . . . is a lyric little bandbox of a ballpark. (page 263)

(b) A jangling medley of incompetent youth and aging competence, the Red Sox were finishing in seventh place. . . . (263)

(c) The affair between Boston and Ted Williams was no mere summer romance; it was a marriage composed of spats, mutual disappointments, and, toward the end, a mellowing hoard of shared memories. (264)

(d) . . . and if this was a tragedy, Williams was Hamlet. (267)

(e) The delicate mechanism of timing and power seemed sealed, shockproof, in some case deep within his frame. (270)

(f) This was what Ty Cobb, the Einstein of average, told him to do. (270)

(g) The dinosaur thrashed around in the .200 swamp for the first half of the season . . . (272)

(h) Two girls, one of them with pert buckteeth and eyes as black as vest buttons, the other with white skin and flesh-colored hair, like an underdeveloped photograph of a redhead, came and sat on my right. (274)

(i) . . . his throwing motion was a kind of muscular drawl. (276)

(j) No calling, no whistling, just an ocean of handclaps, minute after minute, burst after burst, crowding and running together in continuous succession like the pushes of surf at the edge of the sand. (279)

(k) He ran . . . hurriedly, unsmiling, head down, as if our praise were a storm of rain to get out of. (280)

5. "Hub Fans Bid Kid Adieu" is an example of what might be called "creative nonfiction"; it is prose based soundly on fact but with the added dimension of a creative touch. Which parts of the selection —whole sections or particular passages—do you think are examples of creative writing? Explain your choices.

6. On page 277, Updike departs from his usual flowing, moderate-to-lengthy sentences and concludes a paragraph with a series of short, choppy sentences. What is the effect of this switch? Why do you suppose the writer employed it? Does it "work"?

Language: Allusions

On page 266, Updike points out how Williams, "seeking a perfectionist's vacuum, . . . has quixotically desired to sever the game [of baseball] from the ground of paid spectatorship and publicity that supports it." *Quixotically* has two basic meanings, (1) referring to behavior that is foolishly and even ridiculously chivalrous or romantic and (2) referring to behavior based on high but impractical sentiment or goals. How do you know that Updike has used the second meaning in his reference to Williams's desire?

Quixotic is one of many English words based on allusions to names in mythology, the Bible, literature, art, history, etc. Such allusions often convey a special meaning or connotation—as *quixotically* conveys the idea of high but impossible dreams, the kind Don Quixote displayed in Cervantes's novel of that name.

Read the following sentences and explain the meaning or connotation of the italicized word or phrase in each. Use your dictionary for any terms you cannot understand from context.

1. I'm afraid this project is turning into a *Sisyphean task*.
2. I'd describe her as *Junoesque*.
3. We like him, but we find his attitudes rather *Victorian*.
4. I don't care for him much. He's too *narcissistic*.
5. My mother objects to my haircut. She says it's either *Edwardian* or *Byronic*, and she doesn't like either.
6. I don't know how she liked my paper. She took one look at it and gave me one of her *Mona Lisa smiles*.

Composition and Discussion

1. Notice how Updike has presented—in both text and footnotes—ample statistical evidence to back up his points, particularly those points comparing Ted Williams to other baseball greats. Statistics are often useful, but they can be misleading as well. Look at the use of statistics around you: in unemployment figures; in television ratings; in advertisements; in political polls, etc. How well does America use the vast statistics to which it has access? How can people be fooled by statistical information? Be prepared to air your views in an open-discussion period.

2. Analogy—which assumes that if two objects or situations are strikingly similar in one or two particulars they will be alike in many other respects—is an effective, if sometimes misleading, method of development in writing or speaking. Used carefully for illustration, however, analogy is a useful tool for any writer or speaker.

As a research-writing assignment, develop any one of the following sentences into an illustrative analogy, as if it were part of a larger discussion. If necessary, use your library for information on the choice you make.

(a) Man's freedom is illusory and subjective, like the "freedom" of a soaring bird, which ultimately must give in to the pull of gravity and return to earth.

(b) If our society continues in its present direction, it will destroy itself just as the Roman Empire destroyed itself many centuries ago.

(c) Pessimism is like a small infection: unless it is treated and checked, it will spread throughout the entire system and destroy the organism.

(d) Shoes are just like automobile tires.

Grandma Moses

In 1936, because of the arthritis that had stiffened her fingers, Anna Mary Robertson Moses had to abandon her favorite pastime, making embroidered illustrations of worsted yarn drawn through netting. She took up oil painting instead. She was then seventy-six. When she passed her one-hundredth birthday, she was still painting vigorously and, as if for good measure, continued for another year.

The paintings of Grandma Moses are world famous: millions have seen them in museums and in exhibits and showings throughout America and Europe; millions each year send reproductions of them as Christmas cards. As Mrs. Moses herself was, so are her paintings—bright, simple, modest, and direct, depicting "oldtimy" scenes she recalled from a lifetime in upstate New York farm country.

In 1953, Grandma Moses was the subject of a cover story in *Time* Magazine, and, in 1961, her death was noted in *The New Yorker*. Both articles are reprinted here.

Presents from Grandma

In the sunny front room of a trim ranch house in upper New York State, a sprightly little old lady sat working one day last week, an array of paint tubes on the table in front of her. Through the window she could see the fallow corn and tomato fields falling away to the Hoosic River, which curves northwest toward the hamlet of Eagle Bridge (pop. 250). Sycamores edged the riverbank; the hills beyond were quilted with thick-ranked birch and maple trees and patches of frosty pasture land. Anna Mary Robertson Moses—better known around the globe as "Grandma Moses"—sketched in the line of distant hills on a piece of white-coated Masonite. Then she dipped her brush—worn down to the barest bristle—in a can lid of turpentine and rubbed it on the mouth of a tube of burnt umber.[1]

1. **burnt umber:** a dark brown pigment, one of the artist's basic colors.

Peering through her spectacles, chatting as she worked, she added some ungainly vertical strokes of brown in the right foreground, explaining: "This is a butternut tree. When I was a girl there was a butternut tree way down yonder by the river. I used to go down and gather the nuts." She smeared green on the brush and began daubing in leaves. "This is what I like this brush for—you can make leaves so easy with it. Now I'll put on some yellowish green, and whitish green, like you see on the undersides when the wind blows them."

Pointing to the center of the panel, she announced: "There'll be an old mill there, and I guess I'll have some oxen goin' to the mill with a load of grain." Tapping her forehead, she added: "I can see the whole picture right here."

The Oldtimy Things. In the years since she first started painting these rosy visions of her imagination, Grandma Moses has earned a unique place in the hearts of millions, and in the history of American art. Her paintings (more than 1,500 by her own count) have been shown in more than 160 U.S. exhibitions, and in five one-man shows abroad. She is represented in nine American museums and in Vienna's State Gallery; hers is the only *"École Americaine"* [2] picture hanging in Paris's Museum of Modern Art. Grandma's originals—priced at $150 to $3,000 each—hang on the walls of such discriminating collectors as Mrs. Albert D. Lasker, Katharine Cornell, and Thomas J. Watson.[3] Reproductions of her work have entered thousands of less famed American homes, along with Grandma Moses china, fabrics, tiles, and, most of all, Christmas cards. Altogether some 48 million of her cards have been sold in the U.S. Next year, for the first time, they will also be printed in Vienna and distributed in 15 European countries.

The secret of Grandma's success lies partly in her backdoor approach to painting. Most painters make a great display of devoting their lives to art. Grandma Moses, who did not even think of painting seriously until she was 76, devotes her art to her life. It is commemoration, celebration, and thanks for the blessings of her

2. *"École Americaine":* **French**, the American "school" of painting. The term is applied to art and artists recognizably American in style, technique, subject matter, etc.
3. **Mrs. Albert D. Lasker, Katherine Cornell, and Thomas J. Watson [,Jr.]:** respectively, a collector of old and modern French masters and Trustee of New York's Museum of Modern Art; a distinguished American actress; and the chairman of International Business Machines (IBM) Corporation.

many fruitful years. The results are as cheery, nostalgic, yet commonsensical as Grandma herself. Says she: "I like to paint oldtimy things—something real pretty. Most of them are daydreams, as it were." Then she smiles and adds reflectively: "I will say that I have did remarkable for one of my years and experience."

Varnish & Hemlock. Last week Grandma was busily preparing for her own 94th Christmas. She had sent out some 400 cards, penning "Grandma Moses" on each with slow, even strokes of her gnarled hand. Most of her cards went to people who had sent her one the year before. She had carefully clipped the return address from each envelope, and saved it for this Christmas. Some of the cards she sent were reproductions of her paintings, but many were cheaper ones she bought at a church benefit. Grandma frugally cut in two the folding cards with pictures on both parts.

Grandma has decided to have a goose this Christmas, and of course a Christmas tree. One of her great-grandsons—probably eleven-year-old Tom—will go out and cut down a hemlock for her. On Christmas Eve, choral singers will come to her door, and Grandma will give them candy or prunes. Next morning she will have presents for all her 19 great-grandchildren—small trinkets she has saved over the year.

Thinking of Christmas always reminds Grandma of "the smell of hemlock and the smell of varnish." Hemlock is for all the Christmas trees of years past; varnish is for the shining toys. Grandma's main present to her own children at Christmas was always an old hobbyhorse, repainted and left by Kriss Kringle each year. Originally it had been dapple-gray, but it returned year after year repainted in all shades and hues.

In those days the Christmas tree was decorated with strings of popcorn and "cat-stairs" made of colored paper. Amidst the branches would shine a few oranges—a wonderful treasure. There would also be a knife, a comb, or a jew's-harp [4] for the children, along with the hobbyhorse.

Hog-killing traditionally came just before Christmas, and that meant big, juicy spareribs and sausage cakes. "We used to tell people, 'Come and see us during Christmastime.' Why, we'd keep

4. **jew's-harp:** a small, lyre-shaped instrument played by holding the frame between the teeth and striking a flexible steel tongue with the finger.

the table set with plates, ready for anybody to come in and eat, until New Year's." Says Grandma: "Christmas is not just one day."

Back in the Meadows. Grandma's first Christmas was spent "back in the green meadows and wild woods on a farm in Washington County," not far from her present home. She was one of ten children of a frugal farm family. Her ancestry was "Scotch, Irish, English, French, and Indian, and," says Grandma, "that's a good combination, isn't it?" She also takes gentle pride in the fact that one of her great-grandfathers fought in the American Revolution and left a powder horn [5] with the inscription:

Hezekiah King.
Ticonderoga. Feb. 24th 1777
Steal not this horn for fear of shame
For on it is the owner's name.

Grandma's earliest artistic effort was painting paper dolls (with her mother's bluing for the eyes and grape juice for the lips) and making dresses for them of colored paper. One winter her father was ill and passed the time painting a landscape around the walls of a room. Little Anna Mary "got into" the paints. She remembers making "some 'very pretty lambscapes,' as my brothers said I called them," on scraps of slate, wood, and glass. "Father would say, 'Oh, not so bad.' But Mother was more practical, thought that I could spend my time other ways."

Among the "other ways" were ordinary household chores, plus candlemaking, soapmaking, and dressmaking. "Little girls did not go to school much in winter," Grandma recalls, "owing to the cold and not warm enough clothing." Therefore she got only "through the Sixth Reader." [6]

The cold did not stop the children's play. Remembering those days in her autobiography,[7] she exulted: "Wintertime! When zero stands at 25 or 30, when we cannot deny the pleasure of skating till we have bumped heads, and bleedy noses, and the ice is like glass.

5. **powder horn:** a flask for holding gunpowder, usually fashioned from the curved horn of a cow or ox.
6. **Sixth Reader:** *McGuffey's Sixth Eclectic Reader.* Originated by William Holmes McGuffey (1800–1873), McGuffey's Readers were known for their stress on morality and patriotism as much as for their emphasis on literature.
7. **autobiography:** Grandma Moses' *My Life's History,* published in 1952.

Oh what joy and pleasure as we get together, to go for the Christmas tree, what air castles we build as we slide down the hill, who can rebuild what we see on that Christmas tree! Oh, those days of childhood!"

To the Ridgepole.[8] Even in those days, playing with her brothers, Grandma made a habit of excelling. "If they'd climb up a tree," she says, "I'd climb higher. They weren't goin' to outdo me. If they'd climb to the eaves [9] of a house, I'd climb to the ridgepole."

Grandma's childhood was brief. "When twelve years of age," she recalls, "I left home to earn my own living as what then was called a hired girl. This was a grand education for me, in cooking, housekeeping, in moralizing and mingling with the outside world." After 15 years of this education she met and married a farmhand named Thomas Salmon Moses. She remembers, with the certainty of true love, that he was "a wonderful man, much better than I am."

In her autobiography, Grandma gives a memorable description of her wedding outfit: "A going-away costume of a very dark green dress, and jacket the same, a hat, the same, trimmed with a pink feather. The first thing I had on was a chemise, then my corsets, a corset waist, a pair of pantsies, a little flannel skirt, the bustle, a white skirt, then the dress. The dress was made with a skirt lining and wigging [10] stitched on up to the knees, and the dress cloth went over that, a long skirt reaching to the floor. Then an overskirt over that that reached the floor and was tucked up on the sides and the top. Long stockings, black, and high-buttoned shoes. . . . Then I had a stiff high collar and white linen cuffs. My dress was all braided in the front, and the long jacket I wore, that was also braided. We bought the braid in patterns. My gloves were tan-colored, doe skin, they called them. And then, the ring."

Some Sit Down. "I believed when we started out," says Grandma, "that we were a team and I had to do as much as my husband did, not like some girls, they sit down, and then somebody has to throw sugar at them."

8. **ridgepole:** the horizontal beam supporting the peak of a roof and running along its length.
9. **eaves:** the overhanging, bottom edge of a roof.
10. **wigging:** wigan, a stiff lining fabric.

With $600 in savings, the young couple traveled south and rented a farm in the Shenandoah Valley of Virginia. In that valley, Grandma bore ten children and raised the five that survived birth. There, too, she supplemented the family income by making butter and potato chips (a novelty in those times) for sale to the neighbors.

After 18 years in the South, the Moses family moved north again to Eagle Bridge, N.Y. and began a dairy farm there. The children grew up and married. In 1927 Grandma's husband died.

Two of her sons had started nearby farms of their own; Grandma's youngest stayed on with her. The grandchildren, and then great-grandchildren, gave her increasing pleasure. She occupied herself with making worsted pictures (of yarn drawn through netting) until arthritis made handling the needle too difficult.

Says Grandma: "I used to wrap my hands up in scarves and lay them on a chair beside the bed, at night. I couldn't sleep on account of the aching, just like a toothache. Then, one night I got desperate so I got up and hunted the doctor book, the *Family Adviser, Philosophy of Diseases.* The best recipe was: 3 cups of sweet milk every day, and from 3 to 5 drops of turpentine in it. I took it for about three months, and all of a sudden there were no pains any more, but the hardness of the joints stayed."

"Shake, Shake, Shake." It was Grandma's sister Celestia who first suggested that painting might be fun for her. Grandma tried, and found it was. "I painted for pleasure, to keep busy and to pass the time away," she recalls, "but I thought no more of it than of doing fancy work."

When Grandma was finally persuaded to send some of her pictures to a country fair, along with canned fruits and jam, her preserves won prizes but her paintings attracted little attention. Not long after, however, a drugstore in the nearby town of Hoosick Falls, N.Y., put some of her pictures in the window. There they were spotted by a Manhattan collector named Louis Caldo. He bought them all and began trying to interest New York art dealers in Grandma's work. Finally he tried the newly opened Galerie St. Étienne, run by a solemn Viennese expatriate [11] named Otto Kallir, who fell hard for the pictures. Dealer Kallir put Grandma

11. **expatriate** (eks·pā′trē·it): one who chooses to live in a foreign country.

under contract, and her first big show, in 1940, lit the match to a bonfire of public enthusiasm which has been crackling brightly ever since.

Grandma's next show was held at Gimbels department store, which invited her down for the opening. Grandma had not been in Manhattan for years; she later described her visit: "Oh, it was shake hands, shake, shake, shake—and I wouldn't even know the people now. My, my, it was rush here, rush there, rush every other place—but I suppose I shouldn't say that because those people did go to so much bother to make my visit pleasant." A sizable audience gathered at Gimbels to hear Grandma talk about painting. Instead, she told them in detail how she made preserves, and concluded her talk by opening her handbag and showing a few samples. No one could possibly have invented an old lady more refreshing to a jaded urban public.

Doctor Without Cap. In the past dozen years, honors have been heaped upon Grandma Moses. Russell Sage College made her an honorary doctor of humane letters ("Only they didn't let me keep the cap"). She has been given the keys to the city of Albany. President Truman once presented her with an award ("I talked with him, and I could not think but that he was one of my own boys"). General Eisenhower sent her a card from Europe reading: "For Grandma Moses, a real artist, from a rank amateur."

Professional critics have praised her just as warmly. Oddly enough, U.S. critics were, and still are, inclined to temper their praise with a touch of condescension. They note her obvious limitations of draftsmanship and range, and only then admit her ability to evoke atmosphere and create lively scenes. But the European reaction has been full out. A Zurich [12] critic speaks of her "magic spontaneity . . . completely unsentimental, and as untouched as nature herself . . . a phenomenon of our times." Paris's *Arts* votes "thanks to Grandma Moses for the happiness she shows us." Vienna-born Otto Kallir flatly insists that Grandma is "one of the very great painters in America today." In his opinion she outranks even Henri Rousseau,[13] the Paris customs inspector who was the

12. **Zurich** (zŏŏr′ĭk): a Swiss city.
13. **Henri Rousseau** (än·rē′ rōō·sō′): lived 1844–1910.

first modern "primitive" painter to be revered by connoisseurs.[14]

Realism Without Exactitude. Ever since Rousseau's sophisticated friends—Picasso, Braque & Co.[15]—began promoting him at the turn of the century, primitive art has been a subject of controversy. In the first place, few can agree on just what the word is meant to cover. Two things it always stands for are an untrained hand and a childlike eye. Primitives are would-be realists whose charm depends on their very inability to paint photographically accurate pictures. Most of them have trouble with figures (as does Grandma) and make a habit of cluttering their canvases with niggling details (as Grandma does not). Very few have Grandma's luminosity of color, and almost none can match her in creating an illusion of deep space.

Because of these qualities, Kallir believes that the word "primitive" does not apply to her. He urges "natural" as a substitute. Expert Sidney Janis [16] thinks "self-taught" a better word. Grandma herself is not worried about such intellectual distinctions. Grandma simply aims to please.

"As for publicity," says Grandma, "that I'm too old to care for now." The present-day realities of life amidst her family are still what matter most to her. Some 30-odd descendants and in-laws live nearby, and her eldest daughter, Winona, shares Grandma's house. The low, efficient, L-shaped structure—with picture windows, false shutters, garage, and freezer—was put up for her by Grandma's son Forrest and two grandsons. They took the plan from a magazine illustration and finished building it two years ago.

Secluded Sunshine. At 93, Grandma still "makes a batch" of three or four pictures almost every week. She paints each day until she begins to tire: "Then I leave it to do something else; when my hand gets tired, it isn't so stiddy." Sometimes Grandma turns to

---

14. connoisseurs (kon'ə·sür'): experts by virtue of thorough knowledge; those able to evaluate critically the principles and execution of an art form.
15. Picasso, Braque & Co. (pē·kä'sō; bråk): Pablo Picasso (1881–   ), Spanish painter and sculptor; and Georges Braque (1882–1963), French painter; modern innovators who early strove to break away from the detailed sentimentality that characterized much of the art of the turn of the century and to overcome what Picasso called "the tyranny of the eye," or strict realism.
16. Sidney Janis: owner of a Manhattan art gallery specializing in contemporary art.

television, "though it's gettin' to be monotonous," or more likely just chats with Winona. Grandma's hearing is perfect, and she says, "I love the gossip." Now & then she entertains her neighboring great-grandchildren who "come troopin' acrost the field, lookin' like Coxey's Army." [17]

For breakfast and lunch she has coffee and oatmeal, "with lots of sugar—that's for vitality." Her dinners are hearty. "Good eatin's and good keepin's" is Grandma's recipe for health. At 10 o'clock Grandma is ready for bed: "The minute my head hits the pillow I'm dead to the world." She sleeps on an old feather tick [18] under an electric blanket.

For her years, Grandma is in fabulously good fettle, though she does complain that her feet "get clumpy" when she walks. A neighboring doctor drops by twice a week just to keep tabs on her. When people tease her about his being a beau, Grandma points out that "he's 15 years younger than me." The doctor is round in the middle, and, says Grandma, "he wouldn't have such a pot on him if he'd just lay down on the floor and roll over like he did when he was three years old and I first knew him."

Grandma's great and utterly unexpected fame, coming at the close of such a long, useful life, pleases her mainly for the personal contacts it brings her, and bothers her only because it brings too many. A "Do Not Disturb" sign from a hotel room hangs outside her front door to ward off the thousands of tourists who besiege her sunny old age. Yet those who get past that printed plea find that Grandma's main interest, now as ever, is people. Recently a visitor asked the radiant little old lady of what she was proudest after her 93 years of life and labor. The answer could not have been more Christian, or more grandmotherly: "I've helped some people."

17. **Coxey's Army:** Jacob S. Coxey (1854–1951) was a midwestern political reformer. In both 1894 and 1914, he led his army of ragged, unemployed Americans in marches on Washington to petition Congress to adopt a progressive program of aid to the unemployed. (His zeal is reflected in the name he chose for one of his children—Legal Tender Coxey.)
18. **feather tick:** mattress filled with feathers.

Notes and Comment:
On the Death of Grandma Moses

The death of a very old person seems no more natural, no less
an untoward incursion,[19] than the death of a young one. Perhaps
death seems natural only to Nature herself—and even she may
have some doubts. Yet we cannot think of the life, now concluded,
of Anna Mary Robertson Moses without cheerfulness. To live one
allotted span as a farm wife and the mother of ten children, and
then, at the age of seventy-six, to begin another, as an artist, as
Grandma Moses, and to extend this second life into twenty-five
years of unembarrassed productiveness—such a triumph over the
normal course of things offers small cause for mourning. If we do
mourn, it is for ourselves; she had become by her hundredth year
one of those old people who, as old buildings civilize a city or
spindly church spires bind up a landscape, make the world
seem safer. Shaw and Brancusi [20] were examples; Churchill and
Schweitzer [21] still are. They pay the world the great compliment
of being reluctant to leave it, and their reluctance becomes a
benediction.[22] Little is said nowadays about the wisdom of age.
Perhaps such wisdom is dreaded, for there is melancholy in it. Yet
even awkward truths can be gracious and cheering in their expression. Describing her method of painting, Mrs. Moses once said,
"I paint from the top down. First the sky, then the mountains,
then the hills, then the houses, then the cattle, and then the
people."

19. **incursion** (in·kûr′zhən): encroachment (on life).
20. **Shaw and Brancusi** (brong′koosh): George Bernard Shaw (1856–1950),
Irish-born English playwright, author, and socialist; Constantin Brancusi (1876–
1957), Rumanian-born French sculptor.
21. **Churchill and Schweitzer still are:** no longer, however—Winston S.
Churchill (b. 1874), statesman and twice Prime Minister of Great Britain,
died in 1965; Albert Schweitzer (b. 1875), French physician, Protestant minister, philosopher, musicologist, and founder of the famous hospital at Lam-
baréné in French Equatorial Africa, died in 1965.
22. **benediction** (ben′·ə·dik′shən): blessing (from Latin *bene*, "well," plus
dicere, "to say").

"Notes and Comment (On the Death of Grandma Moses)," © 1961 The New Yorker
Magazine, Inc., from *The New Yorker*, December 23, 1961. Reprinted by permission of the
publisher.

Meaning

1. What references or applications are there for the word *presents* in the title, "Presents from Grandma"? Explain the literal sense of *presents* in the title and explain how Grandma Moses gave "presents" to all of us.

2. Do you agree with *The New Yorker*'s opening statement about death? How does it apply to Grandma Moses?

3. What is "On the Death of Grandma Moses" about—Grandma Moses, her death, Death, Life, wisdom, old age? Explain.

4. What is unusual about Grandma Moses' method of painting, as she describes it on page 295? Is her comment also one about life and people?

Method

1. How does the opening paragraph in "Presents from Grandma" set the tone of the article? How does it introduce Grandma Moses? What words, phrases, constructions, and details particularly contribute to establishing the tone?

2. One of the ways a biographer can characterize a person is by presenting the person's own comments and reactions through dialogue or conversation. Notice how *Time*'s reporter has reproduced Grandma Moses' speech. How do her own words contribute to her characterization in "Presents from Grandma"?

3. Which of the other techniques of characterization (see Glossary) have the editors of *Time* used in their profile on Grandma Moses? Do you feel that their portrait of Mrs. Moses is well rounded, complete? Is there anything more about her you would like to know? If so, what?

4. Identify the main divisions of "Presents from Grandma." What sequence of time have the editors used in the essay? Would it have been better to start with Mrs. Moses' childhood and then work toward the present? Why? Why not? How well have the editors selected and limited their material? Have they skimmed over periods of time or over details where it seems logical to do so? Explain your answers, with direct references to the text.

5. Compare and contrast the language, vocabulary, length and complexity of sentences, and emphasis of "Presents from Grandma" and "Notes and Comment: On the Death of Grandma Moses." Would you say that both articles are aimed at the same sort of reader?

6. Both *Time* and *The New Yorker* close their articles with direct quotes from Mrs. Moses. Do the quotations in each case serve the same purpose? What is the effect of each on the rest of the selection? Does each fit in with its article's tone?

Language: "Timestyle"

Look back over "Presents from Grandma" and try to pick out words, expressions, etc. that have a striking effect or unusual ring. Look for compounds and hyphenated words, inverted word order, nouns used as adjectives, deletions in direct quotes, abbreviations and symbols in place of words normally written out, etc. Had you noticed these devices in your first reading of "Presents from Grandma"? Give reasons for your answer. Try to write a short paragraph in "Timestyle," using a person or event currently in the news as your basic subject.

Composition

On page 295, Grandma Moses describes the way she liked to paint: "I paint from the top down. First the sky, then the mountains, then the hills, then the houses, then the cattle, and then the people." How do *you* paint or draw, make a dress, build a model ship, tune-up a car, process a roll of film, prepare for a shopping trip, plan a party?

Draw up an outline showing the major steps in a process you are familiar with. Use the outline as a guide for a brief composition describing the process step by step.

Martin Luther King, Jr.

[1929–1968]

In 1964 the Nobel Peace Prize—consisting of a gold medal and an award of about $50,000—was given to an American Baptist minister, Dr. Martin Luther King, Jr. Ten years earlier, Dr. King had been a virtual unknown, serving quietly as the pastor of a small Baptist church in Montgomery, Alabama. Dr. King, who had been born in Atlanta, Georgia, had come to Montgomery after attending Morehouse College in Atlanta, and after studying at the Crozer Theological Seminary in Chester, Pennsylvania, and at Boston University, from which he had received a doctorate in theology in 1952. He arrived in Montgomery in 1954, a year before the beginning of the Montgomery bus boycott, which, after nearly a year's duration, helped bring about a ruling by the United States Supreme Court that the segregation of public transit facilities was unconstitutional. Dr. King emerged on national newsfronts as a leader of the boycott and, in that connection, as a man who was jailed and whose home was bombed because of his principles and determination.

The year after the boycott ended, 1957, Dr. King was elected president of the newly formed Southern Christian Leadership Conference, a consolidated civil-rights organization. He moved his young family to Atlanta, where SCLC headquarters were located, and became co-pastor of his father's Ebenezer Baptist Church.

Using the SCLC as his base of organization, Dr. King carefully built a civil-rights movement committed to the principle of militant but nonviolent protest and action. As a graduate student, Dr. King had been deeply influenced by the works and principles of two advocates of civil disobedience and passive resistance, the American thinker Henry David Thoreau * and Mohandas Gandhi, leader in the late 1940's of India's struggle for self-determination. Dr. King applied their doctrines to his own situation and times, and found a powerful instrument for achieving social justice.

Over the next decade, Dr. King made a point of being present wherever civil-rights activity was most intense. He led the lunch-

---

* **Thoreau:** his essay "Civil Disobedience" appears in *American Literature to 1900.*

counter sit-ins in Birmingham, Alabama, that had begun in April, 1963; in August of that year he helped organize and lead the March on Washington, a massive demonstration aimed at showing solidarity among the many civil-rights groups and at pressuring Congress to enact a strong civil-rights bill (which it did the following session). Dr. King was credited in 1964 with calming the threat of violence that followed the bombing of a Negro church in Birmingham, in which four little girls were killed. He led a voter-registration drive among Alabama Negroes in 1965. And he did much more during those years to bring his people closer to their goal of equal rights.

Such involvement in the struggle for civil rights kept Dr. King in constant danger, and he knew it. In the early spring of 1968 he traveled to Memphis, Tennessee, to lead a demonstration march in support of the city's striking sanitation workers, most of whom were Negroes. When he arrived in Memphis on April 3, he told a waiting crowd of supporters and newsmen that he knew he might be killed at any time but that he did not fear, because, as he said, "it really doesn't matter now, . . . I've been to the mountaintop . . . and I've seen the promised land." The next night, April 4, Dr. King was slain by a sniper whose bullet struck him as he stood on the balcony of his motel room chatting with friends and SCLC workers.

Dr. King's body was returned to Atlanta for burial. At his funeral, a cortege of thousands followed the mule-drawn wagon that carried his coffin to the cemetery.

After Dr. King's death, the SCLC continued under new leadership. Its hopes are still those Dr. King had expressed in the following address read on December 10, 1964, in Oslo, Norway, when he accepted the Nobel Peace Prize.

Nobel Peace Prize Acceptance Speech

It is impossible to begin this lecture without again expressing my deep appreciation to the Nobel Committee of the Norwegian Parliament for bestowing upon me and the civil-rights movement

"Nobel Lecture" by The Reverend Dr. Martin Luther King, Jr., copyright © the Nobel Foundation, 1964. Reprinted by permission of Elsevier Publishing Company.

in the United States such a great honor. Occasionally in life there are those moments of unutterable fulfillment which cannot be completely explained by those symbols called words. Their meaning can only be articulated by the inaudible language of the heart. Such is the moment I am presently experiencing. I experience this high and joyous moment not for myself alone but for those devotees of nonviolence who have moved so courageously against the ramparts of racial injustice and who in the process have acquired a new estimate of their own human worth. Many of them are young and cultured. Others are middle-aged and middle-class. The majority are poor and untutored. But they are all united in the quiet conviction that it is better to suffer in dignity than to accept segregation in humiliation. These are the real heroes of the freedom struggle: they are the noble people for whom I accept the Nobel Peace Prize.

This evening I would like to use this lofty and historic platform to discuss what appears to me to be the most pressing problem confronting mankind today. Modern man has brought this whole world to an awe-inspiring threshold of the future. He has reached new and astonishing peaks of scientific success. He has produced machines that think and instruments that peer into the unfathomable ranges of interstellar space. He has built gigantic bridges to span the seas and Gargantuan [1] buildings to kiss the skies. His airplanes and space ships have dwarfed distance, placed time in chains and carved highways through the stratosphere. This is a dazzling picture of modern man's scientific and technological progress.

Yet, in spite of these spectacular strides in science and technology, and still unlimited ones to come, something basic is missing. There is a sort of poverty of the spirit which stands in glaring contrast to our scientific and technological abundance. The richer we have become materially, the poorer we have become morally and spiritually. We have learned to fly the air like birds and swim the sea like fish, but we have not learned the simple art of living together as brothers.

Every man lives in two realms, the internal and the external. The internal is that realm of spiritual ends expressed in art, litera-

1. **Gargantuan:** huge. Gargantua is the gentle giant-prince in the French satire *Gargantua*, written in 1534 by François Rabelais (1494?–1553?).

ture, morals, and religion. The external is that complex of devices, techniques, mechanisms, and instrumentalities by means of which we live. Our problem today is that we have allowed the internal to become lost in the external. We have allowed the means by which we live to outdistance the ends for which we live. So much of modern life can be summarized in that arresting dictum of the poet Thoreau: "Improved means to an unimproved end." [2] This is the serious predicament, the deep and haunting problem confronting modern man. If we are to survive today, our moral and spiritual "lag" must be eliminated. Enlarged material powers spell enlarged peril, if there is not proportionate growth of the soul. When the "without" of a man's nature subjugates the "within," dark storm clouds begin to form in the world.

This problem of spiritual and moral lag, which constitutes modern man's chief dilemma, expresses itself in three larger problems which grow out of man's ethical infantilism. Each of these problems, while appearing to be separate and isolated, is inextricably bound to the other. I refer to racial injustice, poverty, and war.

The first problem that I would like to mention is racial injustice. The struggle to eliminate the evil of racial injustice constitutes one of the major struggles of our time. The present upsurge of the Negro people of the United States grows out of a deep and passionate determination to make freedom and equality a reality here and now. In one sense the civil-rights movement in the United States is a special American phenomenon which must be understood in the light of American history and dealt with in terms of the American situation. But, on another and more important level, what is happening in the United States today is a relatively small part of a world development.

We live in a day, says the philosopher Alfred North Whitehead,[3] "when civilization is shifting its basic outlook: a major turning point in history where the presuppositions on which so-

2. Thoreau . . . unimproved end": the dictum, or adage, is from "Economy," the opening chapter of Thoreau's *Walden* (1854). Thoreau then gave an example of what he meant about such "improvements": "We are in great haste to construct a magnetic telegraph from Maine to Texas; but Maine and Texas, it may be, have nothing important to communicate."

3. Alfred North Whitehead (1861–1947): English-born mathematician and philosopher.

ciety is structured are being analyzed, sharply challenged, and profoundly changed." What we are seeing now is a freedom explosion, the realization of "an idea whose time has come," to use Victor Hugo's phrase. The deep rumbling of discontent that we hear today is the thunder of disinherited masses, rising from dungeons of oppression to the bright hills of freedom, in one majestic chorus the rising masses singing, in the words of our freedom song, "Ain't gonna let nobody turn us around." All over the world, like a fever, the freedom movement is spreading in the widest liberation in history. The great masses of people are determined to end the exploitation of their races and land. They are awake and moving toward their goal like a tidal wave. You can hear them rumbling in every village street, on the docks, in the houses, among the students, in the churches, and at political meetings. Historic movement was for several centuries that of the nations and societies of western Europe out into the rest of the world in "conquests" of various sorts. That period, the era of colonialism, is at an end. East is meeting West. The earth is being redistributed. Yes, we are "shifting our basic outlooks."

These developments should not surprise any student of history. Oppressed people cannot remain oppressed forever. The yearning for freedom eventually manifests itself. The Bible tells the thrilling story of how Moses stood in Pharaoh's court centuries ago and cried, "Let my people go." [4]

This is a kind of opening chapter in a continuing story. The present struggle in the United States is a later chapter in the same unfolding story. Something within has reminded the Negro of his birthright of freedom, and something without has reminded him that it can be gained. Consciously or unconsciously, he has been caught up by the Zeitgeist,[5] and with his black brothers of Africa and his brown and yellow brothers in Asia, South America, and the Caribbean, the United States Negro is moving with a sense of great urgency toward the promised land of racial justice.

Fortunately, some significant strides have been made in the struggle to end the long night of racial injustice. We have seen the

---

4. **Moses . . . "Let my people go"**: a quotation from Exodus 5:1. The story of Moses before the Pharaoh is related in Exodus 5:1–12:51.
5. **Zeitgeist** (tsīt′gīst): *German,* literally, "spirit of the times"; the intellectual and moral tendencies that characterize a particular historical era.

magnificent drama of independence unfold in Asia and Africa. Just thirty years ago there were only three independent nations in the whole of Africa.

But today thirty-five African nations have risen from colonial bondage. In the United States we have witnessed the gradual demise of the system of racial segregation. Its Supreme Court's decision of 1954 outlawing segregation in the public schools gave a legal and constitutional deathblow to the whole doctrine of "separate but equal."

The court decreed that separate facilities are inherently unequal and that to segregate a child on the basis of race is to deny that child equal protection of the law.

This decision came as a beacon light of hope to millions of disinherited people. Then came that glowing day a few months ago when a strong civil-rights bill became the law of our land. This bill, which was first recommended and promoted by President [John F.] Kennedy was passed because of the overwhelming support and perseverance from millions of Americans, Negro and white.

It came as a bright interlude in the long and sometimes turbulent struggle for civil rights: the beginning of a second emancipation proclamation providing a comprehensive legal basis for equality of opportunity.

Since the passage of this bill we have seen some encouraging and surprising signs of compliance. I am happy to report that, by and large, communities all over the southern part of the United States are obeying the civil-rights law and showing remarkable good sense in the process.

Another indication that progress is being made was found in the recent [1964] Presidential election in the United States. The American people revealed great maturity by overwhelmingly rejecting a Presidential candidate who had become identified with extremism, racism, and retrogression. The voters of our nation rendered a telling blow to the radical right. They defeated those elements in our society which seek to pit white against Negro and lead the nation down a dangerous fascist path.

Let me not leave you with a false impression. The problem is far from solved. We still have a long, long way to go before the dream of freedom is a reality for the Negro in the United States.

To put it figuratively in biblical language, we have left the dusty soils of Egypt and crossed a Red Sea whose waters had for years been hardened by a long and piercing winter of massive resistance. But before we reach the majestic shores of the Promised Land, there is a frustrating and bewildering wilderness ahead. We must still face prodigious hilltops of opposition and gigantic mountains of resistance. But with patient and firm determination we will press on until every valley of despair is exalted to new peaks of hope; until every mountain of pride and irrationality is made low by the leveling process of humility and compassion; until the rough places of injustice are transformed into a smooth plane of equality of opportunity; and until the crooked places of prejudice are transformed by the straightening process of bright-eyed wisdom.[6]

What the main sections of the civil-rights movement in the United States are saying is that the demand for dignity, equality, jobs, and citizenship will not be abandoned or diluted or postponed. If that means resistance and conflict we shall not flinch. We shall not be cowed. We are no longer afraid.

The word that symbolized the spirit and the outward form of our encounter is *nonviolence*, and it is doubtless that factor which made it seem appropriate to award a peace prize to one identified with struggle. Broadly speaking, nonviolence in the civil-rights struggle has meant not relying on arms and weapons of struggle. It has meant noncooperation with customs and laws which are institutional aspects of a regime of discrimination and enslavement. It has meant direct participation of masses in protest, rather than reliance on indirect methods which frequently do not involve masses in action at all.

Nonviolence has also meant that my people in the agonizing struggles of recent years have taken suffering upon themselves instead of inflicting it on others. It has meant, as I said, that we are no longer afraid and cowed. But in some substantial degree it has meant that we do not want to instill fear in others or into the society of which we are a part. The Movement does not seek to

6. **To put it figuratively . . . wisdom:** this section summarizes and paraphrases from the Bible, specifically, from (a) Exodus 14, which relates the flight of the Israelites from Egypt through the midst of the Red Sea and into the desert wilderness of Shür; and (b) Isaiah 40:4, which reads, "Every valley shall be exalted, and every mountain and hill shall be made low; and the crooked shall be made straight, and the rough places plain."

liberate Negroes at the expense of the humiliation and enslavement of whites. It seeks no victory over anyone. It seeks to liberate American society and to share in the self-liberation of all people.

Violence as a way of achieving racial justice is both impractical and immoral. I am not unmindful of the fact that violence often brings about momentary results. Nations have frequently won their independence in battle. But in spite of temporary victories, violence never brings permanent peace. It solves no social problem; it merely creates new and more complicated ones. Violence is impractical because it is a descending spiral ending in destruction for all. It is immoral because it seeks to humiliate the opponent rather than win his understanding; it seeks to annihilate rather than convert. Violence is immoral because it thrives on hatred rather than love. It destroys community and makes brotherhood impossible. It leaves society in monologue rather than dialogue. Violence ends up defeating itself. It creates bitterness in the survivors and brutality in the destroyers.

In a real sense nonviolence seeks to redeem the spiritual and moral lag that I spoke of earlier as the chief dilemma of modern man. It seeks to secure moral ends through moral means. Nonviolence is a powerful and just weapon. Indeed, it is a weapon unique in history, which cuts without wounding, and ennobles the man who wields it.

I believe in this method because I think it is the only way to reestablish a broken community. It is the method which seeks to implement the just law by appealing to the conscience of the great decent majority who through blindness, fear, pride, and irrationality have allowed their consciences to sleep.

The nonviolent resisters can summarize their message in the following simple terms: We will take direct action against injustice despite the failure of governmental and other official agencies to act first. We will not obey unjust laws nor submit to unjust practices. We will do this peacefully, openly, cheerfully, because our aim is to persuade. We adopt the means of nonviolence because our end is a community at peace with itself. We will try to persuade with our words, but if our words fail, we will try to persuade with our acts. We will always be willing to talk and seek fair compromise, but we are ready to suffer when necessary and even risk our lives to become witnesses to truth as we see it.

This approach to the problem of racial injustice is not at all without successful precedent. It was used in a magnificent way by Mohandas K. Gandhi to challenge the might of the British Empire and free his people from the political domination and economic exploitation inflicted upon them for centuries. He struggled only with the weapons of truth, soul force, noninjury, and courage.

In the past ten years, unarmed gallant men and women of the United States have given living testimony to the moral power and efficacy [7] of nonviolence. By the thousands, faceless, anonymous, relentless young people, black and white, have temporarily left the ivory towers of learning for the barricades of bias. Their courageous and disciplined activities have come as a refreshing oasis in a desert sweltering with the heat of injustice. They have taken our whole nation back to those great wells of democracy which were dug deep by the founding fathers in the formulation of the Constitution and the Declaration of Independence. One day all of America will be proud of their achievements.

I am only too well aware of the human weaknesses and failures which exist, the doubts about the efficacy of nonviolence, and the open advocacy of violence by some. But I am still convinced that nonviolence is both the most practically sound and morally excellent way to grapple with the age-old problem of racial injustice.

A second evil which plagues the modern world is that of poverty. Like a monstrous octopus, it projects its nagging, prehensile [8] tentacles in lands and villages all over the world. Almost two-thirds of the peoples of the world go to bed hungry at night. They are undernourished, ill-housed, and shabbily clad. Many of them have no houses or beds to sleep in. Their only beds are the sidewalks of the cities and the dusty roads of the villages. Most of these poverty-stricken children of God have never seen a physician or a dentist. This problem of poverty is not only seen in the class division between the highly developed industrial nations and the so-called underdeveloped nations: it is seen in the great economic gaps within the rich nations themselves. Take my own country, for example. We have developed the greatest system of production that history has ever known. We have become the richest nation

7. **efficacy** (ef'ə·kə·sē): power to produce a desired or intended effect or result.
8. **prehensile** (pri·hen'sil): adapted for holding or grasping. Monkey tails and elephant trunks are examples of prehensile organs.

in the world. Our gross national product this year [1964] will reach the astounding figure of almost 650 billion dollars. Yet, at least one-fifth of our fellow citizens—some ten million families, comprising about forty million individuals—are bound to a miserable culture of poverty. In a sense the poverty of the poor in America is more frustrating than the poverty of Africa and Asia. The misery of the poor in Africa and Asia is shared misery, a fact of life for the vast majority; they are all poor together as a result of years of exploitation and underdevelopment. In sad contrast, the poor in America know that they live in the richest nation in the world and that, even though they are perishing on a lonely island of poverty, they are surrounded by a vast ocean of material prosperity. Glistening towers of glass and steel, easily seen from their slum dwellings, spring up almost overnight. Jetliners speed over their ghettos at six hundred miles an hour; satellites streak through outer space and reveal details of the moon. President Johnson, in his [1964] State of the Union Message, emphasized this contradiction when he heralded the United States' "highest standard of living in the world" and deplored that it was accompanied by "dislocation, loss of jobs, and the specter of poverty in the midst of plenty."

So it is obvious that if man is to redeem his spiritual and moral "lag" he must go all out to bridge the social and economic gulf between the "haves" and the "have nots" of the world. Poverty is one of the most urgent items on the agenda of modern life.

There is nothing new about poverty. What is new, however, is that we have the resources to get rid of it. More than a century and a half ago people began to be disturbed about the twin problems of population and production. A thoughtful Englishman named Malthus [9] wrote a book that set forth some rather frightening conclusions. He predicted that the human family was gradually moving toward global starvation, because the world was producing people faster than it was producing food and material to support them. Later scientists, however, disproved the conclusion of Malthus, and revealed that he had vastly underestimated the resources of the world and the resourcefulness of man.

9. **Malthus:** Thomas Robert Malthus (1766–1834), British political economist and theorist. The doctrine of Malthusianism suggests that social misery is the result of the tendency of the human population to increase faster than the means by which it is fed.

Not too many years ago, Dr. Kirtley Mather, a Harvard geologist, wrote a book entitled *Enough and to Spare*. He set forth the basic theme that famine is wholly unnecessary in the modern world. Today, therefore, the question on the agenda must read, Why should there be hunger and privation in any land, in any city, at any table, when man has the resources and the scientific know-how to provide all mankind with the basic necessities of life? Even deserts can be irrigated and topsoil can be replaced. We cannot complain of lack of land, for there are twenty-five million square miles of tillable land, of which we are using less than seven million. We have amazing knowledge of vitamins, nutrition, the chemistry of food, and the versatility of atoms. There is no deficit in human resources; the deficit is in human will. The well-off and the secure have too often become indifferent and oblivious to the poverty and deprivation in their midst. The poor in our countries have been shut out of our minds and driven from the mainstream of our societies, because we have allowed them to become invisible. Just as nonviolence exposed the ugliness of racial injustice, so must the infection and sickness of poverty be exposed and healed—not only its symptoms but its basic causes. This, too, will be a fierce struggle but we must not be afraid to pursue the remedy no matter how formidable the task.

The time has come for an all-out world war against poverty. The rich nations must use their vast resources of wealth to develop the underdeveloped, school the unschooled, and feed the unfed. Ultimately a great nation is a compassionate nation. No individual or nation can be great if it does not have a concern for "the least of these." Deeply etched in the fiber of our religious tradition is the conviction that men are made in the image of God, and that they are souls of infinite metaphysical value, the heirs of a legacy of dignity and worth. If we feel this as a profound moral fact we cannot be content to see men hungry, to see men victimized with starvation and ill-health when we have the means to help them. The wealthy nations must go all out to bridge the gulf between the rich minority and the poor majority.

In the final analysis, the rich must not ignore the poor because both rich and poor are tied in a single garment of destiny. All life is interrelated, and all men are interdependent. The agony of the poor diminishes the rich, and the salvation of the poor enlarges the rich. We are inevitably our brother's keeper because of the inter-related structure of reality. John Donne interpreted this truth in graphic terms when he affirmed:

> No man is an *Iland*, intire of it selfe; every-man is a peece of the *Continent*, a part of the *maine*, if a Clod bee washed away by the *Sea*, *Europe* is the lesse, as well as if a *Promontorie* were, as well as if a *Mannor* of thy *friends* or of *thine owne* were; any mans *death* diminishes *me*, because I am involved in *Mankinde*; and therefore never send to know for whom the *bell* tolls; it tolls for *thee*.[10]

A third great evil confronting our world is that of war. Recent events have vividly reminded us that nations are not reducing but rather increasing their arsenals of weapons of mass destruction. The best brains in the highly developed nations of the world are devoted to military technology. The proliferation of nuclear weapons has not been halted, in spite of the Limited Test Ban Treaty.[11] On the contrary, the detonation of an atomic device by the first nonwhite, non-Western and so-called underdeveloped power, namely, the Chinese People's Republic, opens new vistas of exposure of vast multitudes, the whole of humanity, to insidious terrorization by the ever-present threat of annihilation. The fact that most of the time human beings put the truth about the nature and risks of the nuclear war out of their minds because it is too painful and therefore not "acceptable" does not alter the nature and risks of such war. The device of rejection may temporarily cover up anxiety, but it does not bestow peace of mind and emotional security.

So man's proneness to engage in war is still a fact. But wisdom born of experience should tell us that war is obsolete. There may have been a time when war served as a negative good by preventing the spread and growth of an evil force, but the destructive power of modern weapons eliminated even the possibility that war may serve as a negative good. If we assume that life is worth living and that man has a right to survive, then we must find an alternative

10. "No man is an *Iland* . . . it tolls for *thee*": a famous passage from Meditation XVII of John Donne's *Devotions upon Emergent Occasions*, printed here as it appeared in the original edition of 1624.
11. Limited Test Ban Treaty: ratified in 1964; by 1968, 107 nations had signed the treaty.

to war. In a day when vehicles hurtle through outer space and guided ballistic missiles carve highways of death through the stratosphere, no nation can claim victory in war. A so-called limited war will leave little more than a calamitous legacy of human suffering, political turmoil, and spiritual disillusionment. A world war—God forbid!—will leave only smoldering ashes as a mute testimony of a human race whose folly led inexorably to ultimate death. So if modern man continues to flirt unhesitatingly with war, he will transform his earthly habitat into an inferno such as even the mind of Dante could not imagine.[12]

Therefore I venture to suggest to all of you, and all who hear and may eventually read these words, that the philosophy and strategy of nonviolence become immediately a subject for study and for serious experimentation in every field of human conflict, by no means excluding the relations between nations. It is, after all, nation-states which made war, which have produced the weapons which threaten the survival of mankind, weapons that are both genocidal [13] and suicidal in character.

Here also we have ancient habits to deal with and indescribably complicated problems to solve. But unless we abdicate our humanity altogether and succumb to fear and impotence in the presence of the weapons we have ourselves created, it is as imperative and urgent to put an end to war and violence between nations as it is to put an end to racial injustice. Equality with whites will hardly solve the problems of either whites or Negroes if it means equality in a society under the spell of terror and a world doomed to extinction.

I do not wish to minimize the complexity of the problems that need to be faced in achieving disarmament and peace. But I think it is a fact that we shall not have the will, the courage, and the insight to deal with such matters unless in this field we are prepared to undergo a mental and spiritual reevaluation—a change

12. inferno . . . Dante could not imagine: a comparison with Dante's *Divina Commedia*, or *Divine Comedy*, a fourteenth-century poet's vision of (a) Inferno, or Hell, (b) Purgatorio, or Purgatory, and (c) Paradiso, or Heaven.

13. genocide (jen′ə·sīd): the systematic extermination of an entire ethnic or national group. The word is from Greek *genos*, "tribe," plus Latin *-cidium*, "slaughter," and was coined in 1944 to denote the attempted annihilation of Jews under the Nazi regime.

of focus which will enable us to see that the things which seem most real and powerful are indeed now unreal and have come under the sentence of death. We need to make a supreme effort to generate the readiness, indeed the eagerness, to enter into the new world which is now possible, "a city which hath foundations, whose builder and maker is God." [14]

We will not build a peaceful world by following a negative path. It is not enough to say "we must not wage war." It is necessary to love peace and sacrifice for it. We must concentrate not merely on the negative expulsion of war, but on the positive affirmation of peace. There is a fascinating little story that is preserved for us in Greek literature about Ulysses and the Sirens. [15] The Sirens had the ability to sing so sweetly that sailors could not resist steering toward their island. Many ships were lured upon the rocks, and men forgot home, duty, and honor as they flung themselves into the sea to be embraced by arms that drew them down to death. Ulysses, determined not to be lured by the Sirens, decided to tie himself tighty to the mast of his boat, and his crew stuffed their ears with wax. But other sailors learned a better way to save themselves: they took on board the beautiful singer Orpheus, [16] whose melodies were sweeter than the music of the Sirens. When Orpheus sang, who bothered to listen to the Sirens?

So we must fix our vision not merely on the negative expulsion of war, but upon the positive affirmation of peace. We must see that peace represents a sweeter music, a cosmic melody that is far superior to the discords of war. Somehow we must transform the

14. "a city . . . God": a quotation from the Epistle of Paul to the Hebrews, 11:10.
15. Ulysses and the Sirens: Ulysses (or Odysseus) is the protagonist of the *Odyssey* by Homer; the sweet song of the two Sirens—each half-woman and half-bird—lured sailors to their deaths. The encounter between Ulysses and the Sirens is related in Book XII of the *Odyssey*, "Scylla and Charybdis."
16. other sailors . . . Orpheus: the other sailors were Jason and his Argonauts, whose adventures in seeking the Golden Fleece are related in many ancient Greek myths and legends. Orpheus in Greek mythology was the son of the god Apollo and the muse Calliope and was regarded by the Greeks as the sweetest of all singers. His music could make even the trees and the mountains move to follow its source. Jason and the Argonauts used Orpheus's singing to charm the otherwise fatal rocks of the Symplegades, whose gnashing would have crushed the *Argo* as it sailed between them; Orpheus also charmed to sleep the Colchian dragon, thus allowing Jason to steal the Golden Fleece it guarded.

dynamics of the world power struggle from the negative nuclear arms race, which no one can win, to a positive contest to harness man's creative genius for the purpose of making peace and prosperity a reality for all of the nations of the world. In short, we must shift the arms race into a "peace race." If we have the will and determination to mount such a peace offensive, we will unlock hitherto tightly sealed doors of hope and transform our imminent cosmic elegy [17] into a psalm of creative fulfillment.

All that I have said boils down to the point of affirming that mankind's survival is dependent upon man's ability to solve the problems of racial injustice, poverty, and war; the solution of these problems is in turn dependent upon man's squaring his moral progress with his scientific progress, and learning the practical art of living in harmony. Some years ago a famous novelist died. Among his papers was found a list of suggested story plots for future stories, the most prominently underscored being this one: "A widely separated family inherit a house in which they have to live together." This is the great new problem of mankind. We have inherited a big house, a great "world house" in which we have to live together—black and white, Easterners and Westerners, Gentiles and Jews, Catholics and Protestants, Moslems and Hindus, a family unduly separated in ideas, culture, and interests who, because we can never again live without each other, must learn, somehow, in this one big world, to live with each other.

This means that more and more our loyalties must become ecumenical [18] rather than sectional. We must now give an overriding loyalty to mankind as a whole in order to preserve the best in our individual societies.

This call for a worldwide fellowship that lifts neighborly concern beyond one's tribe, race, class, and nation is in reality a call for an all-embracing and unconditional love for all men. This oft-misunderstood and misinterpreted concept, so readily dismissed by the Nietzsches of the world [19] as a weak and cowardly force, has

17. **our imminent cosmic elegy:** that is, our impending doom by nuclear holocaust. An elegy is a meditative poem of lamentation or mourning for the dead.
18. **ecumenical** (ek'yōō·men'i·kəl): universal; worldwide.
19. **Nietzsches of the world:** the followers of Friedrich Nietzsche (nē'chə; 1844–1900), a German philosopher who believed in a doctrine of "superman," i.e., that man is perfectible through his own assertion and effort, without the help of God or other men.

now become an absolute necessity for the survival of man. When I speak of love I am not speaking of some sentimental and weak response, which is little more than emotional bosh. I am speaking of that force which all of the great religions have seen as the supreme unifying principle of life. Love is somehow the key that unlocks the door which leads to ultimate reality. This Hindu-Moslem-Christian-Jewish-Buddhist belief about ultimate reality is beautifully summed up in the First Epistle of St. John:

> Let us love one another: for love is of God; and every one that loveth is born of God, and knoweth God. He that loveth not knoweth not God; for God is love. . . . If we love one another, God dwelleth in us, and his love is perfected in us.[20]

Let us hope that this spirit will become the order of the day. As Arnold Toynbee [21] says: "Love is the ultimate force that makes for the saving choice of life and good against the damning choice of death and evil. Therefore the first hope in our inventory must be the hope that love is going to have the last word." We can no longer afford to worship the God of hate or bow before the altar of retaliation. The oceans of history are made turbulent by the ever rising tides of hate. History is cluttered with the wreckage of nations and individuals that pursued this self-defeating path of hate. Love is the key to the solution of the problems of the world.

Let me close by saying that I have the personal faith that mankind will somehow rise up to the occasion and give new directions to an age drifting rapidly to its doom. In spite of the tensions and uncertainties of this period, something profoundly meaningful is taking place. Old systems of exploitation and oppression are passing away, and out of the wombs of a frail world new systems of justice and equality are being born. Doors of opportunity are gradually being opened to those at the bottom of society. The shirtless and barefoot people of the land are developing a new sense of "somebodiness" and carving a tunnel of hope through the dark mountain of despair. "The people who sat in darkness have

20. Let us love . . . in us: See I John 4:7–16.
21. Arnold Toynbee (b. 1889): English historian and historical theorist. His *Study of History,* from which the quotation is taken, is part of a project aimed at defining and outlining the political, social, religious, cultural, and economic characteristics that make up a great society.

seen a great light." [22] Here and there, an individual or group dares to love and rises to the majestic heights of moral maturity. So in a real sense this is a great time to be alive. Therefore, I am not yet discouraged about the future. Granted that the easygoing optimism of yesterday is impossible. Granted that those who pioneer in the struggle for peace and freedom will still face uncomfortable jail terms, painful threats of death; they will still be battered by the storms of persecution leading them to the nagging feeling that they can no longer bear such a heavy burden, and to the temptation of wanting to retreat to a more quiet and serene life. Granted that we face a world crisis which leaves us standing so often amid the surging murmur of life's restless sea. But every crisis has both its dangers and its opportunities. It can spell either salvation or doom. In a dark confused world the kingdom of God may yet reign in the hearts of men.

22. "The people . . . great light": a quotation drawn indirectly from the many references in the Bible, particularly in the New Testament, to the salvation of sinners (those who sit in darkness) through faith and belief in God (the light).

Meaning and Method

1. Reread page 300. What did Dr. King mean by saying, "Every-man lives in two realms, the internal and the external"? Give specific examples of your own to illustrate your answer.

2. Dr. King said that the problem of spiritual and moral lag expresses itself in three larger problems which grow out of man's ethical infantilism. These problems are racial injustice, poverty, and war. How does Dr. King account for the tremendous movement for the full realization of racial equality?

   Regarding the problem of war, what arguments does Dr. King offer that "war is obsolete" and that it can no longer serve as a negative good by preventing the spread and growth of an evil force? (Review pages 309–12.) Do you agree with Dr. King's reasoning and sentiment?

3. On page 304, Dr. King opens a detailed presentation of his views by saying, "The word that symbolized the spirit and the outward form of our encounter is *nonviolence.* . . ." What did the word mean to Dr. King? What are the physical and moral techniques and principles of nonviolence?

4. Summarize Dr. King's reasonings against the use of violence as a means to an end. Why, for example, did he believe that violence

"as a way of achieving racial justice is both impractical and immoral" (page 305)? What did he means when he said, "It leaves society in monologue rather than dialogue"?

Do you agree with Dr. King's feelings about violence as an instrument with which to achieve racial equality?

5. On page 306, Dr. King spoke about poverty as an "evil which plagues the modern world," in both rich and poor nations alike. He emphasized the evil of poverty by showing the incongruity of its existence in as powerful and rich a nation as America. Enumerate some of the incongruities or contradictions about poverty in America. How did Dr. King attempt to prove that poverty could be eliminated? What suggestions did he offer for alleviating poverty throughout the world?

6. What methods of expository development has Dr. King used in the section on nonviolence (beginning on page 304)—enumeration of many details and particulars, direct analysis, comparison and/or contrast, illustration with examples, direct presentation of reasons and arguments, or a combination of methods? Explain, citing passages in the text that support or illustrate your answer.

7. One of the figures of rhetoric Dr. King uses in his speech is *antithesis,* the use of two contrasting expressions or ideas poised oppositely. When the opposing elements are also parallel in grammatical structure, the device is called *balanced antithesis.* For example, Dr. King says (on page 300), "The richer we have become materially, the poorer we have become morally and spiritually." Other figures of rhetoric in the speech are *repetition* (of a key word or phrase in close proximity, for emphasis) and *parallel structure* (using statements that are similar in grammatical structure).

Read the following excerpts from Dr. King's speech and identify the figure of rhetoric used in each.

(a) He has reached new and astonishing peaks of scientific success. He has produced machines that think and instruments that peer into the unfathomable ranges of interstellar space. He has built gigantic bridges to span the seas and Gargantuan buildings to kiss the skies. (page 300)

(b) Something within has reminded the Negro of his birthright of freedom, and something without has reminded him that it can be gained. (302)

(c) It [violence] is immoral because it seeks to humiliate the opponent rather than win his understanding; it seeks to annihilate rather than convert. (305)

(d) It destroys community and makes brotherhood impossible. It leaves society in monologue rather than dialogue. . . . It

creates bitterness in the survivors and brutality in the destroyers. (305)

(e) We must concentrate not merely on the negative expulsion
of war but on the positive affirmation of peace. (311)

8. Name the figure of speech in each of the following quotations.
Identify the basis for each comparison and, where applicable,
show how the figure of speech is extended through the use of related words. Remember that verb forms frequently serve as
metaphors.

(a) He has built gigantic bridges to span the seas and Gargantuan buildings to kiss the skies. (page 300)

(b) The deep rumbling of discontent that we hear today is the
thunder of disinherited masses, rising from dungeons of
oppression to the bright hills of freedom. . . . (302)

(c) All over the world, like a fever, the freedom movement is
spreading in the widest liberation in history. (302)

(d) Nonviolence is a powerful and just weapon. Indeed, it is a
weapon unique in history, which cuts without wounding, and
ennobles the man who wields it. (305)

(e) Their courageous and disciplined activities have come as
a refreshing oasis in a desert sweltering with the heat of injustice. They have taken our whole nation back to those
great wells of democracy which were dug deep by the founding fathers in the formulation of the Constitution and the
Declaration of Independence. (306)

(f) Just as nonviolence exposed the ugliness of racial injustice,
so must the infection and sickness of poverty be exposed
and healed . . . (308)

(g) We must see that peace represents a sweeter music, a cosmic
melody that is far superior to the discords of war. (311)

(h) The shirtless and barefoot people of the land are developing
a new sense of "somebodiness" and carving a tunnel of hope
through the dark mountain of despair. (313)

9. *Rhythm* and *meter* are literary terms usually applied in an analysis
of poetry but which show up occasionally in discussions of prose.
Hemingway and Faulkner, for example, were known—each in his
idiosyncratic way—for their rhythmic prose. There is definite
rhythm in many of Dr. King's sentences. For example, review the
following sentence from page 311: "Many ships were lured upon
the rocks, and men forgot home, duty, and honor as they flung
themselves into the sea */to BE/emBRACED/by ARMS/that
DREW/them DOWN/to DEATH."* The italicized part of this
sentence is in iambic meter.

Find other passages that seem particularly rhythmic; identify what you think is the meter or rhythm pattern and explain its effect. Does it require, for example, fast reading or slow? even or varying tone of voice?

10. The Bible was a major influence in Dr. King's life and in many instances gave both content and form to his thoughts. In his speeches he often quoted and paraphrased biblical passages and borrowed a biblical diction and style.

How has Dr. King used the Bible in his Nobel lecture? Review in particular the section beginning on page 304 with "To put it figuratively in biblical language . . ." and indicate the effect of the biblical language on the style and the tone of Dr. King's speech.

Is Dr. King's address perhaps *too* effective and appealing in its richness of language? Do you think it runs the risk of pleasing the ear too much, so that the listener or reader is distracted from the message?

Composition

War. Poverty. Racial injustice. These, Dr. King said, are the ills that beset man and that must be cured if man is to survive.

One of the most obvious and often overlooked victims of war, racism, and poverty is the American Indian. The results of a study published in late 1968 revealed that 90 percent of all American Indians live in substandard housing, including tin-roofed shacks, brush shelters, and even abandoned automobiles. The study also indicates that Indian unemployment ranges between 40 and 75 percent, compared with approximately 4 percent for the nation as a whole. Indian children complete on the average about 5 years of school, compared to a national average of over 11 years. Life expectancy for Indians is 43, whereas the national average is 68 years. (Peter Farb, "The American Indian: A Portrait in Limbo," *Saturday Review*, October 12, 1968.)

As a research-writing assignment, use articles in encyclopedias, books on the subject, and articles listed in the *Reader's Guide to Periodical Literature*, to collect information and data on a particular American Indian tribe or on Indian life in a particular section of North America. Explain present conditions, progress, impediments, etc., and offer specific recommendations or suggestions that might help alleviate the problems Indians face.

W. Haywood Burns

W. Haywood Burns was born in 1940 in Peekskill, New York. After attending public schools there, he went on to Harvard University, from which he was graduated with honors in 1962. During the following year, Mr. Burns was the Lionel de Jersey Scholar in Residence at Emanuel College, Cambridge University. He returned to the United States in 1964 and entered the Yale Law School.

With the receipt of his law degree in 1966, Mr. Burns began work in New York City as a staff attorney for the NAACP Legal Defense and Educational Fund. He is also an attorney for the National Office for the Rights of the Indigent.

Mr. Burns has also contributed to the books *Harlem: A Community in Transition* (1964), edited by John Henrik Clarke, and *Southern Justice* (1965), edited by Leon Friedman. Other writings, including articles, poems, and book reviews, have appeared in *Commentary, The Listener, RACE, Freedomways,* and other American and British journals.

His book, *The Voices of Negro Protest in America,* was published in 1963 under the auspices of the Institute of Race Relations, London. The following selection, "Let My People Go," is a chapter from this book and is based on Burns's own "extensive research on and among the Black Muslims" and on two books about the black-nationalist group, C. Eric Lincoln's *The Black Muslims in America* and E. U. Essien-Udom's *Black Nationalism.*

Let My People Go

"Behold, I will send you Elijah the prophet before the coming of the great and dreadful day of the Lord."

—Malachi 4:5

Both the National Association for the Advancement of Colored People and the nonviolent direct-action groups are motivated by a desire to see the American promise fulfilled. Their

"Let My People Go," pp. 61–81 from *The Voices of Negro Protest in America* by W. Haywood Burns. Published by Oxford University Press for the Institute of Race Relations. Reprinted by permission of the publisher.

Let My People Go 319

ultimate goal as organizations is to go out of existence, for they are working for the day when groups of their nature will no longer be necessary and men will be able to move in society without the hindrances of racial prejudice and discrimination.

Not all Negroes, however, share the integrationist motives of these groups. For many it is no longer possible to believe in the so-called American Dream or the white man's good intentions for an honest democracy. The force of oppression has turned such people in on themselves, and their voices of protest have quite another sound, their solutions quite another tenor. Black nationalist organizations claim the membership of thousands of Negroes in the U.S.A., and the number whose lives and thought are in some way directly influenced by these groups is probably in the millions.

Many, though not all, of these groups are separationist in policy, while others lay emphasis on a type of cultural chauvinism.[1] By far the largest and most influential of these militant black nationalist organizations is The Lost-Found Nation of Islam in the Wilderness of North America—known commonly as the Black Muslims. Since the middle of the 1950's, when their meteoric upsurge in membership began, the Muslims have exercised an increasingly important influence upon the nation's racial scene. The movement is significant both in what the mere existence of such a group indicates about American society and for the insights it gives into the mood of a large segment of the American Negro community.

Though it is only in recent years that the Black Muslims have attained their greatest strength and influence in the area of Negro protest, the search for their beginnings takes us back several decades. The history of the modern Black Muslim movement begins some time in the summer of 1930, when a mysterious peddler appeared on the streets of Detroit. He seemed to be of Arab origin, but to this day no one has proved his racial or national background. He sold goods in the Negro section of the city and was patronized by the women, who were interested in his exotic wares:

> He came first to our houses selling raincoats and then, afterwards, silks. In this way he could get into the people's

1. others . . . cultural chauvinism (shō′vən·iz′əm): in New York City the Cultural Association for Women of African Heritage and the Order of Danbhala Ouedo are examples [*Author's note*]. *Chauvinism* means unreasoning or exaggerated attachment to one's race, group, nationality, etc.

houses, for every woman was eager to see the nice things the peddler had for sale. He told us that the silks he carried were the same kind that our people used to wear in their home country, and that he was from there. So we asked him to tell us about our own country.[2]

So great was the interest in the preaching of this man that a hall had to be rented for special meetings. He taught first from the Bible and then gradually groped his way toward a highly personal interpretation of the Holy Scriptures, and finally to an outright attack on biblical teaching. Slowly he evolved a doctrine of his own (though biblical authority is to this day still given some weight if properly interpreted by the Ministers). The hall in which the meetings were held was named "Temple of Islam" (now Temple 1), and there the Black Muslim movement in America was born.

In 1934 this esoteric[3] Detroit cult had collected 8,000 members, when in June of that year Mr. Farrad Mohammad, the mysterious peddler who had initiated the movement, disappeared. Exactly what happened to him is not known. After Farrad Mohammad's disappearance, the direction of the movement fell to his first lieutenant, Elijah Muhammad[4] (Elijah Poole), then a young man in his thirties. In less than three decades after taking control, Elijah has directed and transformed the movement from an esoteric Negro cult in the slums of Detroit to a nationwide sect with mass appeal, one which claims over a quarter-million members (in fact it has probably no more than 100,000 at most) in twenty-seven states and is recognized by many as a sect of orthodox Islam.

The building process was a slow one for Elijah. In the early days there was trouble with the police and local school officials over his operation of parochial schools for Muslim children. Various interest groups, including the Communists and union-busting elements, tried to use this convenient enclave of Negroes to their advantage. The movement has, however, successfully re-

2. He came . . . our own country: [*Author's note*] quoted in E. D. Beynon, "The Voodoo Cult Among Negro Militants in Detroit."
3. esoteric (es'ə·ter'ik): understood by or meant for a few specially instructed or initiated individuals. *Esoteric* can also mean "secret" or "abstruse; lying beyond ordinary comprehension."
4. Muhammad: an alternate spelling of *Mohammed*, just as *Muslim* is an alternate spelling of *Moslem*.

sisted these pressures and at all times has refused to veer from its sole purpose of uplifting the black man in America.

From 1942 to 1946 Elijah was in a federal prison for seditious statements he allegedly made, identifying the Negro's best interest with a Japanese victory in the Second World War. There was no major significant breakthrough in the growth of the movement until the mid-fifties, when Elijah got a column, "Mr. Muhammad Speaks," in the *Pittsburgh Courier* and other Negro newspapers. This was the first time that he had been presented to the Negro public through mass communications media. There was an immediate upsurge in the enrollment of the movement. When the Negro press finally decided to drop Mr. Muhammad's column, his success was already assured; and shortly after the great upswing in membership, the national press began to give the movement coverage. There seems to be little doubt that the coverage the movement has received from press, radio, and television has served to attract more people into its ranks. Those making up the bulk of its membership are the young, the disillusioned recent immigrant from the South, the low-income urban worker, and the socially-rejected in general—those with least to lose from the stigma of being Black Muslims. The frequent observation that this movement has its primary appeal among the low socio-economic class of urban Negroes tells us little, since the vast majority of American Negroes belong to this socio-economic class anyway and are now largely city dwellers.

Beliefs and Goals

Muslim doctrine starts with the premise that the black man in America can never expect equal treatment, since the white man has no intention of ever giving it to him. This hits a responsive note in the hearts of many Negroes, whose experience reinforces this assumption. In denying America's good "intentions" toward the Negro, Malcolm X, leader of the New York temple,[5] says:

5. **Malcolm X . . . New York temple:** at the time the selection was written, Malcolm X was second to Elijah Muhammad in the Muslim hierarchy and was the movement's most articulate spokesman. He broke with Elijah in March 1964, following a dispute that had developed over remarks Malcolm X had made regarding the assassination of President Kennedy in November 1963. Malcolm X then founded and led his own black nationalist group in New York City. On February 22, 1965, he was shot and killed by Negro gunmen as he addressed a rally of his new group.

Do you mean to tell me that in a powerful country like this, a so-called Christian country, that a handful of men from the South can prevent the North, the West, the Central States, and the East from giving Negroes the rights the Constitution says they already have? No! I don't believe that and neither do you. No white man really wants the Black Man to have his rights, or he'd have them. The United States does everything else it wants to do.[6]

The Black Muslims' solution to the American Negroes' problems is separation; they insist on the term *separation* rather than *segregation* in order to avoid the racist charges that are made against them. *Separation,* they hold, is something that is done to equals, with no implication of "superior" or "inferior," as is the case with segregation. They see American society as sick and point to the damaging effects of the slave mentality which they feel still prevails in the Negro community. They often refer, metaphorically, to Elijah as the physician who can cure the Negroes' socio-economic ills. But in order to do this he must first separate the Negro from the malignant influences of the dominant white society. The white man has made separation a fact, the Muslims now call for *total* separation, as a virtue. While the integrationist groups seek to correct some of the flaws in American life, the Muslims embrace a much more ambitious goal—they hope to reconstitute a whole society. To do this they feel that they must reconstruct the whole man. The American Negro must be completely made over. He must become a Muslim—a Black Muslim —and a follower of the Honorable Elijah Muhammad.

Elijah has set forth a twelve-point program for the deliverance of the American Negro. His awareness of the economic precariousness of the American Negro masses is reflected in several points. The program commands:

1. Separate yourself from your slavemaster.
2. Pool your resources, education, and qualifications for independence.
3. Stop forcing yourselves into places where you are not wanted.

6. **Do you mean . . . to do:** [*Author's note*] quoted in C. Eric Lincoln, *The Black Muslims in America,* page 19.

4. Make your own neighborhood a decent place to live.
5. Rid yourselves of the lust for wine and drink and learn to love self and kind before loving others.
6. Unite to create a future for yourself.
7. Build your own homes, schools, hospitals, and factories.
8. Do not seek to mix your blood through racial integration.
9. Stop buying expensive cars, fine clothes, and shoes before being able to live in a fine house.
10. Spend your money among yourselves.
11. Build an economic system among yourselves.
12. Protect your women.

Disillusionment with America has also caused the Muslims to reject America and their citizenship. Malcolm X repeatedly makes the claim that "there are no degrees of citizenship. Either you are a citizen or you are not. There is no such thing as a second-class citizen." The alienation which members of the movement seem to feel is reflected by the answer Malcolm gave when he was asked whether the fact that he was born in America did not make him an American citizen. He replied, "Just because a cat has kittens in an oven, it doesn't make them biscuits." [7]

In order to fulfill their desires, the Muslims say that they must have land of their own. They wish to separate and form a black nation within the United States. The Muslims repeatedly make the cry "Give us some land!" and say that the United States owes them this concession as back wages for the 200-plus years that America benefited from the Negro's involuntary free labor. In a debate at Harvard University Malcolm X outlined some of the details of the Muslim request. He said that the Muslims wanted some land, some tools, and a federal government subsidy for twenty to twenty-five years, in order to get the nation established. Mr. Muhammad explains the importance of land to the Muslims by saying:

We must become, as a people, producers and not remain consumers and employees. We must be able to extract raw materials from the earth, manufacture them into something useful for ourselves. This would create jobs

7. "Just because . . . biscuits": [*Author's note*] Minister Malcolm X, Boston University Human Relations Center, speech. February 15, 1960.

in production. We must remember that without land there is no production.[8]

In this rejection of white American society the Muslims include a rejection of their "Christian-slavemaster" last names. Their former last names are replaced by the letter X, which to them represents the fact that, because of the white man, they do not know their true last names but only those that have come down to them from slavery. As the number of people with the same first name in each individual temple increases, a numerical prefix is added to the letter X to distinguish one John or James from another—thus, John 3X or James 6X. For identification purposes in the society at large, a Muslim will often sign his former last name, preceded by the X—thus Louis X. Smith. Here the Muslim will tell you that the X means "no longer" or "ex."

Not only does the Muslim reject white American society, but he rejects the white man as well. To the Black Muslim the white man is anathema. In his religious mythology the white man is equated with the devil or the forces of evil. The Muslim examines the condition in which he finds himself and his fellow Negroes in America and reasons that someone is to blame for the situation. Once he has gone that far, it is a short step to say that "it is the white man's fault that we are in the condition that we are"—and to hate him for it. The Muslims make no attempt to follow Dr. King's [9] command to hate the evil without hating the evildoer. The Muslims revel in racial glorification of the black man.

A third area of rejection is Christianity. It is cast off as a "white man's religion," a tool of colonialism and the stifler of the proper manly and militant virtues. The Muslims make constant references to the deceitfulness of the Christian missionaries in Africa. They repudiate the doctrine of a heaven or afterlife and say that it has been used as an instrument of subjection of the

---

8. "We must become . . . production": [*Author's note*] "Mr. Muhammad Speaks," *Los Angeles Herald-Dispatch*, November 26, 1960. Also in *In Your Midst—Mr. Elijah Muhammad*, booklet published by Temple 11, Boston. Muhammad says, "The *Black Man* in America has been too long treated as a pariah, despised, neglected, and left to despair, in a country whose soil his blood, tears, and sweat have nurtured. He must therefore begin building enterprises of his own as the first step toward eventual unity of *Black Men*."
9. Dr. King's: for biographical information, see page 298.

African, as well as the American Negro. While the Negro's eyes were planted on the heavens and his soul wrapped up in the expectation of some far-distant joy at the end of his life, the white man was busy scraping up the Negro's gold and looking after his own more immediate desires of earthly pleasure. The Muslims show a great deal of contempt for the "turn the other cheek" doctrine of many integrationists. They are trained never to initiate a struggle, but to be prepared to defend to the death (literally) their principles and their women.

The religion of Islam is meant to replace Christianity. The followers become Muslims and must submit themselves to the will of Allah.[10] They are expected to follow the teachings of the Holy Koran [11] and to observe the proper dietary, fasting, bathing, and praying obligations. Elijah Muhammad made a pilgrimage to Mecca in 1960 and was received by some of the leading Imams [12] of the Islamic religion in the Middle East. There are several points, however, at which the Black Muslims deviate from orthodox Muslim teaching. The most serious of these are their racist doctrines and their deification of Mr. Farrad Mohammad, founder of the movement. Farrad is believed to have been the incarnation of Allah, who made an appearance upon the earth in order to give Elijah the "truth" necessary for the salvation of the black man in the "wilderness of North America." This is one reason that Elijah is regarded so highly by his followers. He is "the Messenger" who has received the message directly from God.

Organization

Elijah Muhammad is a frail little man in his sixties. He is a native son of Georgia, the son and the grandson of Baptist ministers. From his Chicago residence he superintends one of the fastest-growing movements in America. Elijah has the absolute and final word on everything pertaining to the actions of the Black Muslims in America. However, the ministers of the individual mosques [13] are highly enough trained and there are enough "or-

10. **Allah** (al'ə): the God worshipped by Moslems.
11. **Holy Koran**: the sacred scripture of the Moslem religion, in which the revelations of Allah to his messenger Mohammad are recorded.
12. **Imams**: Moslem priests.
13. **mosques**: Moslem temples of worship.

ganization men" under him for Elijah simply to sit back and play the father-role to thousands of black men.[14]

Exactly how many thousands is extremely difficult to judge. Minister Malcolm X says, "Those who say, don't know; those who know, don't say." And this is quite true. Because of the secretiveness of the Muslims about such matters, all figures relating to them have to be speculative. Dr. Lincoln puts the figure at 100,000. Dr. Essien-Udom, who has had a great deal of personal contact with the Muslims, has said that although their rate of conversion is very high, so is the rate of turnover—i.e., many "converts" do not stay practicing Muslims for very long. This may be because the discipline is too rigid, because of the social stigma attached to being a Black Muslim, or for some other reason. At any rate, Dr. Essien-Udom estimates (1962) that there are only about 15,000 registered, *fully active* Muslims, about 50,000 professed believers, and a much greater number of sympathizers. Although this estimate of fully active members might be slightly low, Dr. Essien-Udom's figures probably come closer to a realistic picture. The Chicago, New York, and Boston Muslim followings are supposed to be among the largest in the country, but a visitor cannot help being struck by the very low seating capacity in what are supposedly three of the movement's leading mosques. The *total* seating capacity for all three probably does not exceed 2,500, which gives added weight to Dr. Essien-Udom's belief that it is a small hard core of believers who are the life of the movement and who have attracted most of the attention. Not that the attention paid to the Muslims is unjustified because of their lack of great numerical strength, for every person who has made and kept the commitment to the Nation of Islam there are many more who sympathize with his views.

Each of the eighty temples or mosques is, to a great degree, an autonomous unit. It has its own subgroups, usually consisting

14. **However, the ministers . . . black men:** [*Author's note*] There is ample evidence to show that an additional reason for the Hon. Elijah Muhammad's not being seen in public more often is that his health is failing. More than once in recent years he has failed to put in an appearance at important Muslim conferences where he had been scheduled to address his followers. The question of the line of succession remains unclear; Elijah's position is unique since he alone has had a "direct divine revelation." It is not known whether the leadership will stay in Elijah's family or go to his chief minister.

of "The Fruit of Islam" and the "Muslim Girls Training and General Civilization Class." The Fruit is a paramilitaristic group [15] of young Muslim men who train and drill for physical fitness and act as guards in the temple. This elite corps of Muslim males helps to keep internal discipline and is ready if outside protection is needed. They act as bodyguards for visiting Muslim dignitaries and inspect the proposed itinerary of Mr. Muhammad before any visit, in much the same way as the U.S. Secret Service men act for the President of the United States. The amount known about the inner workings of this group is limited since it is a secret (the Muslims say "private") organization which refuses to discuss its activities or to permit outsiders at its meetings.

The Muslim Girls Training and General Civilization Class is open to the women of the temple. It emphasizes the arts of homemaking and attempts to teach the young Muslim girl to be a good Muslim mother. Women are held in very high regard by the Muslims. They stress the key role that women play in the training and upbringing of men. Elijah often says, "A nation can rise no higher than its women."

In the areas where there are Muslim temples there will always be found Muslim-run businesses and it is Muslim policy to urge members to "buy black" and "hire black." There are Muslim restaurants, barber shops, grocery stores, cleaners, and other types of business establishments. In Chicago there is even a Muslim department store. The Muslims own farms both in the Midwest and in the South. In Georgia they have trucks which deliver fresh fish daily from the sea to their inland markets.

The Muslims have their own parochial schools, some of which are state-accredited—as in Detroit and Chicago, where Muslim children attend the temple school rather than the public schools of the city. In areas where the schools are not accredited, Muslim children attend the schools of the temple in their spare time and on Saturdays. In the accredited Muslim schools the children attend classes fifty weeks of the year, and start to learn Arabic ("the language of their fathers") in the third grade. Race history is emphasized along with the more standard course of study.

---

15. **paramilitaristic group:** a private but unofficial army; a group having a military structure and nature but not official military sanction.

The "history" that is taught in the Black Muslim movement is often no more than a glorified racial mythology. Muslims reject the term *Negro* as a description of themselves and other American colored people, saying that the word is the invention of the white man used to make subjugation of colored peoples easier. They connect the introduction and usage of the term *Negro* with the coming of slavery to America. They say this appellation tells nothing of the history and rich cultural heritage of the black race, for it is nothing more than an indiscriminate lumping together of peoples, disconnecting them from any cultural heritage, obscuring past grandeur.

Muslims believe literally that the "so-called American Negroes" are descendants of "original man" (the white race is a later mutation), and that they are part of the ancient lost tribe of Shabazz which made its home along the banks of the Nile and in the region of what was later to be Mecca. There is a great attempt at identification with the Nile civilizations that flourished in the past.

Race history as taught by the Muslims is distorted. However, there is some basis in fact for many of their claims, facts that are wide open to Muslim overamplification. There is evidence of the past existence of relatively advanced "Negro" civilizations on the lower Nile. During the Middle Ages, there were also large empires of Islamized Africans in the western Sudan. The University of Timbuktu was an important center of Muslim learning. The pilgrimage to Mecca of the African leader Mansa Musa of the empire of Mali in the fourteenth century is still famous in the annals of African history. Mansa Musa caused quite a stir during his visit to the East. He flooded the Egyptian market with so much gold that there was a mild inflation after his arrival.

The belief that Negro origins lie in the East is also reflected in the oral tradition of many West African groups today who hold that their ancestors came to West Africa in ancient times as part of a great migration from the East. It is likewise true that there were African Muslims among the slaves brought to this country, but the number would have to have been very small, since Islam had not made inroads into the areas from which most of the slaves bound for America were taken.

The Muslims have learned well the lesson of mass communications media. They are now applying it with the greatest of zeal in the hope of expanding their membership. Mr. Muhammad has a weekly radio program on many of the radio stations in the different metropolitan areas of the country. His column, "Mr. Muhammad Speaks" is still carried in some Negro newspapers, and the movement now publishes several newspapers and magazines of its own.

Also listed in the catalogue of organs of propaganda is the theatrical production, *Orgena* ("A Negro" spelled backwards). This show was written, directed, and starred in by Louis X, minister of the Boston temple. Louis, upon being converted to Islam (he was previously Episcopalian), left a $500-a-week career as a popular calypso singer to take $70 a week as a Muslim minister. He vowed at this time never to perform again except in the cause of Islam. His own creation now gives him that opportunity. The show consists of a musical dramatization of the history of the Negro, "from the banks of the Nile to the ghettos of America," and a one-act play called *The Trial*, in which the person on trial is the White Man. The verdict is "guilty" and the sentence is "death." The three-hour show is supposed to be both "entertaining and enlightening." It has been presented at Carnegie Hall in New York, Symphony Hall in Boston, and in other major cities in the East and Midwest.

The Muslims have recognized, explicitly or implicitly, the economic precariousness and psychological deprivation faced by the masses of Negroes in American urban areas. They have attempted to provide remedies both for the body and the spirit of the black man. In exchange for economic insecurity, they have offered him the opportunity to join them in their attempts at economic independence. They have set up and run hundreds of business establishments—hiring Muslim and non-Muslim alike. They have opened job opportunities for many—and not in the self-seeking spirit of exploitation but with a feeling for unity, strength, cooperation, and mutual assistance.

They have provided thousands of men and women with a sense of identity and moral direction where in many cases there had been only the empty blackness of the ghetto. Without a doubt, and almost without exception, when a person becomes a Black Muslim there is a great perceptible change. The emphasis on morality and strict discipline creates a new kind of demeanor. The Black Muslim as found in the "Negro" areas of large American cities is usually more courteous, neater, and more respectful of himself and his neighbors than most of those around him.

The existence of this well-disciplined self does not negate the Muslim's militancy, but illustrates that it is not expressed in any overt, boisterous manner. The Muslim appears to be in complete control of himself. He moves with a quiet determination and an inner sense of personal dignity. Perhaps, to a large degree, this stems from the race pride that has been instilled in him by the teachings of the movement and its emphasis upon a knowledge of self. Juvenile delinquency among Muslims is negligible, and the members of the family unit seem to find it easier to assume the traditional roles with father as breadwinner and mother as homemaker.

Muslims have succeeded in changing the ways of living of many convicts and ex-convicts. Muslims proselytize [16] inside as well as outside prison walls. They have taken into their ranks the prostitute, the dope addict, and other deviant or "marginal" types and transformed them. Muslim leaders often say that the Government owes them a debt of gratitude for the job they have done in the social rehabilitation of "hopeless" cases and for the money that they have saved public institutions in doing so. Indeed, it is true that one of the facts that is most striking to observers is the great effect that becoming a Muslim has on the lives of individuals.[17] The Muslims open their arms to the rejects of society, because they themselves have rejected society.

For those who follow him, Elijah Muhammad has succeeded in his grand design of drawing Negroes out from the dominant

16. **proselytize** (pros'ə·lit·īz'): make converts. A proselyte is anyone who has been brought over to any opinion or belief, particularly religious belief.

17. **Indeed, it is true . . . individuals:** [*Author's note*] George S. Schuyler, New York editor of the *Pittsburgh Courier*, and one of the most widely read Negro journalists, wrote in his column: "Mr. Muhammad may be a rogue and a charlatan, but when anybody can get tens of thousands of Negroes to practice economic solidarity, stop crime, juvenile delinquency, and adultery, he is doing more for the Negro's welfare than any current Negro leader I know." *Pittsburgh Courier*, September 12, 1959. One is hard pressed to find evidence to show that Mr. Muhammad is either rogue or charlatan. For an estimation of the man's personal qualities quite different from Mr. Schuyler's, see James Baldwin, "Letter from a Region in My Mind," *The New Yorker*, November 17, 1962.

white society and providing a meaningful existence as free as possible from white contact. But he is not satisfied with this partial success. He claims that land is available to him outside America (presumably somewhere in the Middle East) if he desired to set up his black nation today. He refuses to do this, saying that his goal is not some quarter-million "saved" American Negroes, but every last American black man who suffers under the "pharaohs" in the "wilderness of North America." Elijah Muhammad and the other leaders of the movement tell the American Negro that the solution to the nation's racial problem lies not in efforts to "integrate" American society, but in *separation* from the white man, and in black unity.

Muslims and the Public

Because all temple meetings are closed to whites, the impression that most of the general public have received of the Muslims comes from the mass public meetings that the Muslims hold from time to time. The press, radio, and television coverage of these mass rallies has consistently presented a distorted image of the Muslim movement and has tended to seize on the more bizarre and fantastic elements and to overplay them.[18] The vehemence of the attack upon whites coming from the lips of these Negroes is shocking even to the veteran ears of seasoned white reporters. Mr. Muhammad's theme of "separation or death," which is constantly reiterated at mass rallies, has caused a great deal of misunderstanding. While most have interpreted this as a Muslim threat and reported that the Muslims seek the "extinction of the white race," Elijah Muhammad has insisted that this is a religious doctrine and simply means that God (Allah) will destroy

18. The press . . . overplay them: [*Author's note*] A good deal of attention has been paid in the press to the appearance of George Lincoln Rockwell, leader of the American Nazi Party, at a large Muslim rally. See especially "The Black Crusade," *Sunday* [London] *Times Color Magazine*, April 21, 1963. While it is true that the American Nazis and Muslims have openly expressed sympathy for each other's views on racial separation, this has never amounted to total endorsement. Unwarranted importance has been attached to the fact that Rockwell spoke at this rally—this was an open meeting, and the Muslims offered the platform to *all* solutions of America's racial problems. Rockwell simply availed himself of the opportunity—he is grateful for any platform he can get. [*Editor's note*] Rockwell was shot and killed by sniper fire in a Virginia shopping center in the spring of 1967.

the wicked slavemasters of America unless they "let my people go," in much the same way as he has destroyed wicked rulers in the past. Similarly, the final "Battle of Armageddon" [19] must be understood in a religious context as a war in which the forces of Good will destroy the forces of Evil. It has been wisely remarked that Elijah very carefully treads the line between religious license and political sedition.[20]

Most of the Black Muslim energy is directed toward a day-to-day effort on behalf of the unity and uplift of the Negro in America, but on several occasions in recent years events have catapulted the Muslims into the national spotlight. During Fidel Castro's visit to New York City in 1960 Malcolm X was reported to have had a prolonged and closed consultation with the Cuban leader at a time when no one else was being permitted to see him. Reports intimated that there might have been some sort of alliance or negotiations between the two men. The truth of the matter, according to Malcolm, was that he was a part of the host committee in Harlem, and it was for this reason that he was allowed into the Hotel Theresa in Harlem to speak with Castro. He says that his visit was a brief one and not a prolonged "session." The Muslims are suing the Hearst newspaper syndicate for $3 million for the erroneous and misleading accounts of this event.

Early in 1961 when a group of American Negroes demonstrated at the United Nations in protest at the murder of Congolese leader Patrice Lumumba and continued colonial activity in Africa, the Black Muslims were blamed. The New York Police Commissioner attributed the disturbance to the Muslims and it was so reported in the papers and by U.N. Ambassador Stevenson. The Muslims contend that they were not involved in the incident

19. "Battle of Armageddon": an allusion to the Book of Revelations 16:16, in which a great battle between the forces of Good and Evil is prophesied, the battle to take place at the end of the world.
20. Armageddon . . . sedition: [Author's note] Minister Malcolm X admitted to me that since the forces of evil are represented by the white man and Christianity, and the forces of good by the black man and Islam, the Black Muslim doctrine of the Battle of Armageddon actually amounts to a prediction of an ultimate race war in which the white man is extinguished. When questioned on white Muslims, Malcolm insisted that he has never known any. "A Muslim is one who submits himself to the will of Allah," he said, "and I have never known a white man that would truly submit himself to Allah." Muslims in the Middle East are not white men, he claims. The Black Muslims classify all nonwhites as "black men."

and maintain that other black nationalist groups were responsible. This insistence seems more plausible in the light of past Muslim policy on nonintervention in political matters. At any rate, another lawsuit by the Muslims has been instigated as a result of these allegedly slanderous statements.

On occasion, the Muslims have run into difficulty in exercising their right to practice their religion. In New York State, Muslim prisoners in some of the state penal institutions have been denied the right to practice their own particular brand of Islam. The Muslims have appealed to a higher court. In March 1961, Monroe, Louisiana, one of the thirty cities in Southern and border states with Muslim temples, was the scene of a police raid on a Muslim meeting. Several Muslims were beaten and jailed. They were charged with disturbing the peace, aggravated assault, and aggravated battery. This case also has been appealed.

On April 27, 1962, the Black Muslims again came suddenly to public notice in an internationally reported incident. The incident started when two white Los Angeles policemen decided to question two Negro men who were selling clothes from a parked car on a Los Angeles street. The exact sequence of events that followed is still a matter of dispute, but an altercation developed and a group of Muslims intervened on behalf of the two Negro men stopped for questioning. In the ensuing fray seven Muslim men were shot (one of them killed) and thirteen others arrested and charged with "resisting arrest" and "assault." The two policemen, along with dozens of reenforcements, entered a nearby Muslim mosque, disrupting a service in progress, and searched for a gun that they had heard was hidden there. No weapon of any kind was found. As the trial of the arrested Muslims approaches [May 1963], there is a great deal of public interest in the case— not least because of the shooting of the seven Muslims, all of whom were unarmed in accordance with their Black Muslim teaching (which does not permit members to carry weapons of any sort).

Despite the Muslims' claim that they eschew [21] all weapons, the Los Angeles police have also alleged that the minister of the Los Angeles mosque is guilty of shooting a police officer during the dispute. However, the arrest of the mosque minister on an

21. eschew (es·chōo′): shun; shy away from.

"assault with intent to commit murder" charge was not made until several months after the incident had taken place and the other thirteen Muslims had been arrested.

Recent years have also seen the upsurge of African nationalism exert an increasing influence upon the Black Muslims in America. They identify very strongly with the rising African nations and their militant leaders—especially when that leader happens to be Muslim, like Sekou Toure of Guinea. When African leaders come to the United States they sometimes meet Muslim leaders. Such has been the case with President Nkrumah of Ghana and Jaja Wachuku, then Speaker of the Nigerian House of Representatives.

On the domestic political scene, the Muslims took a sudden new approach after their annual convention early in 1963. In the past, they had avoided American politics as just another part of the corrupt, decadent, unjust American system. In their new line, however, the Muslims show themselves a great deal less alienated and less politically unconcerned than before. By their new acceptance of the political process they demonstrate further that theirs is not in fact a total, out-of-hand rejection of the larger society, but merely a response to the injustice they find in that society. The shift in approach probably reflects a greater awareness of the role politics has to play in social change, or at least it reflects a Muslim awareness of their growing power to influence patterns of thought in the Negro community. The Muslims have begun calling to American Negroes to close their ranks and in the coming 1964 elections to elect candidates "of their own choosing instead of merely existing under those chosen for them by the whites." Malcolm X has declared:

> Twenty million Negroes can tip the political scales in any direction they choose to leap. That's why Mr. Muhammad says we must select candidates from those who honestly represent the black man and can be trusted to look after his interests. Yes, even from among Christians.[22]

Implicitly, this is saying, "Yes, even from among the white man"—a new departure altogether for the Muslims; in the past,

22. Twenty million . . . Christians: [Author's note] [London] Sunday Telegraph, March 24, 1963.

one of the Muslim reasons for ignoring American politics was their belief that no white man could be trusted. Malcolm has also said that the Muslims can already "handle" the Negro U.S. Congressman Adam Clayton Powell [23] and "a number of other Negro politicians." This, of course, depends upon what Minister Malcolm means by "handle," but it is quite true that Powell must take the Muslims into account because of the great power and influence they wield in his Harlem constituency.

The Muslim program as presented to its Negro audience calls for land so that they may set up a black nation within the United States. There is much to indicate, however, that this is a public statement of a goal that Muslim leaders do not expect to obtain, at least not in the near future. There are, of course, different levels of communication. What the Muslim leaders tell their Negro following, what they tell the general public, and what they say among themselves may often be quite different. It seems difficult to believe that Elijah Muhammad, Malcolm X, and other Muslim leaders actually believe that the federal government is going to give them three, four, five, or *any* number of states. Much of present Muslim activity contradicts a real belief in this goal. All over the country Muslims are investing and building up their interests. In Baltimore a large recreation center "to keep black children off the streets" is being constructed; in Chicago plans are complete for a $20 million Islamic center, complete with school, hospital, and mosque. All this activity does not seem the work of a group that expects to be moving out into one geographical area. A man expecting to move into a new house does not expend large amounts of money, time, and energy lavishly furnishing the old. Nor does he neglect the paintwork of the present house, Malcolm is quick to point out. However, it would seem that the Muslims have found this concept and goal of "nation" a very useful one, because it has a romantic and unifying power—and

23. Adam Clayton Powell: in 1964, Powell, long the U.S. Representative from New York's 18th Congressional District (Harlem) and chairman of the powerful House Committee on Education and Labor, became involved in a libel suit that went against him and ultimately resulted in his citation for criminal contempt of court and in the issuance of a warrant for his arrest if he entered the State of New York. Powell remained in self-imposed exile until 1968, when the case against him was settled. Despite Powell's absence, Harlem voters had reelected him in elections in both 1966 and 1968. After the 1966 election, his House colleagues refused to grant him a Congressional seat; he was seated, however, in the Ninety-First Congress, 1969.

unity and advancement seem to be the Muslims' real primary goal, not nationhood.

What the Muslims are developing are communities within larger communities. The way in which they qualify their doctrine of *apartheid* [24] is very interesting. The Muslims ask for separation, but the request is for land in the United States. They do not have the "back to Africa" intentions of the Garvey movement of an earlier day.[25] While they supposedly reject the white man and his ways, the Muslims will often use the white man's values as their criteria. Thus, there is the emphasis on running one's business well, "like the white men do." Muslim standards of dress and behavior as symbols of "having arrived" come straight out of Madison Avenue and a Puritan morality. Of course, for Muslims "arrival" means a different thing than for most people. It mean the coming of their knowledge of the true nature of their condition and of the way out of it through the teachings of the Honorable Elijah Muhammad. The Muslims purport to be separationists, but time and time again they will lament the failing of integration and point to it as the reason for their position. Theoretically, as separationists, they should be pleased when integration does not work.[26]

Nevertheless, the facts must be faced: the Muslims are a group with views which can be described in no other way than "extreme racist," and those who condemn racism in other forms must find the Muslim doctrines unpalatable. It is also true that much of what spurs on the Muslims is a fierce hate for the white man—"the devil." But there is a difference. If there is hate, it is "the hate that hate produced"—hate, or indifference, which may be worse. A nation that too long rejects its own can expect one

24. **apartheid** (ə·pärt′hīt): a system of strict social, political, and economic racial segregation or separation.
25. **Garvey movement . . . earlier day:** Marcus Garvey (1887–1940) was a Jamaican-born black nationalist whose Back-to-Africa movement gained widespread popularity in the United States during the 1920's.
26. **Theoretically . . . does not work:** [*Author's note*] In the teachings at temple meetings and in my talks with Muslim leaders and followers, I have often found this contradiction between attacking the idea of integration and at the same time lamenting its failure to work. Malcolm X and others have admitted to me that what they really want is complete equality—*now*. But since the Government has not seen fit to guarantee this equality immediately, the Muslim can no longer wait and embraces separation as the answer.

day to find its own rejecting it. A man, like a nation, can exist "half-slave, half-free" for only so long. Criticism of the Muslims as racists is valid, but preoccupation with criticism of the plant all too often prevents examination of the soil from which it sprang.

It is not in numbers that the Black Muslims have their greatest significance. In a nation with almost twenty million Negroes, the Muslims are numerically insignificant. The significance of the Black Muslims lies in their importance as social barometers. Theirs is a specific registering of a mood that is widespread, and in some ways even pervasive, in the Negro community in America— a certain anger, frustration, and impatience with the Negro's situation and the rate at which it is being changed. In the nation's black ghettos there are millions who, if they cannot accept all of the Muslims' views, can sympathize with some of them and with the militancy with which they are expressed. And probably at least something of the Muslim indictment of the larger white society for its crimes against the black man hits a responsive note in the heart of every Negro—wherever he might be. The Muslims represent a particular institutionalized version of the more general mood and serve as a vehicle to communicate this mood to the larger society which all too often knows little of the hidden hurt and hidden hate of the black man.

On close examination of both the rhetoric and the teachings of the Black Muslims, it becomes evident that what they are really expressing is a fundamental and deeply-felt disillusionment with the fulfillment of the American promise, and at the same time a great desire for the values that have been denied them. It is what they see as white deceit regarding matters of equality, and not a compulsive racism, that has called the Black Muslims into existence and caused them to flourish.

Meaning and Method

1. In his opening paragraph, Mr. Burns says that the ultimate goal of civil-rights groups such as the NAACP "is to go out of existence, for they are working for the day when groups of their nature will no longer be necessary and men will be able to move in society without the hindrances of racial prejudice and discrimination."

   Do you think that Mr. Burns actually means that the NAACP

is hoping to go out of existence some day? How do the goals of the Black Muslims, the NAACP, and such other organizations as the Black Panthers, Core, and the SCLC differ in methods, philosophies, and goals?

2. Reread the section "Beliefs and Goals," beginning on page 321. Enumerate the major goals of the Black Muslims in the order in which the author presents them. How are the Muslims' goals related to their beliefs and behavior?

3. The author tells us that although many people join but soon leave the Black Muslims, many others join and stay. What is the Muslims' view of themselves? The Muslims have said that they "open their arms to the rejects of society because they themselves have rejected society." How do you account for the Muslims' appeal to Negroes, especially to the so-called rejects of society?

4. The first three paragraphs serve as an introduction to Mr. Burns's essay; the last two, as its conclusion; and the intervening paragraphs, as the body.

Using the sentence outline form, enumerate the main ideas and details covered in the introductory and concluding parts.

5. In the last sentence of the essay's third paragraph (beginning on page 319), we read, "[The Black Muslim movement] is significant both in what the mere existence of such a group indicates about American society and for the insights it gives into the mood of a large segment of the American Negro community."

How do the essay's last two paragraphs amplify this statement and also serve to conclude the discussion? Are the concluding paragraphs consistent with points in the main part, or body, of the discussion?

6. Exposition seeks to clarify and explain by (a) direct analysis, (b) classification and division, (c) drawing comparisons and contrasts, (d) showing cause-effect relationships, (e) defining terms, (f) illustrating and documenting with examples, quoted statements, statistics, etc., (g) detailing the steps in a process, and (h) combining methods.

Reread the paragraphs whose opening sentences are quoted in the following list. Indicate the method of development the author has used. (Remember that a combination of methods may be used.)

(a) Not all Negroes, however, share the integrationist motives of these groups. (page 319)

(b) The building process was a slow one for Elijah. (320)

(c) Exactly how many thousands is extremely difficult to judge. (326)

(d) On occasion, the Muslims have run into difficulty in exercising their right to practice their religion. (333)
(e) On the domestic political scene, the Muslims took a sudden new approach after their annual convention in early 1963. (334)
(f) What the Muslims are developing are communities within larger communities. (336)
7. Mr. Burns has tried to be objective in his account of the Black Muslim movement. He has traced their origin and development, and he has reported many aspects of their beliefs and goals.

What, in your estimation, are some of the positive and negative features of the Black Muslims and their social, economic, political, and religious beliefs and activities? Do you think the author has succeeded in being objective? What does he mean by "criticism of the Muslims as racists is valid, but preoccupation with the criticism of the plant all too often prevents examination of the soil from which it sprang" (page 337)?

Composition and Discussion

1. What do you think of the Muslims' plan for a black nation within the United States? Is this similar to the secessionist movement of the Civil War era? What economic and social problems can you think of that the existence of such a state would create? What other difficulties might arise? Would such a Negro nation give the American blacks a sense of belonging or a feeling of having a "spiritual homeland" with which they could identify?

Write about these and related considerations in a brief expository composition. Before you begin writing your essay, prepare a topic outline of points you plan to discuss.

2. Read the *Autobiography of Malcolm X* (1964; available in paperback), written with Alex Haley. Write a book review, concentrating mainly on what you learn about Malcolm X himself and about the black-nationalist movement in which he was a major participant. Try to explain what the book tells you about history and world problems as well as America's racial strife. If Malcolm X's own account of Black Muslimism seems to be at variance with points in Mr. Burns's essay on the movement, try to explain the difference.

Adelaide Cromwell Hill

"I believe the term *Black Power* is more than a slogan. . . . Black Power is the attempt of a people, my people, to find definition and liberation."

These are the words of Floyd B. Barbour, editor of *The Black Power Revolt*, the collection of writings from which the selection that follows is taken. In his introduction, Mr. Barbour compares the stages of the Negro's development in America, past, present, and future, to the three stages in Dante's *Divina Commedia*— Inferno, Purgatorio, and Paradiso.* American Negroes, he says, have been through the Inferno of slavery and harsh oppression and can look forward to a coming Paradiso; right now, moving forward but still far from reaching their goal, they are passing through Purgatorio. It is with both the Inferno and its relation to the Purgatorio that "What Is Africa to Us?" concerns itself.

The essay's author, Adelaide Cromwell Hill, is a sociologist and teacher. She was born in 1919 in Washington, D.C., and attended the city's public schools before going on to Smith College in Northampton, Massachusetts, where she was a member of Phi Beta Kappa and was graduated cum laude in 1940. She did graduate work in sociology at the University of Pennsylvania (M.A., 1941), Bryn Mawr College, and Radcliffe College (Ph.D., 1952).

Most of Dr. Hill's professional work has been in the fields of teaching, research, and writing, although one of her first jobs was as a parole officer at a school for delinquent girls. She has been a lecturer in sociology at Hunter College in New York, an instructor at her alma mater, Smith, and a teaching fellow at Radcliffe. In 1953 she participated in a State Department-sponsored cultural-exchange program in Israel and Africa, and in 1961 and 1962 was a cultural and educational consultant to the government of the Republic of Ghana. At present, Dr. Hill is a faculty member and the acting director of the African Studies Center of Boston University.

* **Dante's *Divina Commedia* . . . *Paradiso*:** Dante's narrative poem *Divine Comedy* was begun sometime around 1300; its Inferno is a description of Hell; the Purgatorio, of Purgatory; and the Paradiso, of a world of heavenly beauty, light, and song.

Among Dr. Hill's writings are many published articles on sociology and on Afro-American culture. She explains her concern with African affairs this way: "My interest in Africa and the African-American scene has been a part of me as long as I can remember, due to no small extent, in retrospect, to the activities of my grandfather John W. Cromwell, a historian and a founder, along with Alexander Crummell, of the American Negro Academy." Dr. Hill is the coauthor with Martin Kilson of a historical anthology, *Apropos of Africa: Sentiments of American Negro Leaders on Africa, from the 1800's to the 1950's.*

The following essay, "What Is Africa to Us?" was originally read as a paper at the National Conference on Black Power, held in Newark, New Jersey, in 1967.

What Is Africa to Us?

Any discussion of Black Power ultimately requires an assessment of the identity of the Negro American. The elements of this identity, among other things, reflect some expression of it as a state of being and some awareness of its relation to the color of the Negro, which in turn is reminiscent of his African ancestry. This ancestry, in spite of the attempts at degradation, depreciation, or denial, is woven into the Negro's sense of self.

In 1927, before most Negro Americans knew how to express this fact freely, Countee Cullen, with the sensitivity a poet must have, was able to do so in his poem, "Heritage." Cullen wrote:

> What is Africa to me [1]
> Copper Sun or scarlet sea
> Jungle star or jungle track
> Strongblack men or regal black
> Women from whose loins I sprang
> When the birds of Eden sang?

1. First stanza of "Heritage" from *On These I Stand* by Countee Cullen, copyright © 1925 by Harper & Brothers, renewed 1953 by Ida M. Cullen. Reprinted by permission of Harper & Row, Publishers.

One three centuries removed
From the scenes his father told
Spring grove, cinnamon tree,
What is Africa to me?

The answers to this question come from an understanding of
what the Negro American thinks of himself and what he wants for
himself. As the Negro's presence on the American scene has rarely
been fully acknowledged and never fully welcomed, little serious
attention has been given to either question until quite recently.

In considering the question of identity, even in what some
more present-oriented persons insist on calling its newer form, it is
necessary for me to return to earlier days—at least in my own
career—and to reiterate what I have come to believe are some of
the basic ingredients in Negro identity.

Almost thirty years ago, in 1939 to be precise, in the research
necessary for my senior thesis in college, I questioned a group of
high-school girls about certain aspects of their lives. These girls
were all Negroes, lived in Washington, D.C., and were attending
the Negro schools of that city. I put the question to them bluntly:
Are you glad you are colored? Seventy-nine percent said they were
and when asked why, they gave such explanations as, Because
coloreds are prettier than whites; Whites look like witches when
they grow old; God made me colored and that is the way I am
going to stay; or Because I will be able to help the race progress.

These admittedly were the days before self-conscious African
nationalism or the Negro Revolution, and the answers have a kind
of simplistic ring in content. And, of course, these were also the
days before we were preoccupied with the psychological concept
of identity, having neither the theories of Erikson nor those of
Fanon [2] on which to draw. And yet in Washington, away from
the excitement of Renaissance Harlem or strident Garveyism,[3] in
an environment of respectable scholarship and the security of

2. Erikson . . . Fanon: Erik Erikson, psychologist and sociologist, author of
Eight Stages of Man; Frantz Fanon (d. 1949), African radical social philosopher, author of *Black Skin–White Mask*.
3. Renaissance Harlem . . . Garveyism: The Renaissance ("rebirth") in Harlem during the 1920's brought forth a great interest in the creation and appreciation of black music, literature, and art; Garveyism is a black-nationalist
social philosophy based on the teachings of Marcus Garvey (1887–1940),
founder of a "back to Africa" movement.

government jobs, these young girls were aware of their identity—an identity formed and perpetuated within the restrictive features of their society.

Admittedly I was not in the position of probing their unconscious or even unraveling the complex layers of their conscious, and further, this was not a unanimous assessment. Not all of the girls were glad they were colored. Furthermore one could have uncovered other prevalent patterns—the rejection of race, and the "passing" phenomenon so popular, in Washington, on one extreme, and the weak but clear strain of Africa for the Africans, meaning also American Negroes, the rallying cry of Garvey and his followers, on the other. But at this time, these were the extremes; the main stream was an acceptance of one's identity and an acceptance that was neither necessarily passive nor negative, although it could be either. The feeling at that time, however, did not have the fire and international content that later years would supply.

Before examining the changing content of this identity, a brief word on naming or labeling is appropriate. This, too, is a subject that has intrigued me because naming of nomenclature is a most important way of defining and controlling relations between people. *Native* and *foreigner* imply something quite different about the relation and status of the native from *native* and *European*,[4] for example. Also, since language is so important to our species, each communal group has generally named itself and in turn has been named by other groups. Depending on the character of the relationship, the names do not necessarily coincide. Even in the most modern context this is clear: we call ourselves Americans; foreigners call us Yanks.

Against these generalizations, a rather unique situation has occurred with the Negro. On this soil, the Negro has never been given an opportunity to name himself. Denied full inclusion in the terms designated by whites for whites, lacking such tribal terms as American Indians have, or the genuine nationality-based terms of the so-called hyphenated Americans, the Negro has been

4. *Native* and *foreigner* . . . *native* and *European:* Dr. Hill is pointing out that in Africa the blacks are called natives and the whites Europeans, whereas a truer distinction exists between *native,* meaning one born in a particular country, and *foreigner,* meaning one born outside of that country.

given such terms as American society feels are appropriately descriptive. For a brief time in the North, they were called Africans, but more generally for the country as a whole, slaves (slave-black, slave-mulatto, slave-quadroon) but always slave or free men. After the Civil War, briefly, they were called freedmen. Gradually, however, seemingly in an endeavor to please all sections of the country by maintaining in the definition a decent separatism but reflecting an improved status, the term *Negro* was bestowed upon us. And what variant forms it has undergone, what subtleties of meaning it has been able to encompass: *nigger* meaning still slave and evil; *niggrah* meaning still slave but compliant; *negro* with a lower-case *n* meaning not-slave or nonslave—but never a citizen or truly a free man or even a respected individual!

While being named, counted, and classified according to these categories, the "so-called Negroes" (and here especially Malcolm X's adjective [5] seems appropriate) began to react to what they felt as their position reflected in their name. Some preferred *colored* as a gentle reminder of the true description of race relations as it really had been in this country, others preferred *Afro-American* in order to join the other large ethnic hyphenated American communities in this country, and some were so imaginative and creative as to suggest *Negrosaxon*. Gradually, however, reflective of the time—the period between the end of Reconstruction and World War II and the rise of Independent Africa—most Negroes settled for the term *Negro*, insisting only that the first letter be capitalized.

This term then defined or prescribed the limits of their identity: not equal but deserving of some respect. This was the identity of the high-school girls I questioned so long ago. And let me say that in the context of the time, I think it was a solid base from which to develop. I do not feel, regrettably, that Negro high-school students in Boston or Detroit or New York or perhaps even Jackson or Durham would necessarily have felt this way, although it is quite likely, as Horace Mann Bond has indicated, that the basis for identity and motivation would even then have been greater in Durham, Jackson, or Dallas than in Boston, Chicago, or New York. Bond writes in his study of Negro holders of doctorates that

5. **Malcolm X's adjective** (see also page 321, footnote 5); Malcolm X's adjective, which he invariably used to modify *Negro*, is *so-called*.

"among the high schools definitely known to be segregated, whether in the North or South, the high schools that either had been private, or operated on private or state college campuses as laboratory high schools, hold a far higher doctoral production rate than the large urban high schools, and especially higher than the large urban de facto segregated high schools in northern slums. . . . Yet the evidence is that there have been superior high schools in large segregated city school systems: Dunbar in Washington, D.C., Sumner in St. Louis, Mo., where the doctoral productivity was much higher than in such high schools as Du Sable in Chicago, Benjamin Franklin in Philadelphia, and Attucks in Indianapolis, Indiana." [6]

We are saying that a strength and awareness of group potential are essential for the most minimal form of identity to emerge. Or to quote Fanon, "Without a Negro past, without a Negro future, it was impossible for me to live my Negrohood. Not yet white, no longer wholly black, I was damned."

This identification was nourished and shaped, ostensibly at least, within the context of the American experience. It grouped under the same umbrella the wide variety of people from those white in appearance to those of the blackest hues, from those of substantial or comfortable means according to any standards to those for whom welfare payments not only meant survival but advancement, from those whose search for God occurred in the most formal of settings to those whose religious outlet took place in tents or abandoned city stores. So diverse were they that superficially the only bond they seemed to have was the common ability to speak English and almost total inability to speak any language other than English. There was obviously one additional and crucial common fact. According to the social and political rules of this country they were not white. These NON-WHITES as opposed to other non-whites usually referred to in the census as "Other" were not white because some or all of their ancestors had come from Africa. Slavery or the fact of having been slaves is only a

6. Horace Mann Bond . . . Indianapolis, Indiana: [*Author's note*] see Horace Mann Bond, A *Study of Factors Involved in the Identity and Encouragement of Unusual Academic Talent among Under-privileged Populations*, Final Report, Contract No. SAF 8028, Project No. 5-0859, Bureau of Research, Office of Education, U.S. Department of Health, Education, and Welfare, January, 1967.

secondary factor. Realizing it or not, this group of non-whites, the so-called Negroes, derived their identity from their relation to Africa.

Now, as the American Negro begins to understand these facts, he sees himself vaguely and always hesitantly as part of the world's Non-White peoples. This makes him, forces him, to look at India's independence in a way different from that of whites of this planet. It also affects his view of China, of Japan, of Vietnam. But in a more direct and meaningful way it determines and it must determine the view he has of Africa.

There is not the time nor, I feel, at this period of history, the necessity, to review the traditional image of Africa as presented to the Western world in general and to the Negro in particular. It is important only to recall that this image, as just one of the many ways of educating Negroes, was always, with a few weak and spasmodic exceptions, left entirely in the hands of whites; so Negroes saw Africa as whites saw Africa: black, savage, unhealthy, and heathen.

Of course, Americans did not generally view with favor their countries of origin. As a nation of immigrants we were a people who had for one reason or another left our old countries to improve our lot here, to do better than we could have done in the land of our birth. This is true, of course, for all except Africans, who were torn and snatched from their land of birth. It is a bit ironic then that as a "country" of origin Africa has assumed the least favorable image of all the other countries of origin vis-à-vis America. To white Americans in "the land of the free and the home of the brave," no country, not China, not Italy, not Russia, not even France and England, and most assuredly not Africa, is as fair and desirable or beautiful and wonderful as America. Otherwise, why would we have come here? It would then have been totally out of character for Americans to single out Africa as a continent of charm and beauty. But of course we know that is not the entire story—that is not why Africa was described as a dark continent. We know that there was in addition a deliberate effort to deny the culture, the tradition, the wealth, and the beauty of that continent in order to perpetuate the rational basis for colonialism there and slavery here. But for Negroes the image was made even more negative and repulsive by the frequent threat of racists to send us back to Africa!—such forced returns to any country of origin, but especially Africa, had the impact of a life sentence on Alcatraz.

However, since Africa was indeed the basis of our non-white status, it provided from the beginning a fragile source for our identity, which we never completely denied. The naming of our earliest schools *African schools,* our mutual aid societies *African societies,* and the first of our important religious bodies *African Methodist Episcopal,* are but a few examples to prove that Africa was never absent from our self-image—symbolic and remote as it was for so many decades. It was left to Marcus Garvey, however, not only to make us view Africa as potentially merely a boat ride away but to admit, yes, even to proclaim, that our status and our identity was not a negative value but a positive one; we were not just non-white, not just Negroes—however that was defined—we were black.

It has taken almost a half a century and, let it be regrettably admitted, a changed attitude, first by the whites rather than by the Negro, for us really to accept what Garvey was saying. We have witnessed a radical change in the attitude of the larger society toward Africa and coincidentally toward black.

To many people *black* and *Africa* are in a sense synonymous terms—in spite of the range in color types found there. But our identity in its present form requires that the image of both *black* and *Africa* be made positive. Africa could and did change from a continent of *dependent* peoples to a continent of *independent* peoples. Black cannot be changed; we can only change our attitude about it. It cannot be rubbed off or washed off or wished off, and black as a value—except perhaps for the basic black dress once thought so essential for style—has rarely had a positive connotation —in conjunction with Africa or separately. A black lie, the black hole of Calcutta,[7] black death, etc., all illustrate the added strength black gives to whatever is already a bad situation.

But Garvey said we were black, not Negro or brown or colored or some other white euphemism, but black:

7. **black hole of Calcutta:** a small jail cell in the Indian city of Calcutta in which, allegedly, on June 20, 1756, 123 of the 146 British subjects who were confined there died of asphyxiation.

The Black Race,[8] like the white, is proud of its own society and will yield nothing in the desire to keep it pure and ward off a monstrous subjugation of its original and natural type, by which creation is to be judged, as a race responsible for its own, and held accountable in the final analysis for the presentation of itself, before the Judgment seat of God. The Ethiopian cannot change his skin; and we shall not.

Meanwhile, Black Africa began to stretch forth her hands—on her own continent, to the capitals of the world, and to the United Nations, fortuitously for us located in the front yard of our own Negro capital, Harlem. From then on it's been smooth sailing. The community we always had, the identity we always had, were both broadened and enriched by the reality of Africans. We say that black, not just mulatto, high-yellow or what-have-you people, could succeed in this world—and succeed at points of power and decision-making. No longer was the expectation complete to think that only a light-brown-skinned boy could become a doctor or a lawyer. Now quite clearly a black man could be a king and a black woman a real queen.

The feedback on this realization has been tremendously exciting. African heroes and tradition bulwark our long concern with Negro heroes and traditions. It has almost become better to be black than brown or yellow. White society, long accustomed even from the days of slavery to favoring those closer to them in appearance and indeed passing this value on to us as a group, even the ineligible us, now having to associate with and view the power of black kings and queens, no longer favors browns and yellows. To get real credit for pushing civil rights, one must give a black man a visible job, make a black girl your secretary, and welcome a black family into your neighborhood.

This brings us, I feel, to where we are today. Our sense of community has not appreciably changed. We have a separate identity which has been strengthened by having its most basic ingredients, Africa and our blackness, viewed positively by the white world and by us. Africa is no longer the land we never knew.

8. From *Philosophy and Opinions of Marcus Garvey.* Reprinted by permission of Humanities Press Inc., New York, and Frank Cass & Company Ltd., London.

And we here are becoming real people to Africans. It is interesting that this broadening of the base of our identity is emerging at a time in American history when group identity rather than amalgamation or group disappearance is viewed as the more positive value. We are "Beyond the Melting Pot." We no longer proclaim our advancement as one superior people but as one varied people, enriched by our variety. It may be that at last Negroes can be accused of the sin of having a dual identity, of seeing our roots so vehemently that we do not see our homes. I doubt that this will happen except for an occasional person, because Africa is our continental home, not our national home, and Africa is a continent of many nations.

Yet we are indeed free, as few Americans are, to decide from what part of that vast continent we want to think our ancestors came. Other nationalities cannot do this. You are either a Southern Italian or not, a Cantonese or not, an Irishman, or a Scotsman. We can say, and with some documentation to substantiate it, that our slave forebears could have been kings or prophets or farmers or fishermen from Nigeria or from Ghana, from Mozambique or from Kenya. And for the purposes of identity, it does not make much difference which group we choose—they were all black and they all came from Africa. We can glory in the past and present achievement of all Black Africans, and we can cry bitter tears of despair over the flagrant injustices anywhere in Africa from Cape to Cairo and especially from the Sahara to the sea. And let me parenthetically warn you not to forget that in its traditional usage *Black Africa*, a term we did not invent, meant Africa from the Sahara to the Cape, not Africa from the Sahara to the Kalahari or the Zambesi.[9]

We can learn the languages, understand the cultures of that vast area. And we can accept the responsibility of being a block of informed citizens speaking out within our society on matters of foreign policy especially as they affect those areas. This identification in turn will make our young people see a greater need for exercising their suffrage, getting an education, seeking posi-

9. **the Kalahari or the Zambesi:** the Kalahari is a desert plateau rising in southern Africa; the Zambesi is a river in southern Africa flowing through Rhodesia and Mozambique to the Indian Ocean. To Dr. Hill, all of Africa is *Black Africa*.

tions of power. The strength to achieve these goals will come from within our communities revitalized by strengths from Africa. This seems to me to be the basis of our new identity. The identity itself is old; its roots are merely spreading and strengthening.

Meaning and Method

1. "What Is Africa to Us?" attempts to explain, clarify, and define the existence and significance of the Negro American's African heritage. How can an African heritage or the awareness of such a heritage contribute to the sense of identity of the Negro American?

2. In her opening remarks, Dr. Hill quotes ten lines from "Heritage," a poem by Countee Cullen. Express the main point of the poem in your own words.

3. Beginning on page 343, Dr. Hill offers "a brief word on naming and labeling." What does she say is wrong or dangerous in applying group names or labels? Do you agree or disagree?

4. How has the word *black* been used negatively? Why, according to Dr. Hill, must *black* and *Africa* be given positive meanings? Do you agree or disagree with her?

5. "It may be that at last the Negroes can be accused of the sin of having a dual identity, of seeing our roots so vehemently that we do not see our homes." Judging this statement in context (see page 349), explain what you think the author meant by it. What does Dr. Hill seem to mean by *sin?* Do you think Polish-Americans, Italian-Americans, Irish-Americans, American Indians, Mexican-Americans, etc., are liable to the same accusation of "having a dual identity"?

6. On page 342 we read, "In considering the question of identity [of the Negro American], it is necessary for me to return to earlier days—at least in my own career—and to reiterate what I have come to believe are some of the basic impediments in Negro identity."

   How does the author use this statement as the basis for developing her talk? Are the many subtopics or divisions in her talk clearly stated and indicated? What is Dr. Hill's style of presentation? Is she personal, impersonal, or both? How might such elements of style as sentence length, diction, connectives, and transitional devices have differed if a journalist had written the explanation of black identity?

Composition and Discussion

1. The author points out the traditional connotations of *black* in such expressions as a "black lie, the black hole of Calcutta, and black death" (see page 347).

Is the word *black* always used to denote something unfavorable? Does it always carry unpleasant connotations? Is the origin of its unfavorable connotations racial? Is it possible that the unfavorable associations of the word *black* also stem from early man's fear of darkness and night—that is, from his fear of attack by others in the dark, of attack by wild animals, or from the fear of the unseen and unknown hidden by the darkness? Are some "black" expressions found in cultures which have no significant black population? If so, are such expressions based more on mythology, physical reality, or the conditions of the elements than they are on racial or social situations?

Explain the connotations or implications of *black* and *white* in the following expressions: a lily-white reputation; a business operating in the black; a white lie; a black eye; a white-paper report; a black-tie dinner; a white-tie dinner; black is the color of my true love's hair; a white wedding dress; "Black Eyes" (title of a Russian folk song); black is beautiful; the Black Forest in Germany.

2. Mrs. Hill asks, "What Is Africa to Us?" She stresses the psychological and sociological good she believes it would do black Americans to establish a sense of their African heritage.

What is the African identification she seeks? Is it valid in spite of the fact that most Africans regard black Americans as *Americans?* or that it is virtually impossible for a black American to trace his family lines back to an African tribe or village—thanks to the slave owners who destroyed or simply did not keep the family histories of their slaves? or that Africa is a vast land of innumerable tribal, political, geographical, cultural, ethnic, and linguistic differences and divisions? If it is valid, what makes it valid?

Robert H. Boyle

The following selection concerns Dr. Herbert R. Axelrod, a man who has the most extensive holdings in the American tropical-fish and pet business. The author of the profile, which is reprinted from *Sports Illustrated* Magazine, is Robert H. Boyle, who also has an interest in fish: he keeps eight largemouth bass in a 125-gallon aquarium in the living room of his home in Croton-on-Hudson, New York. And this, Mr. Boyle feels, gives him and his subject something in common. In fact, he points out, "Axelrod wouldn't have seen me for an interview unless I'd been a nut, too."

Mr. Boyle is a senior editor for *Sports Illustrated*; he had previously worked for the magazine as a reporter. He has also reported for *Time* and for the United Press, in bureaus in New York, Chicago, and San Francisco.

After graduation in 1949 from Trinity College in Hartford, Connecticut, Boyle received a master's degree from Yale University. To date, he has written one book, entitled *Sport, Mirror of American Life* (1963). He is presently at work on a second book, this one a natural history of the Hudson River and environs. Mr. Boyle has long been fascinated by this river—the village of Croton overlooks it from the eastern bank—and is an active participant in the fight to keep it from a death by pollution.

The Strange Fish and Stranger Times of Dr. Herbert R. Axelrod

Dr. Herbert R. Axelrod is the great panjandrum [1] of the tropical-fish world. Dr. Herbert R. Axelrod—the title and full name are always run together by admirers as though they were one word—

1. **panjandrum** (pan·jan'drəm): a title of mock importance, the equivalent of "big shot," or grandee. The word was coined by the eighteenth-century English dramatist and parodist Samuel Foote. In his sketch "Maria Edgeworth" he described a wedding attended by "the Joblillies, and the Garyalies, and the grand Panjandrum himself."

is without rival in the burgeoning world of tropical fish. Dr. Axelrod is an intrepid ichthyologist [2] and explorer who has made more than 40 expeditions to South America, Africa, Australia, the Fijis, Indonesia, Thailand, India, and the Malay Archipelago. He can, he says, recognize more than 7,000 species of fish on sight, and he has discovered hundreds of species that were lost to science for years or, better yet, were never seen before by man. More than two dozen species of fish have been named after him, and one of these, *Cheirodon axelrodi*, the cardinal tetra, is the biggest seller in the [tropical-fish] world.

Besides being a fantastic discoverer of fish, Dr. Axelrod is a remarkably prolific writer. He has written more than half a dozen major books on fish, all bestsellers. His first book, *Tropical Fish as a Hobby*, is in its ninth printing and has sold more than 80,000 copies. Dr. Axelrod has also churned out more than 100 smaller books and pamphlets on fish, and several hundred articles as well. His typewriter is always busy. Once on a Friday, Doubleday, the publishers, asked the doctor for a book on fish. On Saturday morning he sat down to write and, by the time he stood up on Sunday evening, the manuscript was completed. On Monday it was accepted and published as *Tropical Aquarium Fishes*. It has sold 450,000 copies. As if to show this was no trick, Dr. Axelrod recently sat down for Fawcett and turned out a substantial paperback, *Axelrod's Tropical Fish Book*, over another weekend. The book is lavishly illustrated with hundreds of photographs, most of them taken by the doctor, who, with some justification, regards himself as the finest photographer of tropical fish in the world.

When not traveling up some Amazon tributary by dugout canoe or sitting before a smoking typewriter, Dr. Axelrod is kept busy presiding over the seemingly limitless destinies and rapidly multiplying fortunes of T.F.H. Publications, Inc., of which he owns 75 percent of the stock. T.F.H. Publications, Inc., or TFH as it is known in the trade, is the General Motors of the pet world, and its offices are in, of all places, Jersey City. Here, in the yellow three-story building of his own design, the doctor publishes *All-Pets* magazine, a monthly given over to such articles as "The Four-Toed Tortoise" and "Peafowl, from a Hobby to a Business," and

2. **intrepid ichthyologist** (ik′thē·ol′ə·jist) : one who studies fish fearlessly and tirelessly.

his own very special baby, *Tropical Fish Hobbyist*, which not only has the largest circulation of any aquarium magazine but is, as the cover has proclaimed, THE ONLY AQUARIUM MAGAZINE IN THE WORLD ILLUSTRATED INSIDE WITH COLOR PHOTOGRAPHS!!! Invariably, these photographs have been taken by Dr. Axelrod to illustrate one of his own articles about an expedition he headed, net in one hand, rifle in the other, into some obscure backwater in search of a spotted *Corydoras* catfish. Among the subscribers who have thrilled to the doctor's accounts of rare adventure was the late Winston Churchill, who carried on a correspondence with him about fancy goldfish. Churchill, however, was merely one of a number of world figures enthralled by the doctor. He has been on intimate terms with the Emperor of Japan, Hirohito, a renowned sea-slug specialist; the former King of the Belgians, Leopold III; and the [former] President of Brazil, Huberto Castelo Branco, who has asked Dr. Axelrod to draw up a conservation program for the Amazon.

In addition to publishing magazines, Dr. Axelrod also publishes thousands of booklets dealing with all aspects of the pet world. Among those he has published are such bestsellers as *Modern American Mouse*, *Colorful Egglayers*, *Trick Training Cats*, *Your Terrarium*, *Horned Toads as Pets*, *Monkey Business*, *Snakes as Pets*, and *Rats as Pets*. For some time now, Ernest Walker, former assistant director of the Washington zoo, has been after TFH to publish a companion volume, *Bats as Pets*, but Dr. Axelrod has resisted his friend on the grounds that there are no pet shops selling bats. Walker keeps several free-flying bats in his Washington apartment, and whenever Dr. Axelrod comes to call, Walker, fearful lest his pets escape, opens the door a crack and whispers, "Come in quickly."

At least once a month Dr. Axelrod takes a flying trip to Florida, where TFH owns five tropical-fish farms near Tampa. TFH is the biggest breeder of tropical fish in the world; at last count there were approximately six million fish down on the farms. All in all, TFH so dominates the field of fish that a couple of cosmetic companies, seeking to diversify, recently offered the doctor $7 million to sell out. He refused, because he was making piles of money, and he has used part of the substantial profits of TFH to further the study of fish. Two years ago he reprinted Jordan and Evermann's four-volume classic on systematic ichthyology, *The Fishes of North and Middle America*, which had long been out of print, and presented 2,000 sets to the Smithsonian Institution free of charge. The Smithsonian has been selling the volumes at $25.00 a set, and all the proceeds go toward tropical-fish research and expeditions. On occasion Dr. Axelrod has dug deep into his pocket to finance expeditions by others when he has been tied down by affairs in Jersey City. He dispatched Dr. Jacques Gery of the Laboratoire Arago of the University of Paris to Gabon [3] to search for exotic fish, and Dr. Martin Brittan of Sacramento State College has taken a couple of treks into unexplored Brazil in quest of an elusive blood-red tetra, thanks to the doctor's largess.

In his own spare hours, infrequent though they may be, Dr. Axelrod is fond of playing Bach sonatas on the violin and reading deeply in the sciences. He holds degrees in mathematics, chemistry, physics, and biology and, since he is fluent in French, Spanish, Portuguese, German, Hebrew, and Japanese, can get along in Russian and Polish and grasp the essentials in Hungarian and Swedish, his range of reading is wide as well as deep. The doctor has been a crack golfer, bowler, and swimmer (when only ten he swam fifteen miles from the American shore to the Canadian shore of Lake Ontario), but his favorite sports nowadays are racing pigeons and fishing. He is one of a handful of anglers who have caught an Atlantic sailfish on a fly rod, and when he made his first million he celebrated by building, on the roof of his Jersey City emporium, four of the most luxurious pigeon coops in existence. At noontime he often clambers up to the roof and sends the pigeons flying while he munches on a sandwich. When in residence in Jersey City the doctor always lunches on a double liverwurst on rye sent in from Bauer's Delicatessen, but on the road he is a far more adventurous gourmet. As one might expect, his favorite dish is fish, any kind of fish, but in the jungle he sometimes gluts himself on howler-monkey stew. A good meal counts for a lot with the doctor. In fact, he once broke a trip from an aquarium in Frankfurt-am-Main to Cairo, where he was to inspect fish carvings inside a pyramid, just to stop off in Rome for a highly touted plate of spaghetti.

3. **Gabon** (gà·bôn′): the Gabonese Republic, Africa, formerly a territory of French Equatorial Africa but since 1960 a Republic of the French Community.

This man of enormous energies and myriad talents is also a man of mystery. Rumors abound about Axelrod. One rumor, essentially true, has it that he dwells in splendor in an opulent bomb shelter and fortress tucked into the Jersey coast. Another story goes that, though the doctor is well into his seventies, he does not look a day over forty-five. In point of fact, Dr. Herbert R. Axelrod, ichthyologist, explorer, author, linguist, tycoon, and sportsman, is only thirty-seven years of age. Meeting him for the first time is somewhat like discovering the real identity of the Wizard of Oz.

Dr. Axelrod, a burly six-footer, purposely keeps himself from public view for several reasons. For one, he believes that his private life is his own business. For another, he has no desire to be called at any hour of the night by an aquarist in Oklahoma City whose swordtails have fallen prey, say, to a mild case of *Ichthyopthirius*.[4] For still another, Dr. Axelrod finds most people are bores. He once refused to meet Jacques Cousteau; [5] he thought Cousteau was a bore. Indeed, Dr. Axelrod has been known to interrupt conversations with close friends by yawning in their faces and telling them to leave because he was bored. "I'm not rude for rudeness' sake," says the doctor. "I just don't have time to beat around the bush." When he was younger he worried that he had a personality problem, and he consulted a psychiatrist. The psychiatrist dismissed him at once on the grounds that Dr. Axelrod was the happiest man he had ever met, because he had no inhibitions. Possibly as a result of his complete lack of inhibitions, Dr. Axelrod is tremendously fond of quarrels and litigation. In recent years he has been sued fourteen times, and the filing of each suit gave him as much joy as the discovery of a new species of fish. Several cases arose out of denunciations Dr. Axelrod made of certain fish dealers in *Tropical Fish Hobbyist*, but inasmuch as he considers himself the world's ranking expert on tropical fish, he has no doubt that he will win them all. As a matter of fact, he has so far won thirteen of the lawsuits, with the other one pending. "I like to match wits," says the doctor. "A lawsuit is a chess game. When there's no challenge, I'm not interested."

4. *Ichthyopthirius* (ik'thē·op·thēr'ē·əs): a respiratory disease of fish.
5. Jacques Cousteau: Jacques-Yves Cousteau (b. 1910), one of the world's foremost oceanographers and marine explorers, author of *The Silent World* (1953), an account of some of his undersea adventures.

Dr. Axelrod grew up in Bayonne, New Jersey, just to the south of Jersey City. Bayonne, a grimy oil refinery town fronting Upper New York Bay, is an unlikely place to spawn a naturalist of Dr. Axelrod's stature, but in the days of his youth it still possessed marshlands and creeks unbefouled by oil wastes. The family had little money—Axelrod's father, Dr. Aaron Axelrod, now vice president of TFH, taught mathematics in a local high school—but young Herbert earned pocket money by pressing pants, with characteristic gusto, for an overwhelmed tailor and by catching blue crabs, which he sold to Chinese laundrymen. For a dime he purchased a nondescript pair of pigeons from a fellow urchin,[6] and he housed them in a sawed-off orange crate he kept hidden down alleys and under stoops. Despite his best efforts, the pigeons made their mark on neighborhood porches and roofs, and protesting landlords forced the family to move several times. "I was crazy about the pigeons!" Dr. Axelrod recalls in a typical burst of enthusiasm. "I took them to school and hid them there. I used to take them into my room at night. I couldn't leave them. I didn't know it, but I actually developed the first mobile pigeon loft. It took the Army years to do that, and I did it as a kid!"

In high school Axelrod's passion for knowledge was such that he asked his father to send him to a Jesuit prep school in Jersey City. But since Dr. Axelrod *père* was teaching in the high school that his son was attending he refused, because he did not want to denigrate the teaching abilities of his colleagues. Undaunted, Axelrod *fils* took to cutting school two or three times a week to attend Brooklyn Tech on the sly, because the teachers there were stimulating. Whatever Axelrod did, he did to the hilt. He had an IQ of 181, but he was nagged by doubts that spurred him to further efforts. "I guess I always wanted to show off," he says. "I was an ugly kid, with pimples all over my face. I weighed 110 pounds, and no girl would go out with me. I was obsessed with sex."

At sixteen Axelrod was graduated from high school, and at seventeen he enlisted in an Army officer college training program. He was sent to study engineering at the City College of New York and the University of Delaware. When the Germans almost broke through American lines in the Battle of the Bulge in 1944, all the

6. **urchin:** mischievous boy.

students were rushed overseas, except Axelrod, who was too young for combat. He was apprehended at the gangplank and sent to Fort Lewis, Washington, while his clothes and equipment sailed off to France. At Fort Lewis, Axelrod served out his Army career as a private in an engineering company and whiled away his idle hours as a violinist in the Tacoma Symphony.

Upon discharge from the Army, Axelrod resumed his studies at CCNY, then transferred to New York University when offered a scholarship. His major field was mathematics and, at nineteen, he wrote his first published paper, "The Lattice Theory in Boolian Algebra." He took generous helpings of side courses in languages and sciences. "The more you learn, the easier it gets to learn," he says. While working on his master's degree at NYU he taught an extension course in aquatic life that attracted great attention for its novelty. On Saturdays he took his students out to Long Island, where they explored tidal flats and swamps. He made them eat almost everything they collected. On occasion his enthusiasm for nature became so unbounded that the faculty took alarm. He was once censured by a professor for performing a Caesarean [7] on a guppy.

For a time Axelrod worked as a laboratory assistant to Professor Myron Gordon. When Professor Gordon went on a sabbatical,[8] he recommended that Axelrod teach his course on experimental laboratory animals, most of which were tropical fish. The head of the department, Professor Charles Pieper, asked Axelrod to write out his lecture notes in advance. Axelrod did, and he left them in a pile on Professor Pieper's desk. Professor Pieper happened to be delayed in returning, and in the interim a McGraw-Hill book salesman entered, read through the notes and was entranced. As a result, McGraw-Hill asked to publish them as a book. Axelrod consented, and the subsequent book, *Tropical Fish as a Hobby*, published in 1952, was to make him the leading authority on the subject at the tender age of twenty-four.

7. **Caesarean** (si·zâr′ē·ən): a caesarean (or *cesarean*) section refers to the birth of offspring by surgical incision of the abdominal wall and uterus. The Roman emperor Caesar was reputed to have been born in this manner.
8. **sabbatical**: a year's leave of absence, often with pay, awarded to teachers in some U.S. colleges and universities. A sabbatical year is usually granted every seventh year of continuous service. The term is from Hebrew *shabbath*, "to rest," and is associated with the seventh day of the week, or Sabbath, the day of rest.

In 1950, however, Axelrod, by then engaged on his doctorate at NYU, was called back into the Army at the start of the Korean War. This time he went in as an officer—a lieutenant—and was sent to Korea, where he studied epidemic hemorrhagic fever, a blood disease, as a member of a field medical laboratory. His work called for him to take blood samples to Japan for detailed analysis and, inasmuch as the plane returned to Korea with a cargo of empty blood containers, Axelrod began filling them up with whiskey. He traded whiskey for cigarettes, which he stuffed between the filled blood containers on the flight to Japan. As his import-export business boomed, he also began working on a second manuscript, *Handbook of Tropical Aquarium Fishes.*

On one trip to Japan, Axelrod visited the Tokyo University library, where he pored over the books on fishes. While looking for a misplaced volume, he happened to meet an ichthyologist, Dr. Tokiharu Abe, who showed him a copy of a book, *The Opisthobranchia of Sagami Bay,*[9] that had been written by Emperor Hirohito. Axelrod riffled through the pages, then stopped to point out an error in the scientific name of an opisthobranch. Dr. Abe was incredulous, but Axelrod cited the correct reference in an obscure scientific paper he had just finished reading. With that he bade the doctor adieu, put the incident out of mind, and flew back to Korea with a load of choice six-month-old Scotch.

As Axelrod now recalls it, about a fortnight later he was ordered to appear before General Matthew Ridgway in full-dress uniform. Remembering that a case of whiskey had recently disappeared, Axelrod suspected that military police had seized it as evidence for a court-martial, and by the time he entered General Ridgway's office he was hoping for ten years instead of the death penalty. To his surprise, however, the general had summoned him because Hirohito wanted Axelrod as a house guest. Ridgway wanted to know why, since no American had been asked to see the Emperor since General MacArthur had been relieved of command. Axelrod, forgetting the incident in the library, said he had no idea why he had been invited. Ridgway told Axelrod to accept the invitation and to do his best to get one for the general him-

9. *The Opisthobranchia of Sagami Bay:* opisthobranchia are a large order of mollusks—snails, clams, oysters, squid, octopedes, etc. are all mollusks—having their heart gills located behind their hearts. The term comes from two Greek words, *opisthen* and *branchia,* which mean, respectively, "behind" and "gills." Sagami Bay is a large inlet southwest of Tokyo Bay, Japan.

self. Axelrod said he would see what he could do and went off to Japan, where he spent a week at the summer palace on Sagami Bay collecting marine invertebrates with the Emperor. Hirohito, who was most grateful for having had the error in his book pointed out to him, listened to Axelrod's plea on behalf of General Ridgway and rejected it, explaining that he and the general really had nothing in common. Axelrod said he had to agree. Hirohito then presented him with a jar of preserved eels as a gift for Dr. Leonard Schultz, curator of fishes at the Smithsonian.

Shortly afterward Axelrod was discharged, and he hastened to Washington, where he gave the eels to Dr. Schultz. He also showed Dr. Schultz a draft of the *Handbook of Tropical Aquarium Fishes,* and Dr. Schultz was so impressed with its potential that he agreed not only to collaborate on the work but waive his years of seniority as well and appear as junior author. Not long after this, Axelrod's first book, *Tropical Fish as a Hobby,* was published, and it was such an instant success that McGraw-Hill asked him to return a dozen complimentary copies so as to meet the demand. The book was successful because no one with a working scientific background had ever before written a book about tropical fish and, moreover, Axelrod, unlike previous authors, revealed breeding secrets. His description of spawning *Hyphessobrycon innesi,* the neon tetra, was of great moment [10] to aquarists everywhere.

Since Axelrod had returned home in the middle of the academic year he was unable to resume his doctoral studies and teaching position at NYU until the start of the 1952 fall term. As a returning serviceman, he was entitled to receive his salary anyway, and he used the money to finance trips to British Guiana and Malaya, where he bought tropical fish that he sold from a rented store in Manhattan.

By the time the fall term began, Axelrod was well established in business. He gave up selling fish for the nonce and started *Tropical Fish Hobbyist.* Using mostly pseudonyms to protect his scholarly background, he also wrote, published, and distributed inexpensive booklets on fish and other pets. Within three years T.F.H. Publications, Inc., owned its own printing plant and bindery, and Axelrod was doing so handsomely that he was able to buy out several Jersey City businessmen who had backed him. Meanwhile,

10. **moment:** importance.

he was also busy on his doctorate in biostatistics.[11] The subject of his dissertation was *The Mathematical Solution of Certain Biometrical Problems,* and in it he demonstrated that the statistical procedures used in twenty-five medical and dental research papers were incorrect. "It was a very startling study," says Dr. Axelrod, who is so fond of figures that he multiplies passing license plate numbers while driving around in his car.

Dr. Axelrod's main strength in business is his ruthlessness. A couple of years ago he decided to reprint *Stroud's Digest of the Diseases of Birds,* a solid research work by Robert Stroud, the so-called Birdman of Alcatraz, who spent more than forty years in solitary confinement for murder. Stroud's agent had published the book in 1943, but it had been done poorly. Stroud was eager to see a decent edition on the market but, before giving Dr. Axelrod publication rights, he asked the doctor to endorse his appeal for freedom. "You're a murderer!" Dr. Axelrod exclaimed. "If it were up to me, you'd cook!" Stroud angrily gave the rights to another publisher, but the doctor secured the book for TFH by buying him out. Convicts, incidentally, intrigue the doctor, who has been conducting a pen-palship with prisoners he met when lecturing on tropical fish at the Indiana State Prison. To his amazement, Axelrod found that some lifers had been keeping guppies for more than thirty years despite strict regulations against pets. They had hidden generation after generation of fish in vials strapped to their bodies, and the birth of a new batch was cause for a cell-block celebration. In the interest of science, Dr. Axelrod asked the captive guppy fanciers to keep constant watch on their pets for an intensive around-the-clock study of fish behavior. "After all," says the doctor, "these guys have nothing but time on their hands." To his dismay, however, the prisoners seemed to get sadistic pleasure in keeping prisoners of their own in prison, so to speak, and instead of chronicling fish behavior, they began putting guppies into smaller and smaller containers to see how much confinement they could take before they died. Still, this was not a total loss to Dr. Axelrod, who learned that a guppy can survive in a stoppered inch-long pencil-thin test tube laid on its side.

If there was one turning point in the fortunes of Dr. Axelrod and TFH, it came in 1958, when he took his greatest gamble by

11. **biostatistics:** the statistics of life (*bio-* is from Greek *bios,* life).

publishing the *Encyclopedia of Tropical Fishes,* which he wrote with William Vorderwinkler, editor of *Tropical Fish Hobbyist.* "I did everything that other publishers said I shouldn't do," says the doctor. "We used big pictures. We used big type. They said everything was wrong, that it was a completely lousy book by their standards. They said I was going to ruin myself. I put every cent I had into it, and then I went off to Africa and I said to myself that I'd either come back a millionaire or a bum. The *Encyclopedia* was a success, and we sell 15,000 copies a year. We've been shooting craps in the publishing business for the last 10 years, and we've been winning." In point of fact, Dr. Axelrod is a very lucky crap shooter. He remembers a night in Haiti when he rolled 17 straight passes, then played 21 and beat the dealer. Astounded, the owner of the casino and the croupier, who had been following him around, ominously insisted he stay the rest of the night to play 21 with them. Dr. Axelrod did, and he cleaned them out, too. "They couldn't believe what I was doing," he says as a matter of course, "so I told them I was cheating."

More than anyone else in the world Dr. Axelrod is responsible for the changing tastes in the aquarium hobby today. The hobby started in grim seriousness in Germany 100 years ago, and for years goldfish were the rage. But then, in the 1920's and 1930's, tropicals began to edge in, and in the past few years goldfish have been all but discarded in favor of tropical after tropical, thanks in good part to the expeditions, discoveries, and writings of Dr. Axelrod. In the last five years alone, TFH imported more species of fish than aquarists had seen in all history. Today Dr. Axelrod, TFH, and the U.S. lead the world in tropical-fish expertise, and Germany, the one-time leader, is a distant second.

A living memorial to the doctor is *Cheirodon axelrodi,* the cardinal tetra, which he discovered lurking in a reach of the Upper Rio Negro, a tributary of the Amazon, in 1954. This discovery is regarded as the greatest ever made in tropical fish, but the doctor himself did not know for an entire year that he had happened upon a species [12] wholly unknown to science. The cardinal tetra, an extremely colorful fish, bears a superficial resemblance to its cousin, *Hyphessobrycon innesi,* the neon tetra, and Dr. Axelrod, thinking he had found a race of giant neons, marked them as such

12. **species:** a category of animals or plants subordinate to a *genus,* or biological class.

after bringing back a shipment to the U.S. To his astonishment, they spawned differently from the neons, and he at once sent several specimens to his old friend and collaborator, Dr. Schultz and the Smithsonian, for classification. Upon examination, Dr. Schultz rang up Dr. Axelrod to announce that the fish not only constituted a new species of tetra but, moreover, a close look at their teeth showed that they belonged to a new genus [13] as well. Dr. Schultz described the new fish in February 20, 1956, issue of *Tropical Fish Hobbyist* and assigned it the name of *Cheirodon axelrodi* in honor of its discoverer. Then, on the very next day, in an issue of *The Stanford Ichthyological Bulletin,* Professors George Myers and Stanley Weitzman, outstanding taxonomists [14] in their own right, described a specimen they happened to have, and they called it *Hyphessobrycon cardinalis.* The fight started. Debate raged for more than a year and a half until the International Commission of Zoological Nomenclature convened and gave the nod to *axelrodi.* This contretemps [15] is merely one of a number the doctor has figured in with academic ichthyologists, and their *sotto voce* [16] asides about his being a pushy upstart rankle. "I've been hated for years because I've combined science with business," says Dr. Axelrod, happily putting in the zing. "The guys who criticized me initially for selling science for money are now the ones who try to sell me science for money, including some of my so-called best friends."

Dr. Axelrod's favorite collecting grounds are the Amazon and its tributaries, which support an extraordinarily large and varied number of fishes. "The Amazon River System, I would judge," says the doctor "produces enough protein in one month to feed the world for a year." Most of his jaunts into the jungle are done with Harald Schultz, a specialist on Indian ethnology [17] at the São Paulo museum, who is not to be confused with Dr. Leonard

13. **genus:** general biological class or subfamily.
14. **taxonomists:** experts in the classification of plants and animals, especially suspected new species, which are classified according to scientifically established criteria. The word is derived from Greek *taxis,* "arrangement," and *nomos,* "law."
15. **contretemps** (kôn·trə·tän′): awkward moment; inopportune and embarrassing mischance. The term is from the French.
16. *sotto voce* (sot′ō vō′chē): *Italian,* literally, "under the normal voice"; softly; in an undertone.
17. **ethnology:** the study of man's racial and ethnic group origins, culture, and distribution.

Schultz, much less Willie Schwartz, another Brazilian collecting crony. Harald Schultz has been macheted, blow-gunned, pummeled, trampled upon, and threatened in the course of his field investigations on the tribal rites of hostile Indians, and Dr. Axelrod considers him the bravest man he has ever met. Schultz, in turn, looks upon the doctor as a strong, powerful man, a tremendous genius with a strange personality and a range of accomplishments that can only be likened to Charlie Chaplin's. He also looks upon the doctor as the most foolhardy man he has ever met. Schultz thinks Dr. Axelrod's penchant for swimming with piranhas [18] is a ghastly business—the doctor believes piranhas are not at all vicious and that their bad reputation comes from a bum rap by Teddy Roosevelt, who journeyed up the Amazon in 1913. Schultz was once so put out at Axelrod's grabbing a passing snake by the tail that he refused, on principle, to come to the doctor's aid even though his screams for help indicated that the snake was about to win out. Dr. Axelrod managed to escape unscathed, but Schultz did nothing more than lie in his hammock with a look of anguish. Considering Dr. Axelrod's foolhardiness, he has done reasonably well in the jungle. His only mishap occurred last November when, exhausted from netting rare fish, he settled down to sleep on top of several fire-ant hills that escaped his usually keen eye. He was bitten severely, and he had to spend a month in a hospital in Manaus getting mammoth injections of cortisone.

In Dr. Axelrod's absence, Schultz collects fishes on his own. Named after him is *Hyphessobrycon haraldschultzi*, commonly known as Harald Schultz's tetra, first cousin to *Hyphessobrycon herbertaxelrodi*, the black neon tetra. Not long ago Dr. Axelrod received a letter from Schultz announcing that he had at last found a fish beautiful enough to be named for Schultz's wife, Vilma, and the fish, which has a bright red belly and two metallic blue spots, was subsequently called *Copella vilmae*. In addition to genus *Hyphessobrycon*, Schultz and Dr. Axelrod also have a double entry going for them in *Symphysodon aequifasciata haraldi*, the blue discus, and *Symphysodon aequifasciata axelrodi*, the brown discus. A species of goby, *Butis butis*, rediscovered by Lee Ching

18. **piranhas** (pi·rä′nyəz): small, carnivorous, fresh-water fish of tropical South America; a school of piranhas will readily attack and devour large animals or men.

Eng, a renowned Jakarta [19] fish exporter, is widely known as Axelrod's crazy fish. It so happens that when Dr. Axelrod entered Lee's establishment late one night in 1959, the proprietor shouted, "Dr. Axelrod! I've discovered a new fish!" The doctor looked at the fish, which likes to swim upside down, and remarked, "I doubt that it's new, but it sure is acting crazy." From then on, Lee called it Axelrod's crazy fish.

The honor of bestowing the scientific name on a new species of fish falls to the taxonomist who describes it and not to the discoverer. Fish have been named after Dr. Axelrod largely in recognition of his forays into unknown areas, but the fact is that the doctor has the knack of finding new fish where others have looked long and hard. A prize example of this that he likes to cite occurred in Trinidad several years ago. The island of Trinidad has more fish collectors per capita than any other place in the world. It has been thoroughly combed, so much so that the government has imposed a closed season on collecting for fear that the island's fishes are in danger of extinction. One afternoon, net at the ready, Dr. Axelrod landed at Pearco airport and immediately seined [20] a small pool at the edge of the runway. As onlookers gasped audibly—the doctor vividly remembers the chorus of sucked-in-breaths —the net yielded hundreds of specimens of a bright-red fish that had never been seen before by any Trinidadian, or any taxonomist in the world, for that matter. Flying on to Rio, Dr. Axelrod dropped off some specimens with Dr. Haraldo Travassos of the Museo Nacional, who classified them as belonging to the tetra family. He named the species *Aphyocharax axelrodi*. Ordinarily Dr. Axelrod does not boast about discovering a new species, but he is rather proud of this find, which is marketed widely as the red pristella. "It was like going to a high school ball game and finding five Babe Ruths, four Lou Gehrigs, two Pee Wee Reeses, and one Duke Snider," says the doctor.

Dr. Axelrod's knack for discovering the unusual is not confined to fish. While dining recently in the best restaurant in Bogota, he detected a bitter taste in his cup of Colombian coffee. Draining it down, he discovered a cockroach, and instead of being dismayed he was elated. He took the cockroach back to his hotel

19. **Jakarta** (also *Djakarta*; jä·kär′tä): the capital of Indonesia.
20. **seined** (sānd): fished by means of a net.

366   Robert H. Boyle

room, popped it in a bottle of formalin,[21] and sent it to the Smithsonian in the hope that it might be a new species. If it is, the suggestion has been made that it be named after the restaurant.

The Axelrod knack also extends to people. While returning from the Brazilian jungle for a rest in Manaus, he met a fellow scientist in the elevator of the hotel. The scientist turned out to be Dr. Jean-Pierre Gosse, adviser to Leopold III, former King of the Belgians. Dr. Gosse refused to believe that Dr. Axelrod was *the* Dr. Axelrod—Gosse, too, had heard the rumor that the doctor was well into his seventies—but Dr. Axelrod was finally able to prove his identity by citing the name of a species of fish, *Neolebias axelrodi* (what else?), then under taxonomic dispute at the British Museum. Dr. Gosse introduced Dr. Axelrod to King Leopold, who was staying just down the hall, and Axelrod in turn had his doubts that King Leopold was really King Leopold. The King finally was able to confirm his identity to the doctor's satisfaction, and the two of them had a joyous week together on the Amazon spearing game fish, *Arapaima gigas* by day and *Osteoglossum bicirrhosum* by night. Dr. Axelrod, incidentally, was the first man to capture young *Osteoglossa*, which are carried in the mother's mouth. The fish always swallows her young when speared or netted, but the doctor showed Leopold how to obtain the young by severing the mother's head with a swift slice from a machete. Upon the King's departure for home, Dr. Axelrod presented him with a pet jaguar that had a nasty habit of biting the doctor's ankles, and Leopold, forewarned, gave the animal to the Brussels zoo. Since then the doctor and the King have exchanged visits in Belgium and Jersey City, and last year Leopold presented Dr. Axelrod with a brace of Belgian racing pigeons. They are now ensconced in the luxurious lofts atop TFH headquarters, but the doctor, a member in good standing of the Ideal Racing Pigeon Club, has not entered them against local competition on the grounds that it would be unfair, because Belgian pigeons are the fastest in the world.

In Brazil, Dr. Axelrod has also become very much involved with Willie Schwartz, an eccentric German Jewish refugee who fled the perils of Nazism for the relative safety of the Matto Grasso. Together they helped gather creatures for a couple of Walt Disney's nature epics. One of Disney's more difficult orders

21. formalin: a solution used as a preservative.

was for a pair of rare black jaguars. Schwartz and Dr. Axelrod managed to capture one, but they were unable to come up with another. Finally, Axelrod says, he suggested that they catch a run-of-the-mill jaguar and convert it. They did, Dr. Axelrod administered an anesthetic, and he and Schwartz trucked the beast to a hairdresser in Manaus, where it was bleached and dyed and shipped off to Hollywood.

Life in the wild still spells joy for Dr. Axelrod, but in recent months his thinking has turned more and more toward the booming business of TFH. "I'm really a deep thinker sailing far out into space," says the doctor. "I can sit in a chair for hours just thinking until I'm numb. I'm a great thinker. I go to sleep thinking, and I wake up thinking. I go to sleep with my hands folded behind my head. I have grandiose plans. I never think small!" A couple of years ago, after a bout of deep thinking, Dr. Axelrod seized upon the idea of the Fish-In-A-Flash kit. "It was the most successful flop I've ever been involved with!" he exults. He took the eggs of *Nothobranchius palmquisti*, an East African fish that lays eggs that can survive drought, to a toy trade show in New York and showed how they would hatch in a glass of water. Wholesalers and mail-order houses piled in with $8 million worth of orders. Dr. Axelrod started his own hatchery to produce eggs by the millions for kits, but he had to cease production because the initial customers were disappointed. The hatched fish were almost microscopic, and the customers had difficulty seeing them. "They expected—pop!—two-inch, beautifully colored fish," says the doctor. "It was a bust."

The doctor tried a new scheme last year with Quaker Oats, manufacturers of Cap'n Crunch breakfast food. TV commercials for the product features a Cap'n Crunch, who skippers a ship called the Guppy, and the doctor thought that this looked like a natural. He made arrangements with Quaker Oats to supply a pair of guppies to any tot who wrote in, enclosing a Crunch box top and 19¢, but the deal fell through when the doctor refused to guarantee that the guppies would live. "Who knows what a kid is going to do to fish?" he asks.

The doctor's present grandiose plans fall into two parts. First of all, he aims to corner the entire tropical-fish market. "I have the total approach," he says. "The books, the livestock, the accessories." A short time ago he spent a million dollars to acquire the second-largest aquarium-manufacturing company in the world, and he is rolling his eyes at the largest. He is also aiming to up fish production on his Florida farms, because the size of the tropical-fish market is limited only by the number of fish available. Dr. Axelrod will go to any lengths to increase production. One day last winter he chanced to hear of a fisheries library for sale at $2,000, and, without inspecting a volume, he immediately offered to buy it. "Any one paper in it would be worth $2,000 to me if it gave a hint as to how I could get more fish production," he explains. "It may be that some little trick somebody found out a hundred years ago is just what I need." The doctor is always reading for clues and hints. Several years ago he was perusing an article on salt lakes and brine shrimp, *Artemia salina*, in a Russian fishery journal. The author noted that salt lakes having the right requirements for brine shrimp were found in Russia, Israel, California, and Canada. At the mention of Canada, Dr. Axelrod leaped from his chair. He knew all about the lake in California; a fish-supply house in San Francisco had a monopoly on the brine-shrimp eggs, which are used as food for tropical fish. But Canada was something new. Discovery of brine-shrimp eggs there would be worth a fortune; the eggs bring more than caviar. The doctor ransacked reference literature, but he was unable to find the name of the salt lake. In fact, the best reference he could find mentioned one in Saskatchewan. He put in a call to a pet-shop owner in Winnipeg, who was an amateur pilot. The pet-shop owner agreed to fly up and down Saskatchewan [22] looking for a lake with a white mark around the shore from salt. A month later he called the doctor. He had found not one lake but three, Manitou, Big Manitou, and Little Manitou. Dr. Axelrod mushed north at once. The shores of the lakes were laden with brine-shrimp eggs. The doctor leased the lakes from the Canadian government, and then, in turn, he sold the lease to Wardley's, a tropical-fish supply house in New York, for a five-percent royalty.

For the past year Dr. Axelrod has been reading and rereading Alfred P. Sloan's autobiography, *My Years with General Motors*. The doctor feels that Sloan (assisted by John McDonald) has written one of the great books of the age, and he has under-

22. **Saskatchewan** (sas·kach′ə·won) : a province in west-central Canada.

lined a number of sentences that have special meaning to him and the future of TFH. Among them are: "There is no resting place for an enterprise in a competitive economy," and "The urge for competitive survival is the strongest of economic incentives." The doctor has been applying these maxims to TFH, because the capture of the entire tropical-fish market is only part one of his grandiose plans. Part two calls for TFH to take over the *entire pet market within 10 years*. In that time Dr. Axelrod foresees the gross of TFH swelling from $3 million this year to $20 million by 1970 and $100 million by 1975. "But it's not the money," says the doctor. "It's the power! The pet business is going through a fantastic boom that doesn't look like it's going to stop. The pet business is great."

As part two of his grandiose plan for cornering the pet market, Dr. Axelrod plans to introduce a new pet to supplant the hamster in public affection. The doctor is down on hamsters. "We need a small, hardy animal!" he exclaims, and he has that small hardy animal all picked out. It is the Mongolian gerbil.[23] "The trouble with the hamster is that it is nocturnal, it sometimes bites, and it stinks," says the doctor. "The Mongolian gerbil has a longer tail, softer fur, is not nocturnal, doesn't bite, and doesn't stink. The only difficulty is getting them to breed. I'm going to work on that. Right now I'm trying to tie up all the Mongolian gerbils in the United States."

After getting all the Mongolian gerbils to breed, Dr. Axelrod plans to set up retail pet and hobby shops in department stores, five and tens, and discount houses all across the country. This will give him complete control of the pet market. "The shops will do everything from selling model airplanes and fish tanks to living fish and birds and chameleons and what-have-you," he says. "It will have a garden center. It will sell books, plants, seeds, and microscopes. Everything and anything!"

But for all the fish, all the Mongolian gerbils, and for all the money rolling in, Dr. Herbert R. Axelrod occasionally sinks into gloom. "I'd be happy to be a pauper," he says, "if I could play the fiddle as well as Jascha Heifetz." [24]

23. **gerbil** (jûr′bil).
24. **Jascha Heifetz** (yä′shə hī′fits): Lithuanian-born American violinist; Mr. Heifetz is considered one of the finest violinists in the world.

Meaning

1. Explain the relevance of the selection's title to its contents. Cite some examples of Dr. Axelrod's "strange fish" and "stranger times."
2. Explain which of the following words you think can be applied to Dr. Axelrod or to an aspect of his personality: arrogant, meek, brash, shrewd, confident, overconfident, greedy, foolish, good-natured, ambitious, quarrelsome, lucky, generous, miserly, anti-social, eccentric, gregarious.
3. Reread pages 359–60 and page 360, concerning Axelrod's meeting with (a) Hirohito, the Emperor of Japan, and (b) the King of the Belgians. How did Axelrod regard these men? Was he humble before them? Did he treat them as equals? Was he arrogant and rude?

Method

1. Some of the methods of paragraph development are (a) giving numerous details and particulars, (b) illustrating with at least one example, (c) relating an incident or an anecdote, (d) comparing and/or contrasting elements or ideas, and (e) offering sound reasons and arguments.

    Notice how Robert Boyle begins many of his paragraphs with definite, emphatic topic sentences (for examples, see paragraphs two, three, and four, beginning on page 353). How many ways has he used to develop his topic sentences into full paragraphs? Where does he combine methods? Are his methods of paragraph development suited to his subject and purpose? Explain your answers, citing at least one example for each method of paragraph development you point out.
2. Unity. Coherence. Emphasis. These three qualities are vital to the success of any essay or article. Is this article written in such a way that (a) it has a unified, central theme or topic; (b) its parts are interrelated and linked smoothly to one another; and (c) its parts are arranged in the most effective order? Explain your answers, citing specific points or parts in the article to support them. What would have been the effect if he had begun the article at the point where he takes up Axelrod's early life, which begins on page 357 with "Dr. Axelrod grew up in Bayonne, New Jersey . . ."?

Composition and Discussion

1. Dr. Herbert R. Axelrod is an unusual man, one with some unorthodox business notions and some big plans for the future. What do

you think of his business tactics—past, present, and to come? What do you think of his motives for success in business? Be prepared to explain and defend your views in an open-class discussion. Use illustrations from Boyle's profile and your own reasons to back up your points. As others air their views, listen carefully and be ready to challenge or corroborate a classmate's points.

2. Develop an expository composition based on research into present-day antitrust and monopoly laws. For resource material, consult recent magazine and newspaper articles, encyclopedias, and histories. What problems might Dr. Axelrod face if he tries to "take over" the entire pet industry?

A Glossary
of Literary Terms

Abstract and Concrete Terms: *abstract terms* are words and phrases that refer to ideas, characteristics, or intangible qualities. Abstractions have little or no appeal to any of the senses. Examples of abstract terms are *infinity, mankind, idea,* and *goodness.* *Concrete terms* stand for particular and individual things as opposed to generalities. They usually denote physical realties and therefore appeal to the senses and make us "see" or vividly imagine specific objects or actions. Examples of concrete terms are *red, blink, hard,* and *dime.*

Allegory: a narrative in verse or prose in which concrete characters and actions represent abstact ideas or moral qualities. An allegory carries both literal and symbolic levels of meaning.

An example of an allegory is the play *Everyman,* written in the fifteenth century. Among the symbolic characters whom Everyman meets are Fellowship, Knowledge, and Good Deeds. (See also **Symbol.**)

Alliteration: the repetition of consonant or vowel sounds at the beginnings of words in the same line or successive lines. Although mainly a poetic device, alliteration is sometimes used in prose, as in this verse from the Bible, "Now the man Moses was very meek, above all the men which were upon the face of the earth." (Numbers 12:3)

Allusion: a brief, casual reference to a person, place, event, or artistic or scriptural work that the author expects the reader to recognize. An allusion may be drawn from literature, history, geography, scripture, or mythology. For example, G. K. Chesterton, in an essay on the difference between mere inconvenience and real pain, playfully writes, "They also serve who only stand and wait for the two-fifteen." The allusion is to the last line of John Milton's poem, "When I Consider How My Light Is Spent." Chesterton added *for the two-fifteen.*

Ambiguity: grammatical ambiguity results when a word that has two or more meanings is used in such a way that its meaning in context is not readily understandable. In literature, an author may deliberately use ambiguity, or double meaning, to produce subtle or multiple variations in meaning. To understand the full significance of the context, the reader must search for other meanings of the word or passage.

Analogy: a form of extended comparison which points out the likenesses between very dissimilar objects; it attempts to use a familiar object or idea to illustrate or to introduce a subject that is unfamiliar or complex.

Anecdote: a brief account of an interesting, entertaining, or revealing incident. In writing an expository essay, a writer may use an anecdote to introduce or illustrate his topic.

Antagonist: the character or force that opposes the protagonist; a rival of the hero or heroine.

Anticlimax: see **Climax and Anticlimax.**

Antithesis: the use of opposite or strongly contrasting words, phrases, or statements balanced grammatically against each other for emphasis. For example:

"He knows the world and does not know himself."

—Jean de la Fontaine

Aphorism: a terse, pithy statement expressing a grain of wisdom or truth. For examples:

"Remember, that time is money."   —Benjamin Franklin

"Silence is the virtue of fools."   —Francis Bacon

Argumentation: a type of writing that attempts to convince the reader of the logic and the merits of a particular viewpoint (especially by giving specific reasons and examples), or that attempts to persuade the reader to accept a particular belief or opinion.

Atmosphere: the prevailing mental and emotional climate of a story; something the reader senses or feels. *Setting* and *Mood* help to create and heighten atmosphere.

Autobiography and Biography: both types of literature attempt to present an account of a person's life in a systematic and usually chronological order, using actual facts, events, and available evidence. The *autobiography* is an account written by the subject himself; the *biography* is written by another person.

Character Foil: a character who serves by contrast to set off the qualities of another character. For example, the appearance of a particularly dull, slow-witted, and unimaginative character will strengthen the reader's impression of an amusing, witty, and expressive character.

Characterization: the technique(s) an author uses to develop the personality of his fictional characters so that they are believable persons who act consistently and speak naturally. The basic methods of characterization are the following:

(a) direct analysis by the author of the person's actions, motives, and feelings;

(b) physical description by the author of the person's appearance and actions or description of the person's clothes or physical surroundings, such as the room in which he or she lives or works;

(c) a presentation of the person's thoughts through a stream of consciousness, that is, as thoughts and their associations are formed and run through the person's mind;

(d) presentation of the person's reactions to situations, events, and other people;

(e) showing the reactions of other people to the person's actions or words;

(f) presentation of the person's speech and conversations;

(g) giving the remarks, comments, and conversations of others about the person; and

(h) a combination of two or more of these methods.

Cliché: any trite or commonplace expression that is no longer fresh or effective because it has been used too often. The following are examples of clichés: *the time of our lives, sick as a dog, last but not least, fresh as a daisy, in the prime of life.*

Climax and Anticlimax: *Climax* is the point of greatest intensity of action or suspense in a story. Climax normally follows a buildup through successive narrative incidents. It usually occurs at the narrative's turning point but is sometimes coincidental with the dénouement (French for "unknotting") or final unraveling of the *plot.*

Anticlimax can be either dramatic or rhetorical. Dramatic anticlimax occurs in a narrative in which the climax is unexpected or is not a logical one in terms of the rising action and suspense, or in which the climax is far less than what the reader expected. Rhetorical anticlimax, sometimes purposeful (as in the following example), occurs in sentences or passages whose elements are arranged in an order of decreasing importance or impact. For example:

> "If once a man indulges himself in murder, very soon he comes to think little of robbing; and from robbing he comes next to drinking and sabbath-breaking, and from that to incivility and procrastination."
> —Thomas De Quincey (1785–1859)

Coherence: the logical and clear relationship of one sentence to another within a paragraph, and of one paragraph or part to another within a composition. Coherence is the quality in writing that links and binds the related parts of the composition into a unified whole. It is achieved through the use of transitional words and phrases (*accordingly, on the contrary, first, finally, however, nevertheless*); linking expressions (*this, these, they, it, that, he*); the repetition of key terms; synonyms; and the repetition of the same or similar grammatical constructions ("By his words, . . ." "By his deeds . . ." or "At the beginning, . . ." "At the end . . .").

Comparison and Contrast: in writing, a method used to clarify and illustrate a subject. *Comparison* shows the similarities between two things and *contrast* details the differences between things. They are usually used together, but can be used separately. See also **Contrast.**

Concrete Terms: see **Abstract and Concrete Terms.**

Conflict: the clash between opposing forces. It may be man versus himself (inner conflict), man versus man, man versus nature, man versus society, or a combination of one or more of these types. Conflict may be external (a struggle with physical or outside forces) or internal (a struggle that takes place within the mind of a character). The forces in opposition are labeled *protagonist* and *antagonist.*

Connotation: the associated or suggested meaning of a word, in addition to its literal meaning (see **Denotation**). Words such as *summer, winter, spring, brutal, wealthy,* and *vacation* imply additional meanings beyond their literal meanings.

Context: for a word, the other words and phrases so closely surrounding it that they effect its meaning or use. Context often determines a word's meaning as in the following examples:

> "That book has a fascinating plot."
> "I'd like to build a house on that plot."
> "Plot their fleet's position on the map, Morgan."

For an event or incident, *context* is the situation and circumstances that surround the event; we often speak of a specific event in its historical context.

Contrast: a striking difference between two things. In literature, to heighten or clarify a situation, an author may contrast ideas, personalities, or images. (See also **Comparison and Contrast.**)

Denotation: the literal or "dictionary" meaning or meanings of a word. (See also **Connotation.**)

Dénouement (dā·noo·män'): that part of the plot where the outcome or solution (permanent or temporary) of the main character's major problem is made known; the unraveling of the "knot," or intrigue, that was tied at the complication.

Description: The purpose of description is to make the reader share as intensely as possible in the sense experiences of the writer; that is, the writer wants his audience to see, hear, smell, taste, or touch, in imagination, those things which the writer describes.

In writing, an image or mental picture of a person, place, object, or action can be achieved through an enumeration of physical details, particulars, and sensory impressions.

Dialect: the speech that is characteristic of a particular group or of the inhabitants of a certain geographical region. In literature, dialect can be used as part of a characterization.

Dialogue: the conversation carried on by two or more characters. A monologue is the speech of one person, such as that of someone thinking aloud.

Diction: in a literary work, the choice of the right word or words to convey an idea or impression clearly and effectively.

Empathy: identification with a character in a literary work or a feeling of participation in the work's action.

Episode: one of a progressive series of occurrences or significant events in a story or adventure.

Euphemism: a roundabout way of saying things; the substitution of an inoffensive or bland word or phrase for something possibly offensive or unpleasant; a circumlocution.

Exposition: in fiction, that part of a story or play where the author conveys the background material about the characters and events which the reader must know in order to understand the problem that has to be solved.

In writing, the purpose of exposition is to give information, to explain something, or develop an idea.

Fable: a brief narrative in prose or verse intended to teach a moral lesson. Many fables, such as those of the Greek writer Aesop, are beast fables, in which animals speak and act as if they were human. A writer of modern fables was the late James Thurber.

Fantasy: a work that deliberately employs unrealistic, weird, highly imaginative, or unbelievable incidents. It departs from reality as the reader has experienced it. A fantasy might take place in a dream world, such as that of *Alice in Wonderland*; it might present unreal characters, such as giants; or it might project scientific principles into the future, as in science-fiction stories. A fantasy can be a whimsical form of entertainment, or it can offer a serious comment on reality.

Figurative Language: language that gives new shape or form to the standard or literal manner of expression by means of imaginative devices called *figures of speech*. *Simile, metaphor, personification,* and *irony* are among the most common figures of speech.

Flashback: a device by which an author interrupts the logical time sequence of a story or play to relate an episode or scene that occurred prior to the opening situation.

Foreshadowing: hints or clues (they may be indicated by a word, a phrase, or a sentence) scattered throughout the story to indicate what is going to occur; it is a shadow of things to come. The use of foreshadowing stimulates reader-interest and suspense and helps prepare the reader for the outcome.

Form and Content: in literature, *form* is the structure, pattern, or organization of a work of art that gives it a particular appearance or aspect. A short story is one form of literature; the sonnet is one form of poetry. *Content* refers to the subject matter, ideas, or impressions expressed in the work.

For purposes of discussion, *content* (what is said) may be distinguished from *form* (how it is said), but the overall meaning and effect of a work of art stems from the successful fusion of both form and content.

Frame Story: a story which is placed within the framework of another story; a story within a story. The outer story embodies the reason for the inner story, which is usually the more significant of the two.

Homonym: a word that is distinct from, but has the same spelling and pronunciation as, another word. *Gore,* meaning blood that has been shed, *gore,* meaning to pierce or run through with a horn or spear, etc., and *gore,* meaning a triangular piece of cloth set into a garment, are true homonyms, being alike in pronunciation and spelling but differing in meaning and derivation. *To, two,* and *too; bare* and *bear;* and *sow, so,* and *sew* are *not* true homonyms; they are homophones, being alike in pronunciation only.

Hyperbole (hī·pûr′bə·lē): a deliberate exaggeration for the purpose of emphasis or humor; overstatement.

Imagery: the collective *images*, or pictures and impressions, made with words. Although most imagery makes the reader mentally *see* things, some appeals to the senses of touch, taste, smell, and hearing, as well. Imagery results from the use of figurative language and vivid description.

Immediacy: the quality in writing which makes the reader feel that he is directly involved in the action of the story, not just reading about it. Immediacy is closely related to atmosphere and setting.

Interior Monologue: a device used to present the *stream of consciousness* of a character in a novel, short story, or play. Thoughts, impressions, and free association are set down just as they occur and are expressed by the inner "voice" of the character's mind.

Irony: a figure of speech, humorous or sarcastic, in which the writer's words really mean the opposite of what they seem to say.

A situation may also be ironic when the outcome of an event turns out to be the opposite of what was expected.

Jargon: (sometimes called argot, parlance, shoptalk, and vernacular) the special vocabulary of an identifiable group, occupation, art, science, trade, sect, or sport. *Jargon* can also refer to language full of long words and circumlocutions serving little purpose other than to impress and bewilder the average layman.

Legend: a story about a national hero, folk hero, saint, tribe, people, or historical event that has been handed down from the past, usually by word of mouth.

Local Color: concrete details of dress, speech, locale, customs, and traditions which give an impression of the local "atmosphere" of a particular place.

Stories of "local color" flourished in American literature in the years following the Civil War. Authors wrote about specific regions of the United States, as Bret Harte, the West; Mark Twain, California and Mississippi; and Sarah Orne Jewett, the Maine Coast. An attempt was made to copy local dialects and to depict the characteristic appearance, mannerisms, and customs of the people and the period.

Malapropism: an inadvertent and usually humorous blunder in speech or writing. The term comes from *Mrs. Malaprop*, a character in the comic play *The Rivals*, written in the late eighteenth century by Richard Sheridan. Malapropisms result from the substitution of a word for one similar in sound but greatly different in meaning. Of someone she disliked, for example, Mrs. Malaprop advised, "Illiterate him, I say, quite from your memory."

Metaphor: a comparison or likeness expressed in figurative language without using the words *like* or *as*. One thing is said to be another. For example:

> "Dreams, Books, are each a world."
> —William Wordsworth, "Personal Talk"

Metaphor also involves comparing one thing to another by speaking of it as if it actually were the other. The likeness is often indicated by a verb or a participle. For example:

> "Tiger, Tiger, burning bright/ In the forest of the night,"
> —William Blake, "The Tiger"

Mood: the overall emotional atmosphere or feeling created in a literary work by its tone or tones. (See also **Atmosphere, Setting, and Tone.**)

Motivation: the force which drives a character to some action; the grounds for his behavior. Outside events and environmental influences may cause a character to act as he does, or his action may stem from a need, an inclination, a goal, or a fear within himself.

Myth: a tale or story, related to *legend*, usually focusing on the deeds of gods or superhuman heroes. Myths are the imaginative part of legends and played an important role in ancient cultures by helping to explain or justify the mysteries of nature and the universe, such as the origin of fire.

Narrative: the telling of an event or series of incidents that together make up a meaningful action; a story.

Narrator: one who narrates, or relates, a true or fictional story. The narrator may be a major or minor participant in the action of the narrative, or he may simply be an observer of the action.

Naturalism: a type of extreme literary realism that aims at a detached, mechanistic, and scientifically accurate treatment of man and the environment in which he lives. Like the scientist, the naturalist observes, reports, and analyzes. Naturalism stresses the fact that man, like other creatures in the universe, is subject to the hostile and indifferent forces of nature. American naturalists include

Stephen Crane, Frank Norris, Jack London, and later, Theodore Dreiser, John Dos Passos, and James T. Farrell. Steinbeck's "Flight" is naturalistic in the sense that it looks objectively upon a man reduced to a "natural" state, pursued by man and beast and oppressed and trapped in a natural environment.

Objectivity: the quality of writing that makes it free from the obvious expression of the author's personal sentiments, partialities, feelings, and opinions.

Onomatopoeia (on′ə·mat′ə·pē′ə): the use of words whose sound suggests the object or action that makes the sound. For example, the names of certain songbirds are onomatopoeic in that they imitate the birds' cries: chickadee, cuckoo, whippoorwill, towhee.

Paradox: an apparent contradiction in a statement which nevertheless has at least a grain of truth. In Ambrose Bierce's *The Devil's Dictionary*, the definition for marriage reads, "The state or condition of a community consisting of a master, a mistress, and two slaves, making in all, two."

Paragraph Development, Methods of: There are several ways of developing a paragraph after introducing the main subject or idea in a topic sentence. The methods include: (a) giving many details and particulars; (b) giving specific examples and illustrations; (c) relating an incident or anecdote; (d) offering reasons and arguments; (e) drawing comparison or showing contrast, or both; (f) by giving a definition, and (g) by combining methods.

Paraphrase: the restatement of a line, passage, or entire work, giving the same meaning in another form, usually to clarify or amplify the original.

Parody: the conscious, often exaggerated imitation of a recognizable literary style or particular work with the intention of achieving humor through distortion. Parody is related to *caricature,* which distorts a character rather than a style.

Pathos: the quality in writing that prompts the reader's feelings of sympathy, pity, and sorrow for a character in a work. The term is derived from Greek *pathein,* to suffer. It applies mainly to pathetic situations, in which a character suffers excessively or needlessly through no real fault of his own.

Personification: a figure of speech in which a nonhuman or inanimate object, quality, or idea is given human characteristics or powers. For example:

> "Old Time, the clock setter, that bald sexton, Time"
> —William Shakespeare, *King John,* III, i

Plot: the plan and arrangement of related incidents, details, and elements of conflict in a story. Plot incorporates the situation or problem in which a narrative commences, the resulting complications, the rising action toward the *climax*, and the *dénouement* or final outcome.

Point of View: the manner in which the author presents the events and views the characters in his story. In fiction and nonfiction there are three basic points of view:

(a) *first-person narrator* (*author participant*). The narrative is told by a major or minor character in his or her own words. The author through this "I" narrator is limited to the character's scope of knowledge, degree of involvement, and powers of observation and expression.

(b) *third-person narrator* (*author omniscient*). The author serves as an unrestricted, all-knowing observer who describes and comments upon the characters and action in a narrative. The omniscient author knows everything there is to know about characters—their thoughts, motives, actions, and reactions.

(c) *limited third-person narrator*, in which the author tells the story in the third person by focusing on the actions, reactions, and observations of one of the main characters. Sometimes an author, narrating in the third person, does not wish to indicate that he has any special knowledge about his characters and their behavior. He attempts to keep his personal feelings *objective*, or impartial and detached. In contrast, when the author's opinions about the characters or events in the story are obvious, the writing is called *subjective*.

Protagonist: the main character in a story or drama in whom the action centers; the hero or heroine who is confronted with a problem. (The word was originally used to designate the actor who played the chief role in a Greek drama. The word comes from the Greek *prōtos* meaning "first" and *agōnistēs* meaning "contestant, actor.") See also **Antagonist.**

Realism: literary truth through accuracy; the attempt to present things as they actually are. Realism as a distinct literary movement in America began in the late 1800's with the works and theories of William Dean Howells, who advocated that writers get at truth by treating ordinary people involved in ordinary situations, and without sentimentality or without idealizing them or their lives.

Repetition: the use of the same word, phrase, sentence, idea (or some slight variation of these) to achieve emphasis.

Rhythm: in poetry, the regular and harmonious rise and fall of stress. (As the stress becomes more and more fixed and systematized, it approaches *meter*.) In prose, although rhythm is always present, it is irregular and approximate; prose rhythm is the effective and pleasing arrangement of meaningful sounds in a sentence.

Romanticism: the attempt to present life as it should be or as the writer (and his readers) would like it to be; it pictures life in a picturesque, fanciful, exotic, emotional, and imaginative manner, and often reflects the writer's strong interest in nature and his love of the strange and the supernatural. It is the opposite of *realism*, which deals with the ordinary events of everyday life in an unsentimental and factual manner.

A literary movement called "romanticism" flourished in English literature in the early nineteenth century with the works of writers such as Wordsworth, Coleridge, Byron, Shelley, and Keats, and in American literature in the middle-nineteenth century with the works of authors such as Thoreau, Hawthorne, and Melville.

Satire: the use of ridicule, sarcasm, wit, or irony in order to expose, set right, or destroy a vice, folly, breach of good taste, or social evil.

Science Fiction: a type of *fantasy* that combines man's real knowledge of scientific facts and principles with his imaginative speculations as to what life will be like in the future, as on the moon.

Sentiment and Sentimentality: *sentiment* is a true, noble, or elevated feeling; honest emotion. *Sentimentality* means having an excess of sentiment or feeling; artificial emotion.

Setting: the time and place of the events in a story; the physical background. The importance of setting as a story element depends on the extent of its contribution to *characterization, plot, theme,* and *atmosphere*.

Simile: a stated comparison or likeness expressed in figurative language and introduced by terms such as *like, as, so, as if,* and *as though*. For example:

> "Noise proves nothing. Often a hen who has merely laid an egg cackles as if she had laid an asteroid."
> —Mark Twain, *Pudd'nhead Wilson's New Calendar*

Sketch: a short, simply constructed work, usually about a single character, locale, or incident. A *character sketch*, for example, may be a brief study of a person's characteristics and personality. As in art, a sketch may also be a "rough" or preliminary draft for a longer, more complex work.

Soliloquy: in drama, a speech delivered by a character alone on the stage or apart from the other characters. As a literary device, it is used to reveal character or to give information to the reader or the audience. It is similar to a character talking to himself and thereby revealing his thoughts and problems. (See **Dialogue**.)

Stereotype (Stock Character): a commonplace character who always acts in the same way and shows the same character traits; also, a character who lacks real personality because he possesses or is believed to possess the characteristics of a particular type, group, or class. Examples are the tough private eye, the dull-witted athlete, the hen-pecked husband, and the dashing, quick-witted lawyer.

Stream-of-Consciousness: in fiction, a literary technique by which characters and actions are presented through the flow of inner thoughts, feelings, reflections, memories, and mental images of one or more characters.

Style: a writer's distinctive or characteristic form of expression; the means he uses to express his thoughts effectively. Style is determined by the choice and arrangement of words, sentence structure, the use of figurative language, rhythm, and tone.

Subjectivity: the quality of writing in which the author's opinions, sympathies, personal beliefs, or tastes are obvious and sometimes even dominate his work. Personal essays, biographies, and autobiographies are invariably subjective.

Surprise Ending: in fiction, an unexpected twist of plot at the conclusion of a story; a contrived or "trick" ending. It should be carefully foreshadowed to produce its striking effect. Both O. Henry and Saki (H. H. Munro) wrote stories with surprise endings.

Suspense: the uncertainty, expectancy, or tension that builds up as the climax of a narrative approaches; curiosity regarding the outcome of a narrative.

Symbol: a person, place, event, or object that exists and has meaning in itself and also suggests something further, such as an attitude or a value. For example, donkeys and elephants are donkeys and elephants, but they are also symbols of opposing major political parties in the United States.

Some symbols, such as national emblems or flags, traffic lights and signs, etc., are recognized in about the same way by most people. Other symbols have special or particular meaning in their specific context.

Synonym: a word having the same meaning or meanings as another word or words in the same language, or having the same approximate meaning as another word. Most synonyms are interchangeable but at the same time vary widely in connotation. A standard dictionary of synonyms is Roget's *Thesaurus*. For the word *pride*, for example, Roget's lists the following as synonyms: proudness, pridefulness, self-esteem, self-respect, self-consequence, face, vanity, conceit, arrogance, and boastfulness.

Theme: the main idea of a literary work; the total comment about life that the author wishes to make. The theme of most essays and short stories is, or can be, expressed in a single sentence.

An unconventional theme is a statement about life that may be contradictory to conventional or established beliefs and customs. For example, a *conventional* or traditional theme might be that true happiness is more important than money or wealth. An *unconventional* theme might be that real happiness is not possible where poverty exists.

In an essay, the theme is the basic idea, major premise, or topic to be discussed; the main point. A statement of theme usually appears near the beginning of the discussion.

Tone: the attitude of the writer toward his subject, his characters, and his readers. He may love or admire his subject or be highly amused by his characters. He may wish to anger his readers or to amuse them. The author conveys his feelings through his choice of words and his arrangement of words and sentences.

Topic Sentence: a clear, brief, complete statement of what will be discussed in the paragraph; it is usually, but not always, placed at the beginning of the paragraph. (See also **Paragraph Development, Methods of.**)

Understatement: the representation, through unemphatic or restrained wording, of something as less than it actually is, usually in order to achieve a subtle effect. A news reporter describing a politician's greeting by a crowd as "less than enthusiastic" would be using understatement.

Unity: the singleness of purpose, theme, or topic (or all three) in a composition. Unity is the organizing principle that binds a work's subordinate parts together. Unity occurs when all of a work's individual parts relate to a central theme or main point.

Vignette: a brief yet significant sketch of a person or event. The meaning of a vignette is usually implied rather than stated. It often forms part of a longer work.

The
Language Arts
Program

Throughout the text, language arts principles and activities have been integrated with the presentation of literature. Most of the language arts activities appear in the *Meaning, Method, Language, Composition,* and *Discussion* questions and exercises that follow each selection. Other aspects of the language arts are introduced and discussed in the section introductions, and still others—particularly those concerning the origins of words—are covered in footnotes to the selections.

General Skills

Author (appreciating author's personality), 259; (recognizing author's attitudes), 66, 171, 232, 253, 260, 282, 350

Characterization (inferring character of author or subject), 54, 65, 98, 120, 156, 222, 223, 252, 296; (recognizing techniques of characterization), 7, 8, 10, 11, 18, 66, 98, 134, 184, 213, 231, 244, 282, 296

Comparing and/or contrasting selections, characters, etc., 21, 54, 183–84, 253, 296

Conflict, 7, 55, 66, 97–98, 157, 198

Context, 213

Dictionary, 158, 198, 232, 243, 245, 284

Drawing conclusions from the text, 20, 55, 66, 86, 120, 135, 157, 170, 184, 198, 213, 222–23, 231, 244, 296, 337–38, 338, 350, 370

Extending discussion beyond the immediate text, 170, 171, 183, 184, 198, 223, 244, 252, 314, 315, 337–38

Foreshadowing, 9, 86, 135, 157

Humor (appreciating humor), 88, 231, 234, 243, 244; (recognizing humorous techniques), 231; (recognizing seriousness in humor), 98

Levels of language, 296

Library research, 172, 284–85, 317

Outlining, 338, 339

Paraphrasing main points, 65, 317

Purpose, 282, 283, 297

Relating all parts of the selection, 296

Summarizing, 252, 314–15

Theme, 14, 20, 54, 55, 171, 184, 213, 222, 223, 232, 252, 261, 296, 350

Titles, 98, 135, 212, 260–61, 281, 296, 370

Tone, 232, 244, 259, 296, 317

Variety (in sentence length), 259–60, 296, 350

Literary Types and Terms

Allusion, 70fn., 73fn., 84fn., 188fn., 227fn., 229fn., 237fn., 238fn., 240fn., 241fn., 263fn., 264fn., 272fn., 275fn., 277fn., 279fn., 282, 283–84, 292fn., 294fn., 300fn., 301fn., 302fn., 310fn., 311fn., 312fn., 332fn., 340fn., 342fn.

Analogy, 282, 284

Antithesis, 315

Argumentation, 225

Atmosphere, 156, 170, 253

Autobiography and biography, 225, 244, 296

Characterization, 7, 8, 9, 11, 14, 17, 19, 54, 55, 65, 66, 86, 98, 120, 124, 134, 156, 171, 184, 213, 222, 223, 231, 244, 252, 281, 283, 296

Coherence, 296, 370

Comparison and contrast, 120–21, 184, 282, 237–38, 338, 370

Conflict, 7, 55, 66, 97–98, 157, 198

Connotation, 54, 55, 67, 98, 183, 213, 281, 296, 314, 350, 351

Context, 213

Definition, 338

Denotation, 55, 67, 98, 296, 314

Description, 65, 66, 225, 252

Dialect, 184

Dialogue, 20, 66, 296

Diction, 223, 296, 317, 350

Emphasis, 244, 370

Exposition, 66, 85, 225, 338

Figurative language, 17, 316

Foreshadowing, 9, 86, 135, 157

Hyperbole, 86, 244

Imagery, 17, 19, 20, 54, 253, 260

Immediacy, 212

Irony, 135, 171, 183

Journalism, 121, 225–226

Local Color, 2, 86

Malapropism, 229fn., 231

Metaphor, 98, 282

Mood, 55, 259

Motivation, 120

Mythology and folklore, 172, 174fn., 182, 183, 204fn.

Narration (narrative), 66, 134, 183, 225

Narrator, 65, 66, 86, 134, 157, 198, 212

Naturalism, 2–3

Objectivity, 2, 157, 259, 339, 350

Outline, 338, 339

Parable, 171

Paradox, 121, 229fn.

Paragraph development (methods of), 315, 338, 370

Parallelism, 315

Paraphrase, 65, 304fn., 315

Parody, 122

Personification, 11, 157

Plot, 171

Point of view, 19, 134, 135, 157, 198, 253, 260

Protagonist, 7

Pun, 231

Realism, 2

Repetition, 54, 315

Rhetoric, 315

Setting, 7, 13, 19, 54, 55, 66, 170, 253, 259

Simile, 7, 8, 282

Vocabulary Development

Speaking and Listening

Compare and contrast main
points in different selections
(253)

Evaluate use and misuse of statistical information (284)

Panel discussion on American
race relations today (339)

Explain connotations of specific
words and phrases (351)

Agreeing or disagreeing with author's conclusions (351)

Expressing personal view on business ethics (370–71)

Composition

Narration:

Narrating and describing a specific incident, using stream-of-
consciousnes technique (pages
20–21)

Writing obituary notice for
story's central character (21)

Narration recounting childhood
holiday occasion (213)

Using anecdotes to recount humorous incidents (233)

Description:

Describing and narrating specific
incidents, using stream-of-consciousness technique (20–21)

Describing specific locale through
use of numerous details (66–
67)

Describing a specific room or
place (253)

Description conveying mood or
personal impressions of place
where you grew up, or where
you wished you could have
grown up (261)

Step-by-step description and explanation of a process (297)

Exposition:

Comparing and contrasting attitudes in story and specific
poems (21)

Defining term through examination of denotation and connotations (66)

Comparing and contrasting views
of life in two stories (66)

Essay comparing and contrasting
regional types (87)

Expressing agreement or dis-
agreement with critical interpretation (135)

Explaining a specific term by defining it in your own words
(158–59)

Explaining views on qualities
necessary for coping with
twentieth-century life (184)

Relating theory on mob action
or behavior to theme in story
(199)

Defining friendship by explaining what it is and what it isn't
(213)

Comparing and contrasting
themes in different selections
(253)

Step-by-step explanation and description of a specific process
(297)

Report on social, economic, and
health conditions of Indians
in America (317)

Direct analysis of racial issues
and problems in America and
of Black Muslims' proposed
solutions (339)

Explain and analyze connotations of specific words and phrases (351)

Argumentation:
Arguing pro or con on city versus country life (55)
Defending or refuting critic's view of story's central character (158)
Using examples to substantiate argument expressed in story and in poem quoted in story (199)
Arguing for or against author's statement on Black identity in America (351)
Defending personal view on contemporary business ethics (370–71)

Book Reviews, Library Research:
Review of one of Hemingway's full-length works, emphasizing theme and quality of writing (121–22)
Report on evidence of scapegoats in past or recent cultures (172)
Using library research for development of composition on a specific topic (284–85)
Research and writing about living conditions and problems of Indians in America (317)
Book review of *Autobiography of Malcolm* X (339)

Parodies, Letter-writing, and Outlining:
Devising parody of Hemingway style using passages in other stories (122)
Series of humorous letters between customer and department-store manager (245)
Using outline as basis for essay on Black Muslims (339)